D0375124

Innovating for Health

Innovating for Health:
The Story of Baxter International

By Thomas G. Cody

with foreword by Dr. Michael E. DeBakey

Baxter International Inc.
Deerfield, Illinois, 1994

ISBN 0-89434-152-9

Dedication

There is only one person to whom this book can be dedicated. That is Bill Graham. He is the architect of the modern Baxter. In a real sense, this is his book. Personal insights into this remarkable man are best captured in remarks made about him on two occasions by Gaylord Freeman, a long-term friend and colleague of Graham.

Those occasions were Bill Graham's receipt of the Business Statesman Award from the Harvard Business School Club of Chicago in 1983 and a Baxter "alumni" dinner honoring him on February 10, 1989. Gaylord Freeman's eloquent and witty remarks are excerpted in the appendix.

The history of Baxter is also dedicated to all Baxter people from its inception in 1931 to the present. As much pride as the former CEO takes in the company's business and financial performance, he is even prouder of the Baxter tradition of outstanding people, whether they made their principal contributions to meeting medical needs within the company or moved on and made them elsewhere.

TABLE OF CONTENTS

PART FOUR: A MAJOR TURNING POINT IN BAXTER'S HISTORY

PART FIVE: ANTICIPATING HEALTH CARE REFORM

FOREWORD

When Bill Graham asked me to write an introduction to *Innovating for Health*, it revived many memories, and I was willing to oblige despite the many competing demands on my time. I am glad I did take the time because this book is much more than the usual corporate history, providing, as it does, an account of a number of important medical developments, including several in which I was fortunate to play an early and timely role.

As contemporaries, Bill Graham and I have witnessed these many developments in medicine and health, although from very different perspectives. *Innovating for Health* reminded me that I was graduating from medical school at about the time that Baxter was being formed in Chicago. It turns out also that Bill Graham joined Baxter just before I became affiliated with Baylor 45 years ago.

The account of Baxter's developmental work on artificial organs, beginning with dialysis, in the fifties and the sixties, held particular interest for me. That was certainly an exciting era. In the early thirties, as a medical student, I had devised the roller pump, which was subsequently adapted by John Gibbon to become an integral part of the heart-lung machine and led to the advent of open-heart surgery. In 1957, we performed the first successful resection with graft replacement of a fusiform aneurysm of the entire aortic arch, using the heart-lung machine. In 1964, our team performed the first successful coronary artery bypass procedure. Then came heart transplantation, and on August 31, 1968, my surgical team performed the first multiple organ transplantation—two kidneys, a lung, and a heart from one donor going to four different patients.

I have said in some of my addresses that the exciting era of the sixties paved the way for today's major developments. One of those developments is the left ventricular assist device. In 1966, we performed the first successful use of a mechanical ventricular assist device in a patient. In those days, we worked with the Baxter Heart-Lung Oxygenator and that is when I became acquainted with Baxter and with Bill Graham. The company was strongly committed to medical development and worked closely with surgeons. Baxter is in the forefront of that important work with the Novacor Device. Baxter is still a leader in blood oxygenation equipment, catheters for angioplasty, and other cardiology products. In the eighties, with the availability of cyclosporin to mitigate the rejection problem, cardiac transplantation became more beneficial. Baxter is now working on a promising new anti-rejection substance, Anti CD45, for kidney transplantation.

Innovating for Health also recounts how, at some considerable risk, Baxter moved early to make its critical-care products available to patients in other countries, becoming an integral part of those different medical systems wherever it operates. A good part of my own work in recent years has been in other countries, assisting with the development of the health-care system. Mindful of the global medical needs, I commend Baxter for its worldwide efforts. Baxter's persistence in market development in Japan should be particularly interesting for readers.

I was also an early user of Baxter Viaflex solution containers. Pioneering the use of flexible biocompatible packaging for solutions as well as blood products was an outstanding medical development. It was beneficial for patients, responsive to the needs of physicians and hospitals, and cost-effective. It was characteristic of the practical way Baxter looked at its role and responsibilities in the sixties and early seventies. Developmental work on Viaflex dates back much earlier, all the way to the early fifties. The company persisted with the development for many years before achieving success. It is an excellent model for other companies to study and emulate.

Our medical and health-care systems now face the most vexing problems I have seen in my career since 1932. The challenges are not restricted to the United States; they are building in nearly every country around the world. We face problems of cost, ethics, and—yes—technology too. Too often these days new technology seems promoted for financial reasons and applied in a way that is not consistent with the best and most balanced practices. We must maintain our technological lead in medicine for the welfare of our people and the nation, but we must do it in a more responsible way. There is much in Baxter's history to help decision-makers as we debate the future direction and dimensions of health care in this country. I particularly recommend that readers study how Baxter went about identifying patient needs and managed development processes in a quiet, efficient way.

Few subjects are as gripping, vital, and dramatic as clinical medicine and health care. *Innovating for Health* provides an excellent perspective on the march of medical progress over the past sixty plus years. The book should be of interest to physicians and other health-care professionals, policy-makers, and all of us whose lives are touched by the health-care system and medical technologies.

Before we decide where we are going in health care, we have to be clear on where we have been. This book provides that perspective. I recommend that you read beyond this introduction. I am certain you will enjoy it and learn more about the realities of health care.

Dr. Michael E. DeBakey
Houston, Texas

PREFACE

> Between my finger and my thumb the squat pen rests;
> snug as a gun.
> I'll dig with it.
>
> Seamus Heaney, "Digging."
> From *Death of a Naturalist*.[1]

As a history of Baxter, this book obliges its author to call as little attention to himself as possible. I'll honor that obligation. Others—those who closely directed the research and writing and whose imprint is on it as surely as mine and also the outstanding people of Baxter, past, present, and future—should occupy center stage. There are, however, several thoughts I must express.

This is my third book, the second about Baxter. I didn't set out to become a company chronicler. It just turned out that way. My first book about Baxter was an independent undertaking to tell the story of the 1985 merger with American Hospital Supply Corporation and the events that followed.[2]

This is a totally different kind of book. First, the company sponsored and supported it. It rests on a more solid foundation of research and scholarship. And every aspect of the work was directed and reviewed by an executive group made up of William B. Graham, Baxter senior chairman, now in his forty-ninth year of company service, together with Raymond D. Oddi and Lincoln Dowell, both retired Baxter executives.

I wish I could say that the basic ideas about the structure and thrust of the Baxter history were mine because they are, I think, fresh and original. Those ideas are not solely or principally mine, however. They came, by and large, from these three men, principally Bill Graham, and from discussions among all of us.

Yet in the four plus years I was engaged in this work from 1989 through 1994, my independence and objectivity as a researcher and writer were not limited. Bill Graham wanted an objective and accurate history of Baxter, not a book about Bill Graham or Bill Graham's point of view. So in the end, the pen rested between my finger and thumb. I take responsibility for the research, the writing, and for errors and omissions. Working with the project executive committee was an inspiration for me, particularly the countless hours I had the opportunity to spend with Bill Graham, as his keen mind alternately illuminated and dissected the historical facts I dug from the dusty archives. He is truly a giant of a man!

John Steinbeck said in remarks prepared for a 1939 NBC radio interview, "Boileau said that kings, gods, and heroes only were fit subjects for literature. The writer can only write about what he admires."[3] Our concepts of literature and business literature have certainly changed since 1939, when Steinbeck made that remark and Baxter was a struggling less-than-one-million-dollar enterprise still perfecting commercial IV solutions and preparing to introduce the Transfuso Vac. The Transfuso Vac borrowed from the development experience of the IV solution Vacoliter to simplify the function of direct blood transfusion. John Elliott developed the concept. Dr. Naurice Nesset of Baxter perfected and commercialized it. Whether the reader finds heroes here or not, I certainly do admire the company and its people.

Baxter's most senior people energetically supported and encouraged this history through its long preparation, particularly Vernon R. Loucks, Jr., elected president of Baxter in 1976, CEO in 1980, and chairman and CEO in 1987.

On a sad note, the preparation of the Baxter history was begun by a well-known Chicago writer, Mr. Herman Kogan and his son, Rick Kogan. Mr. Kogan died suddenly in the spring of 1989. It was after that I became involved. While Mr. Kogan had not begun to write at the time of his death, I was able to build on and incorporate much of his research.

Innovating for Health aptly conveys all the central themes of Baxter's rich history. First and most important, is the theme of Baxter's continuing contribution to today's health picture, from which many of us—but sadly, not all—have benefited so greatly. Next is the theme that is so central to the company's and its CEO's view of itself. That is, Baxter is an integral part of the total health care picture, a full partner, if you will, in nearly every aspect of patient care and well-being in this country and around the world. So we've tried to cover the many trends and developments over sixty years, in what may be the most dynamic and fruitful system the modern world has yet created. The late 20th century health care system, particularly in the United States, which accounts for about 40 percent of the world's estimated health care expenditures and investments, is extraordinarily diverse. It is composed of medical professionals of great skill and dedication, non-profit and for-profit institutions, government at all levels, universities, businesses, communities, and others. Let's hope that in making the necessary decisions about 21st century health care, the richness and strength of that diversity will be recognized and preserved. More specifically, we have tried to show in detail why Baxter, as an organization, presents such a robust picture of health. We're not concerned just with financial results, although those by themselves are impressive enough. The story of Baxter's more than 60 years shows how wise and patient strategies, fierce commitment to innovation and leadership, good people, and an eager willingness to embrace continuous change all mesh together to produce superior results. In many respects, this story is about change. It is structured around key turning points in Baxter's growth and development. For example, in 1983–84, the company faced change of such magnitude and velocity that its own health appeared for a time to be threatened. There have been many other turning points in Baxter's history. They make up much of the drama of the story.

Researching and writing Baxter's history proved not as difficult as settling on a title for the finished work. We went through proposed titles like biotech companies go through investment capital. For some period of time I wrote under the assumption that the title of this book would be *Hit 'em Where They Ain't*. Sports analogies are always popular for describing management strategy and tactics. This is one of Bill Graham's favorite expressions to paint the picture of how Baxter overcame its early limitations to grow and become successful.

Wee Willie (William Henry) Keeler used the expression "Hit 'em where they ain't" to explain his batting style of punching the ball through the infield and away from outfielders. Despite his small stature (5 feet 4 inches tall and 140 pounds), Wee Willie played 19 seasons in the major leagues with four different teams. In 2124 games he had 8591 at bats and 2962 hits—of which only 34 were home runs. As of 1988 his lifetime batting average of .345 was still the fifth highest in the entire history of major league baseball.[4] He was elected to the Baseball Hall of Fame in 1939, at the same time that Baxter was still perfecting commercial intravenous solutions and preparing to introduce the Transfuso Vac and Plasma-Vac. Even though that title was discarded in favor of one more descriptive of Baxter's characteristics and accomplishments, you will still hear echoes of "Hit 'em where they ain't" because it so aptly portrays company strategy, particularly from 1945 to 1983.

Acknowledgements

I acknowledge with love the support given me by Kathy, my wife for almost 38 years, and our two children, Kathy and Kitt. Writing is a solitary pursuit and it is important to be able to set down the pen and find them there. I'd also like to acknowledge the importance in my life of the bond with my three brothers: Jack, who died suddenly in 1991; Bill, who had been courageously battling cancer for the whole time I've been engaged in this history and died in 1993; and Dick.

As usual, many, many people have been helpful and instrumental in getting Baxter's history into print. Also as usual, I can single out only a few for acknowledgement. Several senior officers read successive manuscript versions carefully and critically and made many helpful suggestions. Three Baxter stalwarts—Dr. Bob Ausman, Dr. "Patt" Patterson, and Dave Bellamy—provided scientific and medical advice and review. The three typify in different ways the spirit that has shaped Baxter. All were immensely helpful. During the early part of the project another part of the team was Pat McBride, who wrote the definitive book on the artificial kidney.[5] Carol Summerfield, editorial director of J. G. Ferguson Publishing Company, was a valued advisor as well as an editor, thoroughly professional, infinitely patient with the complications that attend a book of this kind, and a pleasure to work with.

As we raced for the finish line, we were fortunate to have John P. Rojewski join the Baxter history team. A twenty-eight year Baxter finance department veteran, he helped validate and clarify the Baxter financial data used throughout the history. He was also immensely helpful in the myriad project management tasks necessary to move ahead to book production and distribution. John, thanks for all your help. After Jill Carter became director of corporate communication, she became an integral part of our team. We greatly appreciate her many contributions.

Ray Oddi made contributions in so many different ways to this history. It was clear during my work why he was such an important part of Baxter management for so long a time. Quietly, good-naturedly, but insistently, he kept everything moving along on track. Ray's financial expertise, his broad, successful management experience and knowledge, and his insistence on accuracy and clarity are important ingredients of this work. Without him, I am convinced the book might never have seen the light of day. It was he who recommended that I be chosen to do the research and writing. Although during the difficult days of the project I didn't always thank him for the opportunity, I certainly do now.

The medical illustrations necessary for a full understanding of Baxter's products and services were drawn by Peg Gerrity, past president of the Association of Medical Illustrators. I thank her for her outstanding contribution. And, again, I'd like to thank Dr. Bob Ausman, who oversaw the development of the illustrations, carefully improved the captioning, read drafts, offered me encouragement, and helped in countless other ways. An author of 12 medical volumes, who embarrasses me as a writer with his facility and speed, Bob Ausman epitomizes for me what a physician should be.

And certainly not least, Vern Loucks, chairman and CEO of Baxter, provided the necessary resources and support, encouraged me to write the best and most honest history I could, was candid and open with me (which is one of his traits), and then rode me about how long it took to get the book done. He is a man of action, not accustomed to waiting four years to see the result.

Conclusion

A final thought. In the course of this undertaking, I've read innumerable corporate histories. Corporate history is, it must be said, an uninspired and uninspiring literary genre. It is to be expected, therefore, that you would begin to peruse this one with a certain amount of jaundice.

I would not have picked up the pen to dig with it had I not been convinced that Bill Graham and Baxter would insist on a corporate history that was different and better. After all, the company has approached strategy in a distinctive manner. Its financial planning and use of resources have been creative over the years. And its success in understanding and meeting medical needs is truly unique.

Through the many patient therapies in which Baxter has made pioneering contributions, most notably parenteral nutrition, kidney dialysis, blood therapy, hemophiliac treatment specifically, heart surgery (through early development of oxygenation equipment and through other devices for cardiovascular treatment and care), and more recently through creation of alternate site systems and services, hundreds of thousands of human lives around the world have been saved, extended, and improved. Since the early days of Dr. Ralph Falk, the company has been dedicated to quality of patient care.

The story of Baxter's first sixty some years and its strategy over those years is remarkable and dramatic enough in itself. We've tried to do more, though, than let the story tell itself. It's our hope that readers within and outside the Baxter family will judge that we've been successful in bringing the story to life and perhaps at the same time making a broader contribution to management history and scholarship.

A Word on Approach and Style

The form chosen for telling Baxter's story is what might be called dramatic or documentary history. The framework is built on specific key events—strategic decisions, breakthroughs in serving medical needs, reactions to market shifts and competitive threats, and other turning points—which determined the company's character and long-term direction. Historical chronology flows from and around those events.

In order to bring you, the reader, into the drama of these events, we have recreated conversations, painted the personal aspirations and motivations behind strategic decisions, and tried to illuminate the beliefs and personalities of the people involved. Where these techniques are used, they are guided by strict standards of research and scholarship. Descriptions are based on examinations of Baxter written records, interviews and reinterviews with participants in key events, and research of external sources. Where there were conflicts, as there sometimes were among various sources, I used the best judgment I could to establish the real facts. The final manuscript underwent a rigorous review process. I feel comfortable and confident, therefore, in vouching for the accuracy and validity of this historical work.

However, historical accuracy was only one of the primary objectives for Bill Graham, Ray Oddi, Link Dowell, and me. Another equally important objective for this book was to "educate" Baxter employees and customers. That requires critically examining the broad significance of the events in which Baxter has been involved and which it helped shape. It also means making these events relevant for what we hope will be a wide variety of readers. And since health care is an almost universal concern and one of our most pressing public policy problems, we wanted to make a contribution to understanding of the $800 billion U.S. system (probably $2 trillion for all health care systems around the world). Additionally, we believed there were important strategy and management lessons to be learned from Baxter's experience. So this is not the usual inward-looking corporate encomium. At least, we certainly hope it's not.

Throughout Baxter's sixty plus year history, we keep looking "outward" at the development of the nation's health care and hospital system. That system has frequently been challenged by change over that six decade span. When Baxter began in the early thirties, U.S.

hospitals were developing diagnostic capability, but had few weapons for treating the disease states diagnosed. Through much of the depression-era thirties, the dominant clinical problems were tuberculosis, lobar pneumonia, polio, rheumatic fever, syphilis, and erysipelas. And pharmacology consisted of morphine, aspirin, cathartics, bromides, barbiturates, and digitalis.[6] Now hospitals and health care professionals command an incredible array of diagnostic weapons and treatment. And we are on the threshold, with biotechnology, of even more dramatic discoveries and advances. So the challenges are becoming more complex and difficult: How can the imperfections and inequities of the health care market be dealt with? What about the enormous and rapidly-growing cost of the U.S. system? Are we being defeated by our own successes? If the perspective of Baxter's history can contribute in a secondary way to understanding these difficult questions, that also would be a desirable outcome.

Constant and profound changes in health care caused difficulties in finalizing Baxter's history. It's a challenge to put current history in perspective. Perhaps that's why some other corporate histories are content to package the more distant past. In 1993 on the brink of national health care reform, Baxter experienced a year filled with setbacks and disappointments. We deal with these events directly in concluding chapters because they are a part of the story and because the cycles of risk and change are greater in health care—and becoming more so—than in other sectors. Baxter has faced and surmounted many such challenges over its more than sixty year history. That is in part what lends drama to this history and makes Baxter a dynamic organization.

End Notes

1. Seamus Heaney, *Selected Poems 1966–1987* (New York: Farrar, Straus and Giroux, 1990).

2. Thomas G. Cody, *Strategy of a Megamerger* (Westport, Connecticut: Quorum Books, 1990).

3. John Steinbeck, *Working Days: The Journals of the Grapes of Wrath* (New York: Penguin Books, 1990) p. xxi.

4. Joseph L. Reichler, ed., *The Baseball Encyclopedia, Seventh Edition* (New York: Macmillan Publishing Company, 1988).

5. Patrick T. McBride, *Genesis of the Artificial Kidney* (Deerfield: Baxter Healthcare Corporation, 1987).

6. Lewis Thomas. *The Youngest Science: Notes of a Medicine Watcher* (New York: Viking Press, 1983) pp. 27–32.

PART ONE

THE EARLY YEARS

1931 TO 1945

Baxter International can best be characterized as a strategically driven company. William B. Graham proved himself to be one of the early master corporate strategists. Vernon R. Loucks followed and enriched that tradition, developing a unique and successful strategy for a much larger and more complex organization ($1.3 billion sales when he became CEO in 1980 and almost $8.9 billion in 1993).

Although Baxter has long been known as a strategically driven company, in its first 14 years it had no clear, comprehensive strategy. Instead, what direction it had came from the personal commitment and vision of founder Dr. Ralph Falk to improve overall patient care. That commitment, summed up in the phrase "Innovating for Life," continues to be an important theme in the philosophy of Baxter.

In the beginning, though, the company's primary focus was survival. How the company grew beyond that stage to become a model of the strategic approach in the business world is an aspect of this history that should be of the broadest interest.

Because Baxter began without control of any essential natural resource, with only a "derivative" technical advantage licensed from a small California company, and without a recognized market need or a distribution system that provided competitive advantage, its success and growth had to rely on innovative management strategies. Indeed, demand for its initial products had to be created in the true sense of the word.

CHAPTER

I

THE BATON IS PASSED

"As a new chief executive I'm fortunate. I'm prepared for the job and the challenges we face. The company has momentum after 25 years of record-setting results. This year's net earnings should beat 1979 by 15 percent."

Vernon R. Loucks, Jr., who had been elected chief executive officer of Baxter Travenol Laboratories, Inc. at that morning's board meeting (May 3, 1980), was talking with a visitor about the passing of leadership and his strategic outlook.

He was only the third CEO in Baxter's 50-year history.[1] The first, Dr. Ralph Falk, founded the company as Don Baxter Intravenous Products, Inc. in 1931. The second, William B. Graham, a former patent attorney, joined Baxter in 1945 when its annual commercial sales were $1.6 million.[2]

Loucks had big shoes to fill. Graham, 68 years old when he passed the baton to Loucks, had been the architect of Baxter's success for 27 years and had functioned as de facto CEO from the time he joined the company. He was elected president in 1953 and became CEO when Falk died in 1960. There was no question, inside or outside the company, whose imprint had shaped Baxter as an innovator and world leader in hospital products and medical specialties. In the eyes of many, Baxter was Bill Graham and Bill Graham was Baxter.

Loucks was 45. A graduate of Lawrenceville, Yale, and Harvard Business School, and a former U.S. Marine Corps officer, he had joined the company on January 17, 1966, after a stint in management consulting. He was six-feet five-inches tall, handsome, and very personable—the "CEO from central casting," some called him. At Yale he played football as an end and kicker on the Jordan Olivar-coached team, which won the first Ivy League football championship, going undefeated in league play and losing only to Colgate. He was first baseman on the Yale baseball team in his freshman and sophomore years.

Originally, Loucks answered a Baxter ad for an assistant to the president of the still-new international division. He ended up going

William B. Graham

to work as Graham's assistant. He still chuckles when he recalls that first meeting with Graham. Graham said, "You know, if you do come to work here, you may not like it. And we may not like you. But if that's the way it works out, Baxter is a great place to be from."

His election as president and chief operating officer in 1976 came after several very successful assignments, including an important stint in Europe for the international division in 1968, that provided him with unique experience in an independent environment.

"You know, it will be difficult to follow Bill Graham," Loucks told his visitor. Usually informal, he was still in full dress from the morning board meeting: navy suit, pale blue shirt, and red-and-black rep tie. He shed his coat and tossed it over the arm of the office sofa as he continued.

"Look at our record. Over 25 years of more than 20 percent growth in compound earnings per share! In the 1970s our net income growth

Vernon R. Loucks, Jr.

rate was even higher—24 percent, I think—which was triple the average rate then for the Fortune 500.

"The stock market has rewarded our performance. Baxter common stock value has recently been growing 22 percent a year. And I remember a day in 1973 when our stock peaked at about 70 times earnings. That's one of the reasons we've had six two-for-one common stock splits. If trends continue, you'll see a seventh.[3] One thousand dollars invested in Baxter stock in the early days of Bill Graham's leadership[4] is worth $150,000 now.

"Bill and I are both proud of the participation of Baxter employees in the increased value of their company. That began with our 1945 profit-sharing plan, which was heavily invested in Baxter stock. Later we added an employee stock purchase plan and, for a while, even guaranteed the value of the stock for employees who needed to sell. We also introduced stock options early, and they were broadly distributed. This was part of the Graham philosophy that all employees should share in the company's gains—and yes, its risks too. Let's face it. It was also a way of controlling fixed-expense dollars.

"As the company's performance kicked into high gear, our PE ratio went up too, and the profit-sharing plan continued to invest in Baxter stock, so that employees got a 'triple-kicker.' Someone coined the label, 'The Morton Grove Millionaires.'[5] This became one of the Baxter traditions."

After a brief pause to answer a congratulatory phone call, Loucks continued on a different tack.

"I have three strategic objectives in mind as I look ahead. One, of course, is to continue our record-setting financial performance as long as we soundly can. However, that certainly will be interrupted at some point. All periods of setting records do come to an end; we have to be prepared for that.

"The second is to get more new products and technology in the pipeline, and they have to be the right ones. Graham's philosophy of hitting lots of solid singles gets more and more difficult as we continue to grow in size. I have the feeling we are going to have to change our stance to try for more triples and home runs. In order to fill up the pipeline, we're going to invest more in development. That will, of course, affect our future earnings. And *services* may represent an opportunity for the Baxter of the future that's even more attractive than products. We're going to explore that direction.

"The third is to continue on our general strategic path, but progressively adapt it to changing market conditions. Hospital buying groups are affecting the economics of our business. American Hospital Supply's Corporate Program is a winning response to the situation. We've got to find ways to turn these developing market problems into Baxter opportunities.

"By now our financial successes are probably better known than our innovations in patient care. Seeking out unmet medical needs in hospitals, and, in so doing, shaping the hospital products industry as we know it today, built our financial record. I've got to drive those basic strengths in a way that's appropriate to our rapidly changing marketplace.

"I know of few other companies with a comparable record of patient care innovation. It began 50 years ago with Baxter's pioneering commercial intravenous solutions. Making it possible for hospitals to safely administer essential fluids and nutrients intravenously without dangerous fever reactions was, in many respects, the beginning of modern, long-term hospital care and treatment.

"The original sugar and salt solutions in distilled water have become dozens of varieties of solutions used in every health care field, and along the way they've saved countless human lives.

"Beginning with IVs, we became and remained market and technical leaders in virtually every product area we've entered. We've never been content with being just one step ahead in product innovation. Once IV solutions were made stable, we moved on to disposable tubing, which eliminated the problem of patient reactions to reused rubber tubing that wasn't adequately clean and pyrogen-free. We introduced lighter, 'one-way' bottles and many new solution products. In 1970, Baxter revolutionized IV therapy with Viaflex plastic container packaging.[6] The plastic containers are easier to ship and store, unbreakable in use, and—most important for patient benefit—are a completely closed system which prevents air and contaminants from entering the bloodstream."

Loucks continued to recite the company's long record of innovation: about ten years after pioneering commercial IV solutions, Baxter brought out the Transfuso Vac and then the Plasma-Vac containers (1939 and 1940 respectively), making modern blood therapy possible. These developments were based on blood filtration work done by Dr. Warren B. Cooksey of Detroit's Henry Ford Hospital, and more extensive work by Dr. John Elliott, laboratory chief at Rowan Memorial Hospital in Salisbury, North Carolina. Before 1939, blood was usually transferred directly from donor to recipient. That procedure could take as long as six hours, and as many as five people were needed to perform the procedure. Needless to say, the much quicker and safer Baxter products soon proved their worth by saving thousands of lives in World War II.[7]

The list of Baxter's firsts is a long one. Baxter was one of the first companies to undertake the commercial marketing of human blood plasma in 1952.[8] It was the first to concentrate factor VIII for treating hemophilia. (Before that, plasma or serum was used for treatment, which taxed the patient's system with large volumes of liquid.) Baxter worked with the Cohn fractionation process to produce a concentrate. It scored another first in successfully bringing the Fenwal blood handling and blood component separation system to market beginning in 1959.[9]

In 1956 Baxter developed the first commercial artificial kidney, based on the work of Dr. Willem Johann Kolff. Kolff had gotten the cold shoulder from two other companies (Mead Johnson and Abbott) before he talked to Baxter. Although there was a medical need, no one could figure out how to make a market out of the need. Twenty-four hours after meeting Graham, Kolff and Baxter had an agreement. As there is with any "trailblazing," there was initial customer resistance; the machines couldn't be given away. It took strong conviction, years of effort, and a long-term investment philosophy to turn kidney dialysis into a viable business. Dialysis may have helped more people more dramatically than any other single thing Baxter pursued. In 1977 the company introduced CAPD,[10] another significant advance in dialysis technique, based on the work of Dr. Jack Moncrief and Robert Popovich in Austin, Texas. By 1980, five thousand patients around the world were on this form of treatment, which provides lifestyle as well as medical benefits.

In 1962, a Baxter team working with the University of Minnesota Medical School and a young intern there, Robert K. Ausman (who later joined Baxter), developed the first commercial heart-lung oxygenator, necessary for open-heart surgery.

As these and other Baxter innovations illustrate, the company has continually sought and been open to new developments from every source, both inside and outside the company. That approach to innovation has been an important part of Baxter's philosophy.

"One development captures for me the essence of Baxter's approach to innovative patient care," Loucks continued. "It's a drug named Synthroid [levothyroxine sodium]. Yes, in those days we worked in pharmaceuticals as well. At any rate, in 1951 Baxter introduced Synthroid tablets and injections, which as pure chemical forms were superior to the desiccated animal thyroid products then on the market for deficient function of that gland. Smith–Kline brought out a product similar to ours at about the same time. If we'd known about the Smith–Kline introduction, we might not have proceeded with ours. Neither product caught on. After a market blitz that went nowhere, Smith–Kline withdrew and went on to more promising opportunities. One of their sales executives said that introduction was like 'dropping a sheep down a dry well.'

"We didn't have the luxury of a lot of choices, so we hung in there. Sales limped along. I'm told that Bill Graham himself pored over sales results by territory. Then based on the results of the Kansas City sales representative, George Kraft (who went on to become a dynamic sales manager), we found the key. It turned out that doctors were prescribing Synthroid only for *new* patients. After titrating and adjusting existing patients for the more variable animal product they were already using, they weren't about to go through the process again to switch them to this new chemical substance. We were able to take that into account in our marketing and sales plans. By 1956 or 1957, Synthroid tablets were a success. Today in 1980, even though patent protection is long expired, Synthroid tablets are one of our more profitable products and our only entry on the top-selling prescription list. If you're going to be a market leader, you have to learn how to overcome initial resistance. When it comes to improving patient care, you learn to take the long-term view and to pursue it with patience and persistence."

Loucks glanced at his watch. "While our fundamentals appear strong," he concluded, "I am concerned about how they will be affected by trends in the hospital marketplace. This company's success has been due in large part to superior strategy. Now we are going to have to adjust that strategy, progressively but substantially, because of our changing relationships with providers and with patients. At the same time, of course, we must continue some of the key strategic thrusts that have worked so well for us over so many years."

EFFECTIVE TRANSITION

Loucks' transition to chief executive officer held promise for the future. Not only was Loucks a popular choice, but transition issues had been thoroughly thrashed out between him and Graham, with some outside assistance from Marvin Bower of McKinsey & Company, the dean emeritus of management consulting. In addition, there would be continuing opportunity for counsel with Graham, who continued as chairman until 1985, when events caused him to move to senior chairman, a position he still holds.

Employees and managers accustomed to Graham's strong personal direction were generally surprised at the seeming ease with which he stepped aside; once the baton was passed, he never intruded in the decision-making of the new CEO.

BAXTER'S "CONTRARIAN" STRATEGY

Baxter strategy was intensively reviewed during the transition, but it wasn't substantially altered. The period between 1983 and 1984, however, would be the watershed from which a new strategy emerged. The original strategy had taken shape in the late forties and early fifties as Graham began to set the course. From the start, the objectives were to create the greatest shareholder value by pioneering improvements in patient care. Because Baxter's cash flow and product line were still very limited, the initial strategy was determined by operations and resource constraints, rather than by any grand vision.

"We tried to be the Wee Willie Keeler[11] of hospital and medical products," Graham says. "His slogan was 'hit 'em where they ain't.'

"We had to hit a lot of solid singles to succeed. Since we were up at bat so often, we learned to rely on innovation from every part of the company and from outside it as well. We concentrated on what we did best, which was chemistry, engineering, and product application in areas like sterile packaging, later plastics and fluid technology, and RF (radio frequency) sealing.[12] Since we didn't want to call attention to what we were doing, we never pointed to the outfield fences and talked up our batting or slugging average. Maybe that's why Baxter didn't become more widely known for many years. We planned our investments carefully and strategically in order to sustain all the initiatives we had going. Why this 'contrarian' approach, which today is considered a model strategy? Because the only model in the forties and fifties was the pharmaceutical companies. It was clear to me we couldn't hit directly at them. We didn't have the financial resources then. It's becoming obvious now that the Wee Willie Keeler approach gets more difficult as our organization grows bigger."

NEW LEADERSHIP STYLE

In their discussions of the transition, Graham and Loucks spent a lot of time talking about the inevitable shift in leadership style and how it might affect the performance of key people in the Baxter organization. Graham had run a taut ship and made most of the key decisions himself. This had inevitable repercussions on the way Baxter employees worked and felt about the company.

"Many of us were in awe of Bill Graham," said Gabriel Schmergel, who joined Baxter right out of graduate school. "When I joined Baxter in 1967, he was already attracting superior people in terms of mental capacity and drive, including many Harvard Baker Scholars. There's a story about Dolph Bridgewater, who joined Baxter from McKinsey, one of the world's most respected management consulting organizations. McKinsey had always prided itself on recruiting the top HBS scholars. In one of his first Baxter management meetings, Bridgewater realized with surprise that more than half the participants were Harvard Business School Baker Scholars.

"Within the context of being told 'what Bill Graham wanted' you were given every chance to show what you could do," said Schmergel, himself a Harvard Business School Baker Scholar, and now CEO of Genetics Institute. "The atmosphere was electric. The psychic rewards were there. We were all overworked and underpaid. Long-term Baxter stock appreciation made up for tight pay ranges. If you did your job, you were left alone and given more responsibility. Interesting, isn't it? The reward for outstanding performance was to get *less* management attention! I was, fairly quickly, vice president for Europe with almost five thousand people reporting to me.

"Bill Graham had a lasting impact on my career and the way I run Genetics Institute. I'd sum it up this way: Graham always had a road map, but he was prepared to zigzag with the road. He was personally charming, but merciless about results. He had a keen eye for people with superior mental capacity and lots of drive. And he took everything about the business very personally. Anything that didn't go right he took as a personal affront. It took me a long time to grasp that last point. Now I'm the same way in running Genetics Institute. Confronted with tough decisions here, I often say to myself, 'I wonder how Bill Graham would have handled this one'."

In their discussions of leadership style, one subject Loucks and Graham frequently discussed in the months leading up to the transition was product cost and corporate cost structure.

"We've traditionally done a good job of controlling and driving down product costs, Bill," Loucks said at a meeting in early February 1980. "IV solutions sold for about 60 cents a liter back at the beginning, in the thirties. If those prices had escalated just 5 percent a year—even without doing all the more complicated adjustments for comparison—they'd be over $8.00 today. And here we are, selling better, safer solutions in the same price range of 60 to 70 cents while maintaining margins and increasing profitability through product and manufacturing innovation.[13] It's great value for hospital customers and a remarkable accomplishment by Baxter. You've said to me many times that the strategy that evolved in the fifties was based in large part on the hard reality that Baxter margins were nowhere near as wide as they were for the pharmaceutical industry. I also remember your pointing out way back that you thought our product mix was okay to carry us to a sales volume of $250 million, but beyond that we might have to consider some new directions. That time has finally come in 1980 with our volume having passed one billion dollars. What those new directions will be I'm not yet sure. Beyond CAPD [Continuous Ambulatory Peritoneal Dialysis, a patient-managed technique for peritoneal kidney dialysis, which Baxter pioneered in the late seventies and early eighties] we don't have what we need for major new thrusts already in our pipeline. One of my first initiatives will be to drive IV solutions and other costs down further through planned programs. We'll reinvest our gains from those programs in more R&D to speed up the flow of new products to market."

Graham was fully supportive even though his view of the fullness of the Baxter R&D pipeline was somewhat different from that of Loucks.

1980 PROCEEDS TO A STRONG CLOSE

The 1980 annual report showed Baxter's earnings up 15 percent and net sales at $1.374 billion, up 15 percent from 1979, just as Loucks had predicted. In addition, stockholders' equity grew 18 percent from the prior year to $852 million, and the number of Baxter employees decreased somewhat to 32,232.[14]

In contrast, the company's first annual report for 1951, after Baxter's initial public stock offering at $17 per share, showed net sales at $11.3 million and net profit at $705,000. The company ended 1951 with 1,033 employees, less than the total number of shareholders (1,148) after its first public stock offering.[15]

With such a positive annual report, Loucks and Graham, and indeed the whole organization, faced Baxter's sixth decade with confidence. The eighties were going to be a changing and turbulent time for health care in the United States and, to varying extents, in other developed countries. There was nothing new about this, however. Every preceding decade, including the first, had been filled with change and challenge, inevitable in the health care business.

It is hoped that through the lens of these events, the reader can more easily see the significance and relationship of earlier developments, as the history of Baxter now reaches back to the company's uncertain beginning in 1931.

This history is presented in five parts. Part One covers the early years—1931 to 1945. While there certainly were dramatic and significant milestones during these years, they proved to be a prelude to major discoveries and inventions. The early history is dominated by the actions and inspirations of several individuals whose work came together fortuitously. They grappled with war, disease, and infection to position the company to contribute to modern medicine.

The modern Baxter began to emerge in the years following 1945. This phase is the subject of Part Two: Strategy Formation, 1946 to 1962. Then Part Three, the longest of the five parts, covers the Growth Years, 1962 to 1980, the time most closely identified with Bill Graham. Of course, despite the heading for this part, growth certainly did not end in 1980. In fact, at that point, Baxter's most dramatic increase in size and scope of service to hospitals was still on the horizon.

A painting of quarantine signs from the era before modern medicine.

Part Four covers one of the most important turning points for Baxter. Soon after Loucks became CEO in 1980, the U.S. hospital industry was battered by attempts to rein in health care costs, specifically by federal policy changes in hospital reimbursement. The company's principal market changed suddenly and dramatically. Loucks' strategic response was equally rapid. It included the 1985 merger with former rival American Hospital Supply Company and the 1987 acquisition of Caremark. When the dust settled, many felt that Baxter was a totally different company. Certainly it was many times larger. Large scale had become at least as important as a competitive requirement as Baxter's traditional speed and strength of market niche leadership.

The concluding section—Part Five, Anticipating Health Care Reform—traces developments from the decade of change in the eighties into the even more uncertain nineties. The last chapter ventures a look into the future based on current trends.

From time to time in each of the history's five parts, the viewpoint shifts to examine developments and strategic decisions from the perspective of hospitals and closely related health care segments.

Since the general history of hospitals in the United States has been well covered elsewhere,[16] only hospital and clinical medicine developments directly related to the Baxter story are included.

END NOTES

CHAPTER I

1. Baxter's fiftieth anniversary was commemorated the following year on October 20, 1981. Actually, Dr. Donald Baxter, as described a little later, served briefly as the company's first titular president.

2. Baxter's military sales were about to wind down abruptly with the conclusion of World War II.

3. A seventh Baxter two-for-one common stock split did occur later in 1983.

4. The base year for this growth comparison is 1954.

5. Morton Grove, Illinois, was the headquarters of Baxter Laboratories from 1947 to 1975. After headquarters moved to Deerfield in 1975, the Morton Grove facility continued to be used as a laboratory and distribution center. It was sold in 1988.

6. Viaflex plastic bags were first introduced in Canada, then in the U.S. in 1970, and later throughout Europe. They replaced glass bottles.

7. For a detailed history of blood therapy in World War II, including many specific references to Baxter products, see Brig. Gen. Douglas B. Kendrick, "Blood Program in World War II" (Washington, D.C.: Medical Department, U.S. Army, 1964).

8. The plasma was marketed by Hyland Laboratories, acquired by Baxter in 1952.

9. Fenwal Laboratories was acquired by Baxter in 1959.

10. Continuous Ambulatory Peritoneal Dialysis is a system of disposable bags to infuse dialysate and then remove waste product which has been filtered through the patient's peritoneal membrane.

11. See preface (p. xiii) for Wee Willie Keeler's remarkable player statistics.

12. Electronic or RF (radio frequency) sealing of thermoplastics was a difficult problem in terms of both medical product reliability and quality and production efficiency. Baxter worked on this technology for years, going all the way back to the time in the early fifties when Dave Bellamy (then with Fenwal) experimented with this process in an old mill building in Ashland, Massachusetts.

13. Actual pricing data for Vacoliter solution in 1934: 60 cents. Escalated at 5 percent annual rate to 1990: $9.22. Comparable selling price in 1990: 66 cents. Baxter Finance Department.

14. Baxter 1980 annual report.

15. Baxter 1951 annual report.

16. Rosemary Stevens, *In Sickness and In Wealth: American Hospitals in the Twentieth Century* (New York: Basic Books, 1989) is an example.

CHAPTER

II

MAKING A TOUGH INVESTMENT DECISION

On an early June morning in 1931 Dr. Ralph Falk was in his small office at Boise's St. Joseph's Hospital before seven a.m. He had some patient work to attend to before a ten o'clock meeting with his brother, Harry Falk, who was arriving from Los Angeles by overnight train. Ed Snow, Ralph Falk's attorney, was to join them.

Several bottles of intravenous solutions made by Dr. Donald E. Baxter, which Dr. Falk had brought back from an April meeting at Baxter's Glendale, California laboratory, caught his eye, reminding him of his concerns about the venture they were going to decide on later that morning.

His concerns were not about the product itself. Even though more work was clearly needed, particularly on the solution's shelf-life stability, Falk had had the opportunity to use the Baxter commercial product in his own surgery practice. Some of his St. Joseph's colleagues had used it as well. The patient results were excellent, and medical data Dr. Baxter had given him in Glendale had been corroborated.

No, Falk was concerned instead about the prospect of another investment with his younger brother, Harry. Harry had started two businesses earlier, with Ralph providing the lion's share of the capital. Both businesses had failed.

First, Harry Falk had gone into the cattle business. While the first shipment to market was in transit, cattle prices plunged to half of what they had been. The loss came to about $16,800—well over 50 percent of the investment ultimately made in this new venture.

Then Harry had the idea of shipping fancy, fresh Idaho potatoes to Eastern retail markets under the name Potatocrat. There was nothing wrong with the idea of gourmet fresh foods, but the economic morass of the Depression was clearly not the time to launch it. With that business struggling, his Boise warehouse burned down. Despite the fact that Harry owned a Boise insurance agency, the warehouse was not insured.

Harry pulled up stakes to make a new start in Los Angeles. He met Dr. Baxter of Certified Laboratory Products at a social gathering, which resulted in their forming a cosmetics company, Antonie's of Hollywood, named after one of Falk's daughters. As Dr. Baxter progressively focused his attention on intravenous solutions, Harry became convinced there was an opportunity in that business for him and his brother.

Harry's track record did not exactly inspire confidence in his newest business proposal, Dr. Falk thought to himself. On occasion, he had said to family and friends, "I hope Harry doesn't think the reason I work as hard as I do at my medical practice is to generate cash for his business ventures." The remark was always made affectionately and in good humor, but there was an edge in his voice at the same time.

The earlier results of Harry's entrepreneurial enthusiasm were not the only concerns, however. The economic wreckage of the Depression made it the worst of times to risk financial resources that had somehow survived the last two years.

From the market's roller coaster ride of early 1929, Black Thursday on October 24, and then the stock market crash on Tuesday, October 29, stock prices didn't stop falling until November 13, 1929.[1] By that date the New York Stock Exchange List had lost an estimated 40 percent of its market value. The economic slide was just beginning. In 1930 the American Federation of Labor estimated that 43 percent of all construction workers were out of work. The YMCA in New York's City's Bowery was feeding 12,000 unemployed a day. Unemployed workers rioted in New York, Cleveland, Detroit, and Washington, D.C.

As Dr. Falk reflected on the decision he had to make, the economic havoc was still mounting. From 1929 to 1933, national income fell from $88 billion to $40 billion. Farm income plummeted from $12 billion to $5 billion. Automobile production dropped to 20 percent of its 1929 high of 5 million cars. American steel production bottomed out at 12 percent of capacity. In July 1932, the Dow Jones stood at 58, from 452 in September 1929.

From 1929 to 1932, factory wages were slashed from $12 billion to $7.6 billion. The average weekly wage collapsed from $25.03 to $16.73. Wheat prices fell from $1.65 to 39 cents a bushel, cotton from 17 cents to 6 cents a pound, and corn to 33 cents from 81 cents a bushel.

This was not an auspicious time to persuade hospitals to pay up to 75 cents a liter for commercially prepared solutions they could make themselves for a direct cost that was much less—not when they were laying off their own employees—no matter how good the Baxter product proved to be.

Harry Falk, too, had a chance to reflect during his overnight train ride from the west coast. As he watched the night landscape slip by the train windows, he concluded there were two clinching arguments to use with his brother. One was this was a business, unlike cattle and potatoes, which his brother understood as a doctor. The second was that if they didn't seize the opportunity to take Baxter solutions into national distribution, someone else certainly would. Maybe it would be a company like American Hospital Supply, whose sales were flattening for the first time since its founding in 1922.

Despite Harry's failures, the Falk brothers had a solid business background. Their father emigrated from Germany in the 1860s. He crossed the Panama Isthmus by mule, and then traveled to Boise, Idaho, from San Francisco. There he was joined by other brothers from Germany and started a successful dry goods store. The store was sold many years ago, but still operates.

There were four Falk sons: Leo, who ran the store; Ralph (born in 1884); Harry; and the youngest, Ted, and two daughters, Anne and Bella.

Ralph Falk II believes that his father had been interested in medicine from childhood. "But," Ralph said, "my grandfather was just as determined that his second son would become an engineer. Kindly but firmly, he refused to pay my father's way through premedical school. My father borrowed his way through Cal Berkeley, and then went on to Cooper Medical School in San Francisco. I don't know why he transferred to Jefferson Medical School." Ralph graduated from Philadelphia's Jefferson Medical College, interned at Augustana Hospital in Chicago, and had a thriving medical and surgical practice in Boise. Soon after the end of World War I he stopped delivering babies, and by 1931 he had restricted his practice to diagnosis and surgery.

Ralph Falk was committed to improving the quality of patient care. One of the stories he was fond of recounting in later years was how he had diagnosed and cured, after others had failed, parrot fever (psittacosis) in Mrs. William Borah, the wife of the U.S. Senator from Idaho.

Dr. Falk's diagnostic skills were advancing, consistent with what was happening then in medicine. He was concerned, moreover, with operative and post-operative complications that he saw among patients. This stimulated his keen interest in safe IV solutions.

THE TEN O'CLOCK MEETING

Following a decade of consumerism and marketing in the 1920s, hospitals had become marvels of engineering with their surgery amphitheaters, modern air handling, efficient kitchens, and supply systems. In addition, an increase in the number of government hospitals had prompted physicians and voluntary hospitals to form closer alliances that would lay the foundation for hospitals to become centers of medical technology—first in radiology, then oxygen therapy, blood collection, and anesthesiology. Despite this modernization, however, hospitals were still seriously deficient in aseptic procedures for surgical instruments, intravenous solutions, and rubber tubing used in intravenous and blood procedures.[2] It was becoming understood that solutions which avoided patient pyrogenic (fever) reactions could hasten and assure their recovery and even shorten their hospital stay. Dr. Falk was well aware of this, and as he sat in his office at St. Joseph's pondering the problem of the proposed business proposition, he also knew this was not another of Harry's speculative schemes. Hospitals had a definite need for Baxter's product; he just didn't know how to persuade them that they did.

When Snow and Harry joined Dr. Falk in his office a little after ten o'clock, they found him shaking a Baxter solution bottle. They watched as particulate settled out and clouded the solution.

"Look, Harry," Dr. Falk said, "the product still needs a lot of development. While I know it works with patients, the appearance will turn off doctors and nurses. More important, hospital admissions and revenues are declining. The only thing that's keeping the patient census up is more non-paying patients are being admitted to government hospitals."

Dr. Falk's sense of national trends proved correct. Hospital revenues depended on paying patients, who accounted for nearly three-quarters of their budgets. Since the Depression, however, patient revenues in nongovernment hospitals were dropping significantly (17 percent from 1929 to 1933). As yet there were no hospital insurance programs; it would be another five years before the standards for insurance were set.

C. Rufus Rorem became head of the American Hospital Association's Committee on Hospital Services. Within a year he developed the national standards for what would become Blue Cross Plans. By 1940, there were 71 plans with 4.4 million enrollees.[3]

Dr. Falk continued to enumerate his concerns. "Baxter solutions will no doubt be successful, but how long will it take? A lot of missionary work with doctors and other operating room personnel will be necessary.

"It's true, surgeries and all kinds of lab tests have been increasing,[4] but we'll have to see what happens now. Who can afford to pay for these procedures in times like this? Anyway, most of the surgery is routine—tonsillectomies, adenoidectomies, appendectomies, and deliveries[5]—and that doesn't represent much in the way of IV solution potential. There are going to have to be other medical developments before solutions begin to reach any volume.[6]

"I'm figuring on an investment, with others, of $35,000.[7] That's a bigger risk, Harry, than we took with either cattle or potatoes."

"I don't see how we can lose this time," Harry answered. "Direct sales are already being made in California. All we have to do is get the word out in the eastern territory."

Snow seemed to side with Harry. "The rights you'd be acquiring from Don Baxter, Ralph, have real value," he said. "If worst comes to worst, you could recoup some of your investment by selling the rights to someone else."

Before the ten o'clock meeting was over, it was relatively certain the venture would proceed if an agreement could be reached with Baxter. The positive decision was as much due to Dr. Falk's keen interest in what Baxter solutions could contribute to patient care and the correction of post-operative complications from hospital IV practices as it was to the business reasons that had been discussed.

INCORPORATION OF DON BAXTER INTRAVENOUS PRODUCTS, INC.

A few months later, on October 19, 1931, Don Baxter Intravenous Products, Inc. (DBIP) was incorporated in Delaware.[8] Capitalization was one thousand shares of authorized $100 preferred and one thousand shares of no par common. There were 22 common stockholders and 21 preferred holders, both groups dominated by the Falk family and Dr. Baxter.

Harry Falk relocated from Los Angeles to Glenview, Illinois, to begin his sales efforts.

The first formal board meeting was held on October 26, 1931, to elect the corporate directors and officers. They were:

The first production team from the 1933 Glenview plant.

Dr. Donald E. Baxter, president and director,
Dr. Ralph Falk, treasurer and director,
Harry Falk, general manager and director,
Fred Mann, vice president and director, and
John McGonigle, secretary and director.

Soon after, on October 30, the board authorized reimbursement of Ralph Falk for the following start-up expenses: $750 for corporate life insurance; $500 incorporation costs; $3,000 advance royalty payment to Don Baxter; and $1,000 balance due on 21,600 one-liter bottles for eastern inventory. That took an almost 20 percent bite out of paid-in capital.

THE PROMISE OF MODERN INTRAVENOUS THERAPY

It was a rocky road for the new company in the 1930s. Product development problems were not overcome until the end of the decade, and general hospital acceptance wouldn't be achieved until much later.[9] The initial accomplishment of gaining safe access to the human body's internal distribution system, however, was extraordinary. Intravenous solutions were an early triumph of combining medical science and engineering—more common now in diagnostics, other medical instrumentation, and biotechnology, but relatively unusual then.

Much work remained to be done with Baxter solutions, however, and the new company was immediately taxed to complete the solving of many product problems. In 1936, the first Ph.D. scientist, Dr. Naurice Nesset, joined the company, bringing with him a missionary zeal for technology leadership and product quality.

Co-workers of that era recall a quality quiz Nesset liked to give new production workers. "What's the ultimate test of quality for this bottle of solution?" he'd ask. After thinking, the worker would invariably say, "The ultimate test is for me to take the solution myself." "No," Nesset would say. "I want you to be so confident of this solution that you'd administer it to one of your children."

Whether Nesset knew that Baxter had done exactly that—had experimental solutions administered to his own son in addition to taking them himself—is unknown. Dr. Baxter had treated his son at Los

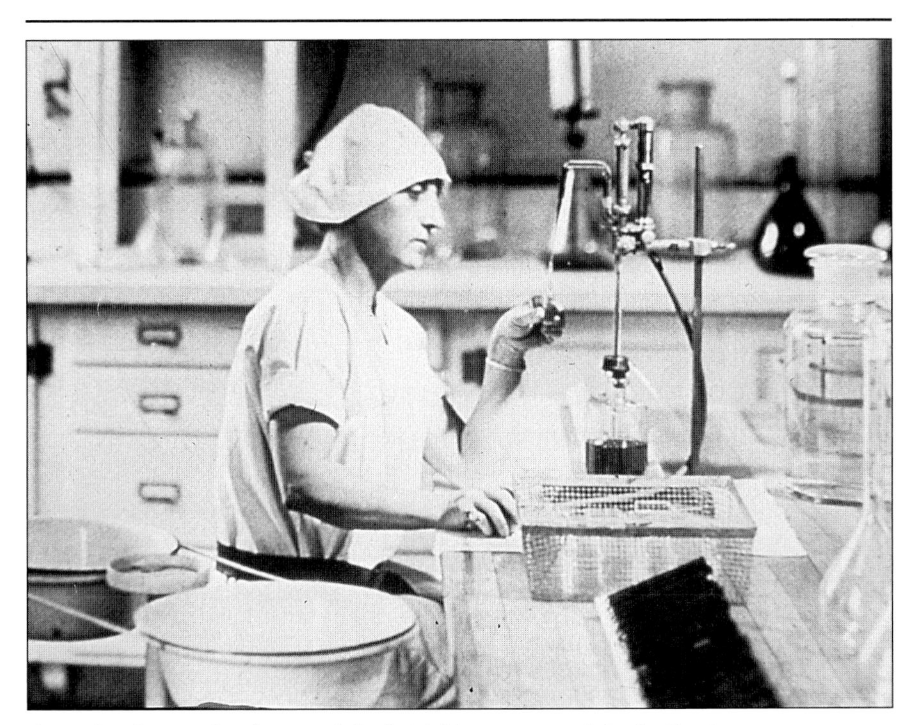

A production worker in one of the initial intravenous labs for Baxter.

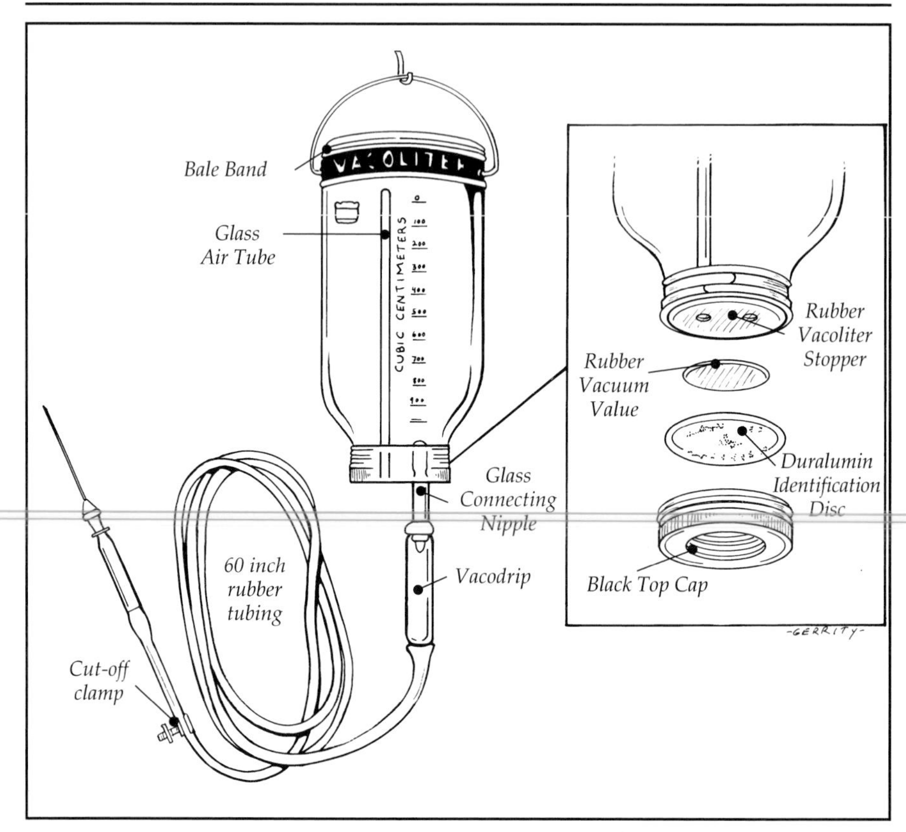

The Vacoliter Container: *The illustration shows the assembled Vacoliter container and parts which made up the product. This glass container was among the first marketed by Baxter. It underwent several improvements and was in common use before the advent of polyvinyl intravenous infusion solution containers.*

Angeles Children's Hospital and himself at Cottage Hospital in Santa Barbara. More than a demonstration of patient safety, Baxter's experiments also showed that his system saved time and money. One of the techniques some doctors had used to lessen the risk of pyrogenic (fever) reactions was hyperdermoclysis, the injection of solution deep into the tissue with a long needle. This procedure required the doctor or nurse to stay with the patient for an hour or more to watch for the warning signs of fever, and that cost money. Thanks to the dedication to product quality and patient safety by such people as Dr. Falk and Dr. Nesset, by the end of the decade of the Depression, the new company had already greatly surpassed its progenitor, Don Baxter, Inc., in technology as well as market share.

Despite Dr. Falk's early concerns about launching a new business in the middle of the Depression, his timing turned out to be fortuitous. Soon after 1931, hospital treatment of patients became more aggressive. Admissions data from 1935 and 1936, for example, show sharp increases in hospital treatment of pneumonia. From 1935 to 1940 the number of deaths occurring in hospitals grew from one-fourth to one-third of all deaths, showing how much more acute care was being provided in the hospital setting.[10]

Baxter's formation thus coincided almost exactly with the emergence of modern clinical medicine. DBIP, which became Baxter Laboratories, Inc. (BLI) in 1935, contributed significantly to these major changes in the health care environment and at the same time benefitted from them.

END NOTES

CHAPTER II

1. Materials in this paragraph and the next two are taken from William K. Klingaman, *The Year of the Great Crash: 1929.* (New York: Harper & Row, 1989).

2. For an excellent discussion of practices in Boston's Peter Bent Brigham Hospital in 1933, see Dr. Carl Walter "Finding A Better Way" in *The Journal of the American Medical Association.* Vol. 263 (Mar 23-30, 1990). (Carl Walter was an operator of one of the nation's first blood banks and a founder of Fenwal Laboratories, which was acquired by Baxter much later in 1959.)

3. Rosemary Stevens, *In Sickness and In Wealth: American Hospitals in the Twentieth Century* (New York: Basic Books, 1989), 140-69.

4. William G. Rothstein, *American Medical Schools and the Practice of Medicine* (New York: Oxford University Press, 1987).

5. Stevens, *In Sickness and In Wealth.* These procedures accounted for 51.9 percent of hospital admissions from 1929-31.

6. The most notable development of the era was Sulfanilamide in 1937, which ushered in modern clinical medicine. See Lewis Thomas, *The Youngest Science* (New York: Viking Press, 1983).

7. $35,000 was the planned investment level; the actual investment was $27,500.

8. Information in this section is taken from early DBIP board minutes.

9. Actually, product and production problems weren't fully resolved until the advent of disposable solution bottles and plastic, disposable tubing (patient administration sets).

10. Stevens, *In Sickness and In Wealth.*

CHAPTER

III

THE EARLY YEARS: 1931-39

Before proceeding with the flow of events, it would be helpful to go back to the origin of the California company, Don Baxter, Inc., and the individual who struck the initial technical spark in intravenous solutions, Dr. Donald E. Baxter.

Dr. Baxter was born in Southington, Ohio, in 1882. After attending Hiram College in civil engineering, he transferred to Baltimore Medical College. About this time, dispensaries were rapidly expanding their care in urban centers, and hospitals were beginning to expand their medical education activities.[1]

Before graduating in medicine from the University of Louisville in 1909, he worked for a time in surveying and civil engineering. As far as is known, he never had a medical practice as such. Except for World War I, when he served with the military in France, he worked principally with the Rockefeller Foundation. Before the war, he worked on post-poliomyelitis care in New York City and, after the war, with victims of cholera in China. Dr. Baxter is thought to have engineered the first inclined ramp for wheelchair patients while in China.

Having contracted tuberculosis, Dr. Baxter returned to California in 1921 and established a laboratory on Gardena Avenue in Glendale. There he experimented with a variety of products: nitrous oxide (laughing gas), X-ray and stereoscopy equipment, a polio cure, birth-control products, and cosmetics.

In addition, Dr. Baxter had a continuing interest in solutions and worked on improving them. He was strongly influenced by a 1923 paper by Dr. Florence Seibert of the National Tuberculosis Association. In her paper, Seibert traced patient fever reactions to pyrogens that were produced by bacteria in distilled water and that remained in solutions even after elimination of the bacteria themselves. By 1928, using himself as a test subject, Dr. Baxter had found a method of using a baffle to prevent reflux (backflow) in producing IV solutions under vacuum and thus eliminating pyrogens. By 1929 he was producing small quantities of commercial solutions. He disposed of his cosmetics interests to a local chemist, and in 1930 Certified Laboratory Products was renamed Don Baxter, Inc.

It was during this period of early commercial development that he and Harry Falk became associated. Baxter may have been interested in licensing his development to Ralph Falk because of his own capital limitations or in order to continue to do laboratory development work on this and other products, or both. There is no way of knowing with certainty because his activities would continue for only a few more years.

INTRAVENOUS AND PARENTERAL THERAPY: DEVELOPMENT COINCIDES WITH TRENDS IN HOSPITAL CARE

Modern intravenous therapy based on Dr. Baxter's early work came along at just the right time to be a part of a series of major changes and improvements in patient care, such as increasing emphasis on clinical specialization and anti-infectives.

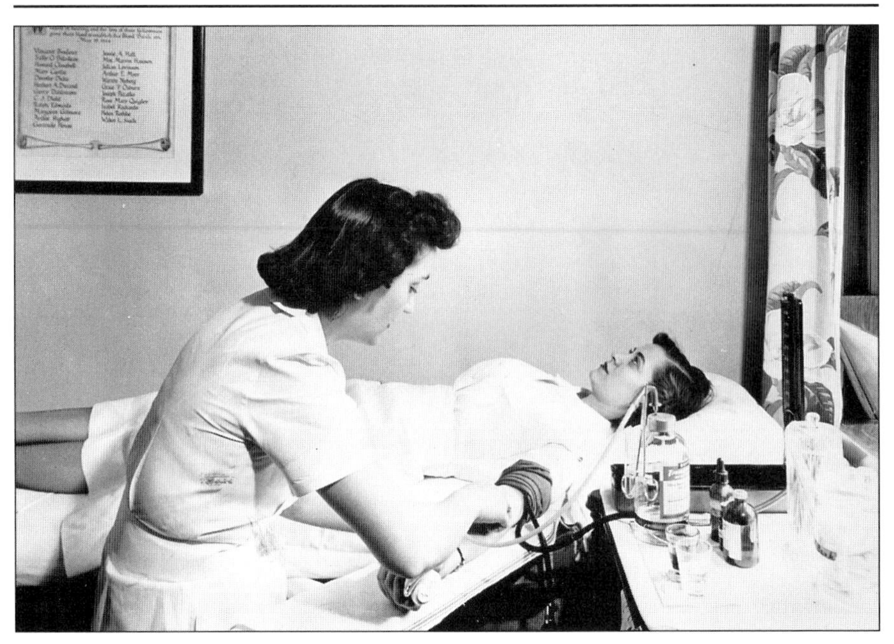

Early parenteral therapy required considerable supervision by a professional medical team.

Parenteral therapy is the administration or infusion of fluids, nutrients, or medicines through pathways other than the alimentary canal in order to (1) correct shock, (2) meet nutritional needs when the gastrointestinal tract isn't functioning, (3) infuse drugs, and (4) correct blood profile and blood pressure.

Medical interest in the infusion of solutions dates to Sir William Harvey's description of the circulatory system and Sir Christopher Wren's animal injection experiments in the seventeenth century. In 1831, Dr. William Shaughnessy described the benefits of solutions therapy. In that same year, saline solutions were administered to cholera patients with mixed results. Widespread use of commercial solutions, however, had made little progress in the hundred years since. Physicians were reluctant to use IV solutions because of their experience with hospital-mixed products. Even as doctors began to use solutions less cautiously, however, they didn't necessarily use them less sparingly. They had to learn the appropriate and adequate quantities of IV solutions to speed post-operative recoveries and, in some cases, to shorten hospital stays. It was not until the demands of battlefield medicine in World War II that the appropriate quantities of solutions began to be better understood.

EARLY PROBLEMS

The enormous task facing the new company, then, was to accomplish initial market introduction and entry—sufficiently to generate some modest cash flow—while at the same time continuing to press ahead with product development and patient administration work that had only begun at this point. The effort to overcome basic product problems was to continue throughout the thirties.

Harry Falk's optimism and his brother's investment faith were severely tested in 1932, the first full year of operation. While Harry busied himself with sales promotion, renting warehouse space at Chicago's Navy Pier, and then moving the office from Jackson Street to space adjacent to American Hospital Supply on Jefferson Street, hospital orders were not increasing. Dr. Falk's letters and his occasional visits from Boise reminded Harry that cash flow was tight and growing tighter.[2]

Several separate problems—including customer resistance to the price of the new solutions—discouraged sales: cloudiness or turbidity in the solution caused by microscopic glass particles that flaked off the container during storage, contamination of the solution caused by its reaction with the rubber bottle stopper, and discoloration of the dextrose caused by the sterilization process. Dr. Naurice Nesset worked with Owens Illinois Glass Company to solve the first problem through a process known as "1845 treat." The sulphur dioxide finishing treatment to glass provided an effective barrier to interaction between the container and the solution it held.

The stopper problem was resolved later by a colleague of Dr. Baxter's, Dr. Arthur Cherkin, who developed a "secret" tung oil formulation. Dr. Cherkin was Don Baxter's first senior scientist. He contributed significantly to most of the important steps in commercialization of IV solutions. His wife, Adina Cherkin, recalls working all night with him in the early 1940s in the small Glendale laboratory "analyzing drip samples." At the same time, he was pursuing his Ph.D. degree in biochemistry at the University of California, Los Angeles. Much later, he was caught up in the conflict between Don Baxter, Baxter Laboratories, and American Hospital Supply Corporation, and left the company. He subsequently joined the staff of the California Institute of Technology. Cherkin died in 1981.

Ed Nawoj, who started with Baxter in October 1937 as a chemist, recalls how the "secret formula" was kept in a locked safe, and the "paint," as they called it, was mixed only by him or under his direct supervision.

"Even after we got the paint formula from California, it didn't work with our stopper, which was different," Nawoj said. "Under Dr. Nesset's direction, we tried dipping the stopper in a chlorine solution so the paint would adhere. For a while, we had workers in gas masks outside the plant working with the chlorine solution. However, the chlorine changed the pH of the solution, so we switched to a sulfuric acid treatment. On this single problem we went through a whole process of manufacturing development. We had to. We wouldn't have made it over the long-term without solving the glass-coating and stopper problems." The dextrose discoloration problem was solved gradually through improved sterilization techniques and tight quality control, together with improved stopper coating.

All of this was at the root of the sales problems Harry Falk was experiencing in 1932. With sales still flat in August, a discouraged Ralph Falk decided to inquire about whether Eli Lilly & Company might have any interest in the commercial solutions business. His proposal was assignment of his rights for a one percent royalty. His back-up position was the outright sale of the company for $10,000 or less.

Encouraged by Josiah Lilly's[3] preliminary interest, Dr. Falk went to Indianapolis with Vacoliter solution samples to pursue an agreement with the Lilly company. Discussions there ended on a note of strong mutual interest, and Dr. Falk returned to Boise believing a deal could be struck. Time passed, however, with no follow-up word from Lilly.

Pondering the next step at St. Joseph's Hospital, Dr. Falk noticed how cloudy the solution samples on his desk had become, and that heightened his apprehension. He took the initiative and contacted Josiah Lilly. What he learned bore out his concerns. Mr. Lilly told him with some sharpness that the solution samples left for analysis in Indianapolis had clouded and discolored, and the company was not interested in further discussion. The Lilly option had quickly evaporated. Just as quickly, it was replaced by a very different option, which was adopted and implemented before year-end. The direction set in December 1932 soon alleviated Baxter's short-term sales problems, but at the same time it created long-term issues and conflicts that were to continue for years into the future.

BAXTER MAKES AMERICAN HOSPITAL SUPPLY ITS EXCLUSIVE DISTRIBUTOR

Problems with solutions were not the only reason Harry Falk was having trouble selling Baxter's products. He was also discovering how hard it was to sell to hospitals. Hospitals then and now are complex organizations with many reasons for caution about change, and they tend to make decisions about new approaches and products slowly and grudgingly.

Occasionally, Harry would talk to Foster McGaw of American Hospital Supply about his sales problems. McGaw was one of the five men who founded American Hospital Supply in 1922. He was the sales management sparkplug of that organization, having had earlier sales experience in the infant hospital supply business. Much later, McGaw would become the major owner and chief executive of American Hospital after the death of the dominant original investor, Harry Drake. McGaw was to become, starting in 1932, and continuing for almost 30 years, an important outside factor in Baxter affairs.

Harry Falk and McGaw had been crossing paths with increasing frequency in 1932. Harry became more and more convinced that an American distribution agreement was the answer to Baxter's immediate business problems. They ran into each other at hospital shows and conventions, and one or the other would obliquely bring up the possibility of a distribution agreement between their two companies. Harry Falk clearly thought it was a solution to his business problems because, after the American deal was done, he went on to execute other exclusive distribution contracts with Ingram and Bell in Canada, A. B. Christaens in Belgium, and in other countries. Paying royalties upstream and distribution discounts downstream would become a headache of major proportions.

McGaw's motivations for the distribution agreement may have been more complex. Of course he saw the promise of the fledgling Baxter solutions product, and his own distribution sales in 1932 had been flat. Beyond that, it's possible that he was thinking ahead to what later emerged as a major American Hospital Supply priority. After he became controlling stockholder and chief executive in 1947, McGaw emphasized backward integration from supply distribution into manufacturing. It's also likely that as McGaw watched Harry Falk's early unsuccessful attempts to manage the small Baxter business, he thought to himself that there was an opportunity for a more dominant and active role for him and American Hospital Supply to play.

With these potential "control" issues hovering in the atmosphere, Harry Falk, John McGonigle, and Ed Snow met with Drake, Charles Hough, and McGaw of American Hospital in mid-December 1932 to hammer out details of an exclusive distribution agreement for the 37 eastern states for "products known as D-glucose and/or normal salts together with combinations of either or both of said articles in Vacoliter solution dispensers and/or Ampules." The solutions were to be shipped directly from Glendale, California, to American Hospital's Chicago and Pittsburgh warehouses. Baxter's board approved the contract on December 20, 1932.

This contract, in ever more complicated form, was to continue to be renewed until 1962,[4] 30 years later. Many believe it was the Baxter solutions volume that enabled American Hospital Supply to build its modern warehouse and distribution system.

As for McGaw, he was to exert influence on Baxter's destiny for many years in a variety of ways. On June 14, 1935, he was elected to the Baxter board and was granted 250 shares of Class A (nonvoting) Baxter stock. He resigned from the board on November 30, 1943, at a time when there were Baxter-American contract disputes. (He later told one of his associates that disposing of his Baxter stock was the single worst business decision he ever made.) Later, in 1950, he acquired the California company, Don Baxter, Inc., for American Hospital Supply Corporation, despite the fact that Baxter Laboratories held a first-purchase option. Baxter promptly filed a lawsuit contesting American Hospital's acquisition.

GROWTH AND CHANGE TO 1935

First-year Baxter sales in 1933 through the new American Hospital distribution agreement were modest. The company had revenues of $55,881, yielding a net profit of $3,589.

The more predictable volume of sales from American's distribution system, however, did allow Baxter to establish its own manufacturing facility, a five-thousand-square-foot converted automobile showroom, in Glenview, Illinois, where Harry Falk lived. Dr. Baxter came from California to provide assistance in planning and start-up, and two Don Baxter, Inc. employees, Wayne Brandon and Argyle Campbell, joined the initial staff of eight at the Glenview operation. Brandon served for a number of years as general manufacturing superintendent. Baxter remained in this facility, in a constant state of reconstruction and expansion, until August 1947 when its new Morton Grove, Illinois, Headquarters and Laboratory were ready for occupancy and the Glenview property was sold to Kraft Foods.

McClay "Mac" Cole was Baxter employee number 17. Months before his employment in 1936, Mac Cole was playing cards at the gas station on the corner of the Baxter plant property. (The property had been the site of the region's first Model T dealership.) The players heard a commotion outside and looked out to see a punch press that had fallen from a truck. "Come on, give us a hand,' said the man attempting to unload the truck. "I'll pay you to help us get this press into the plant."

The man was Brandon. After the work was done, Cole said to him, "I need a job. Are you hiring?" Brandon said he would get in touch with Cole, but never did.

Many months later, while fixing a car for a Baxter employee, Cole went into the plant. Brandon said to him, "Where have you been?" and hired him on the spot.

The gas station run by Frank Schmidt and his brother continued to figure in the story. The station operators kept a five-foot-tall black bear that they had raised from a cub as a mascot. One night Cole got a call from the Glenview police. "Meet us at Baxter," they said. "There's something strange going on there. Could be a break-in."

When Cole and the police got into the plant, they saw the bear tied to a post where the station owners had sheltered him for the night. The bear was twisting the caps off every solution bottle he could reach, and was thoroughly drunk and blown up like a huge balloon.

Cole's first job at Baxter was brushing solution bottles at 35 cents an hour. He moved up to filling the bottles. He received a nickel raise after his first year. It was almost five years before he received another raise. Cole ended up working for Baxter for more than fifty years, retiring in 1986. During his years of employment, his brother and his son worked at Baxter, and Cole met his wife there.

Mrs. Cole recalled one visit by Harry Falk to her department while she worked at Baxter. Her boss announced, "Clean this place up. Some of you get over here and tidy up these product storage shelves. Harry Falk is on his way over here."

Falk was a very small man, and Mrs. Cole says his head was barely visible over the factory partition before he entered the area. After he left the area, one of the employees grumbled, "We didn't need to clean up the shelves. Mr. Falk can't see up that high."

Running into Baxter employees in the neighborhood was not uncommon in the early years. Mac Cole recalled one afternoon in the Morton Grove barber shop. He was talking with some of his friends in the shop when a figure with a towel draped over his face suddenly sat up and extended a hand. "So you're Mac Cole. I've been looking forward to meeting you. I'm Bill Graham."

CHANGE OF OWNERSHIP AND NAME

In late 1934, Dr. Baxter initiated discussions with Dr. Falk about selling his 40 percent interest in the company. The board of directors, in a Portland, Oregon, meeting on October 29 and 30, 1934, authorized the company to buy back Dr. Baxter's preferred stock for $10,000. In early 1935, Dr. Falk bought Dr. Baxter's common stock for a reported $8,000.[5] On May 20, 1935, the board approved a name change to Baxter Laboratories, Inc. and a new capital structure of 1,000 common shares, 1,000 preferred shares, and 250 Class A (nonvoting) shares. Dr. Falk became president and Harry Falk was made executive vice president.

Not too long afterward, on July 20, 1935, Dr. Baxter died at the age of 53. Stricken with a cerebral hemorrhage in Las Vegas, he died on Amelia Earhart's plane en route to medical facilities in Los Angeles, according to unsubstantiated reports from several sources.

He was succeeded at Don Baxter, Inc. by his second wife's brother, Emory Beardsley. For a number of reasons, including the restricted western territory, the market and technical influence of that company waned. American Hospital Supply sought to reverse that trend when it bought the company in 1950.

FOCUS ON MANUFACTURING AND QUALITY

With the approval of Baxter solutions for general use in 1934 by the American Medical Association's Council on Pharmacy and Chemistry, the solutions market began to attract competition. Cutter Laboratories entered the business in 1934. A Chicago company named Hospital Liquids came in about the same time. In 1937, Abbott Laboratories introduced its IV solutions product line.

Recovery from the Depression continued and the likelihood of world war loomed. As hospital sales were slowly growing, Baxter Laboratories, Inc. was growing in depth and technical competence. This growth owed much to talented people who came aboard at that time. Owen Kompelein joined the company in 1936. His first job was mixing fibrol (a laxative) for Falk-Baxter, a sideline venture promoted by Harry Falk. Nawoj came aboard in 1937 and Ted Gewecke was recruited at about that time. Dan Borgen was added to the technical staff in 1938, and a bacteriologist, James McLellan, shortly after. Owen Fess became a part of Baxter in 1940 and Karl Bauman in 1941.

Nawoj remembers that period as being very stimulating and exciting because there were so many important things to be done that all one had to do was look around and take one's pick.

"Some people just naturally rise to the occasion," Nawoj said. "That happened with me and later on it certainly happened on a much larger scale with Bill Graham."

There were a number of critical things that needed doing in the late thirties. Autoclaving (steam sterilization) of the finished product was continually improved as sales volume increased. Product testing routines also became more rigorous. There were three major tests: the "black-and-white" test was for checking solution clarity; the "hammer" test was the procedure for checking vacuum in filled Vacoliter solution containers; and "shooting rabbits" was taking the temperature of rabbits injected with small amounts of batch solutions to test for pyrogenic reactions.

These procedures were carefully replicated in an expansion plant in College Point, New York, which opened in 1936 to service the growing network of American Hospital Supply warehouses, ten in number by the end of the decade. Expansion also began in Canada in 1937, culminating with the construction of a manufacturing plant at Acton, Ontario, in 1940.

Product expansion also continued. There were 20 different solution products by 1939. Work was continuing on tubing and other accessories needed to administer solutions to patients.

In the black-and-white test, the black background shows light particles in the solution, and the white background shows black or colored particles.

The operation most graphically remembered by production employees of that era is salvage. Vacoliter solution bottles, like milk bottles, made three or four trips back to the plant, along with stoppers and tubing, for salvage and reuse. All sorts of ingenious equipment were devised for removing the stopper from the used Vacoliter solution container, usually resulting in new ways to shatter and explode them.

"Nobody liked salvage," one employee of that time said. "Customers didn't like it, nor did they take adequate care with products intended for reuse. Truckers disliked it and gave poor service, and Baxter employees didn't want to be assigned to salvage." The problem didn't go away until years later when first tubing, and then the containers themselves, were converted to one-way disposables.

In keeping with the tenor of the times, labor unions began to make incursions in the Baxter work force. Harry Falk didn't help that situation. One of the stories about early management-labor relations tells of Harry coming upon a group of workers idling, and ordering that they all be fired. It turned out they were on an authorized break.

Born in Chicago in 1912, John Schlesser went to work for Baxter Laboratories in 1940 as the war approached. Schlesser had a 14-acre farm on Milwaukee Avenue in Niles near Oakton. He had a roadside farmstand and later a greenhouse. He had a new house on which he wasn't able to get a mortgage, so he needed a job to supplement his farm income. Schlesser recalled, "I had friends in Wheeling who worked for Baxter in Glenview. So I went there to apply at 3:30 one afternoon and John Storner hired me to go to work the next morning. Storner told me my pay would be 45 cents an hour, but it turned out when I got my first paycheck it was 50 cents an hour. I went to work breaking glass [in the salvage area]. There were still dirt floors in that part of the plant. We were changing over to a new two-liter bottle and that made the work even tougher. One day Storner said, 'We need people. Tell some of your neighbors to come around.' I told him Baxter ought to hire more women. When more women began to show up, there weren't enough rest room facilities for them. They took over and forced the men out of one of the plant rest rooms.

"I left to spend more time working my farm. I came back and worked in Morton Grove from 1948 to 1952. I didn't like it as much. It had gotten too modern for me."

One of the women hired in 1943 was Jane Meyer. She stayed with Baxter until 1983. Jane met her husband, Art, at Baxter. He was a supervisor at Baxter and worked with the company from 1943 to 1978. Meyer started in salvage at 25 cents an hour. She recalled, "Bottles came back from hospitals covered with mold. Of course, we wore no gloves or protective clothing. When raises came, they came at 2 cents an hour. Then I moved to the production line. I loved it. I was one of the people active in getting the union out of Morton Grove. People said it was because my husband was a supervisor. It wasn't, though. The union wasn't doing anything for us.

"Baxter was a great place for romance in those days. A lot of men coming back from the war married women they met and worked with at Baxter."

REMARKABLE SUCCESS IN MANAGING "DOWN THE COST EXPERIENCE CURVE"

IV solutions may be one of the more remarkable examples of American manufacturing inventiveness in regard to cost management with a product where technology changed rapidly, product value was continually increased, quality requirements were stringent, and customer needs kept evolving. Baxter's continuing commitment to manage costs took root about this time.

It was also at this time (1938) that the U.S. Food & Drug Administration was formed from earlier antecedents, and the modern New Drug Application (NDA) process began. Product quality requirements thus became more demanding. Much later, the F.D.A. added Good Manufacturing Practices (GMP) and Good Laboratory Practices (GLP) to be rigorously adhered to.

Through all the product variety and change, solution costs were inexorably driven down at rates and to levels that IV competitors were generally unable to match. This continued through a major change from glass to plastic packaging. The philosophy of "best manufacturing cost" applied to other Baxter products where the volume was considerably smaller. It also led to some interesting pricing and competitive decisions which are described later.

By 1939 war seemed imminent. The dark days of the Depression were drawing to a close. Baxter Laboratories' sales reached $787,000 in 1939, yielding net profits of $180,000. About half of American Hospital Supply's sales that year came from Baxter solutions, although the relationship between the two companies was uneasy and was to worsen in the forties.

For comparison, IBM in 1939 had total sales and service revenues of $39,474,000, yielding operating profits of almost $12,000,000. Sears Roebuck reported sales of $617,414,000. More relevant to Baxter's business, Merck & Company had 1939 sales of $20,060,000 with profits of $1,856,000. Abbott Laboratories, an early competitive entrant in the solutions business, had total sales of $11,485,000 with profits of $2,488,000.[6]

1935 HOSPITAL SALES PICTURE THROUGH THE EYES OF A SALESMAN OF THAT ERA

Through their contact with customers, salesmen of the early period played an important role not only in sales but in product development as well. Eben "Bud" Erickson[7] joined American Hospital Supply from Union Carbide on March 1, 1935, to sell Baxter solutions. He recalls what it was like to be a salesman of that period.

"Dr. Falk taught me how to fill a tube and needle set, unseal the bottle, and regulate the vacodrip to 60 drops a minute. The hospitals were buying ampules from pharmaceutical companies containing 50 percent dextrose in saline, and then they'd add sodium chloride to make it isotonic. Almost all the hospitals I called on were having difficulties with severe patient reactions, but they didn't want to admit it.

"Hospital objection to commercial solutions was based on price. I would point out that hospitals might pass on the small charge in the patient bill and even add a markup. Because of the strong resistance, I'd also suggest that the hospital buy a safeguard stock of 5 and 10 percent dextrose and saline, and I would train the nurses so it could be used in case of an emergency.

"A lot of my early work was service. One of my first sales was to a Jacksonville, Illinois, hospital, and they called to say they couldn't use the solutions because they had a lot of deflocculant material in them. I called Dr. Nesset in Glenview and drove down to get the solutions. In front of my car heater on the way back, the solutions cleared up. Then we realized that the cold weather had partially frozen these bottles and precipitated some of the dextrose.

"A few hospitals reported patient reactions when using the Vacoliter. So I dug into that and learned they weren't using distilled water to clean the reusable tubing and weren't cleaning needles properly. That led to the production of sets, which was a vital step forward."

MILESTONES

1930s

1931	Incorporation of Don Baxter Intravenous Products, Inc.
1931	Vacoliter container patent application.
1932	Exclusive distribution agreement with American Hospital Supply.
1933	Opening of Glenview manufacturing laboratory.
1934	American Medical Association Council on Pharmacy and Chemistry approves Baxter solutions.
1935	Dr. Baxter sells his interest in DBIP. Company is renamed Baxter Laboratories, Inc. Dr. Falk becomes CEO.
1935	Death of Dr. Donald Baxter.
1936	First expansion plant opened in College Point, New York, to serve growing American Hospital distribution network.
1937	First international expansion into Canada leading to manufacturing laboratory in Acton, Ontario.
1939	Introduction of Transfuso Vac container.
1939	Baxter annual revenues near $800,000.

END NOTES

CHAPTER III

1. In Baltimore in the late 1800s there were 18 dispensaries, the largest of which treated 10,000 patients annually. See William G. Rothstein, *American Medical Schools and the Practice of Medicine* (New York: Oxford University Press, 1987), Part III.

2. DBIP board minutes. 8 percent dividends on preferred stock were "passed" until June 30, 1934. Salaries for officers and directors (except Harry Falk) were not paid until October 15, 1934.

3. Josiah K. Lilly Sr. was the son of founder Eli Lilly, who served as president of the company from 1898 until 1932, when he retired and became chairman. He was replaced by his son, Eli. Source: Anita Martin, Eli Lilly and Company archivist.

4. While the contract was terminated in 1962, certain supply provisions carried forward through 1964.

5. Company documentation of the buy-out price does not exist. The $8,000 estimate is from Ralph Falk II.

6. Abstracted from *Moody's Manual of Investments: American and Foreign*, reports of 1940 and 1943.

7. Patrick McBride, interview on the occasion of Baxter's fiftieth anniversary.

CHAPTER

IV

THE WAR YEARS: 1940-45

In an era darkened by the shadow of widening world conflict, Baxter Laboratories developed a second major health care contribution, related to its pioneering work in commercial solutions and as significant as solutions. The company ended the era with management changes in 1945 which greatly expanded its horizons. Despite its technical achievements, Baxter was not an established, far-sighted enterprise until those 1945 changes.

BLOOD THERAPY BREAKTHROUGH . . . IN TIME TO MEET WAR NEEDS

Baxter's development of commercial blood collection and transfusion equipment came at just the right time, with the first product, the Transfuso Vac container, ready for production in late 1939.

However, just as with intravenous solutions, the few years of commercial development followed centuries of medical experimentation with blood transfusion. Medical progress was agonizingly slow. Only 347 transfusions worldwide could be identified by Landois up to 1875.[1] Then in rapid succession came blood-typing work in 1900; discovery (1914) of sodium citrate's effect of preventing blood coagulation; pioneering blood studies by Raus and Turner of the Rockefeller Institute (1916); and somewhat later Florence Siebert's identification of pyrogens (1923). Robertson ran a blood bank (although it wasn't called that) for the British Army in World War I.

This work seemed to cease after the war, except for the Soviets, who reported in the early thirties on their transfusion work using cadaver blood.

Progress quickened in the mid-1930s. Dr. Bernard Fantus is generally credited with operating this country's first blood bank in 1936 at Chicago's Cook County General Hospital, and with coining the blood bank name.

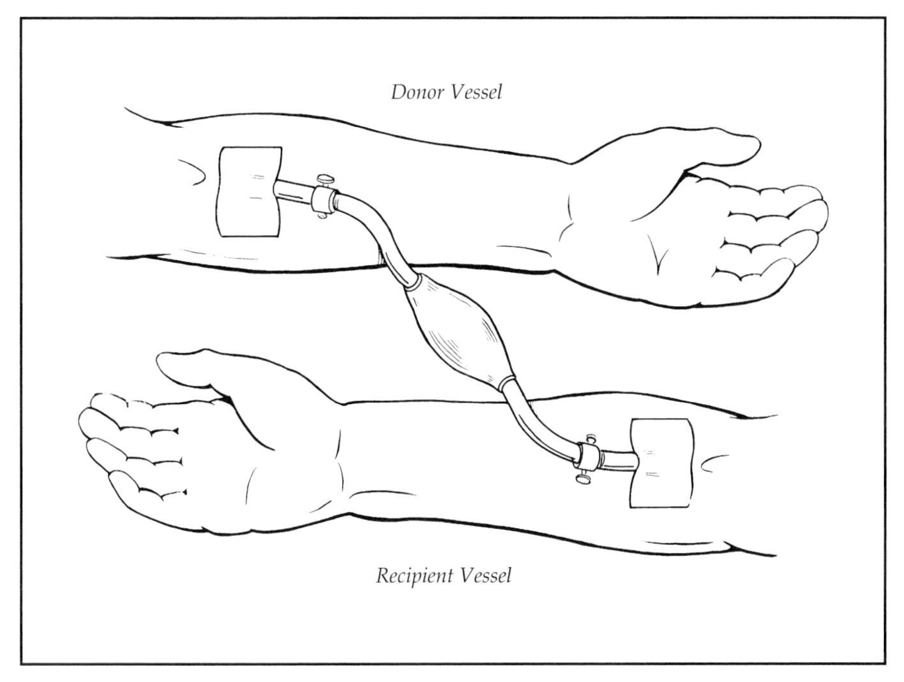

Early Methods of Direct Transfusion: *Before blood storage was perfected, the most common method of transfusion was to make a direct transfer from donor to recipient following confirmation of major blood type compatibility. The equipment shown facilitated the transfusion process. Because careful study of minor incompatibilities was not possible and since the equipment was reused following cleansing and sterilization, the number of reactions associated with blood transfusion was considerably higher than encountered in modern times of donor, storage, and administration management.*

The American National Red Cross created local panels for blood donation in 1937, but little progress was made until the United States was drawn into World War II and the Red Cross Blood Donor Service was operated under the guidance of the National Research Council. The British Ministry of Health asked their Medical Research Council to create a national blood bank service in 1939.

Prior to these blood therapy developments, there had been attempts at systems for collecting, storing, and administering blood to overcome the limitations of direct donor to recipient transfusion. All of them, however, suffered from similar problems. Storage time was short. Cell destruction (hemolysis) sometimes occurred, even during that short storage time, due to mechanical damage. There were febrile and other patient reactions, and these earlier systems were still extraordinarily labor-intensive. Introduction of air into the patient's system could cause life-threatening embolisms. The Transfuso Vac apparatus was intended to solve these problems.

There was no question about the critical medical need, but uncertainty about market potential and profitability lingered for some time. The overwhelmingly successful use of blood and plasma for casualties during World War II established, in the most dramatic human fashion, the significance of Baxter's innovation. The early war years saw such dramatic events as the first long-distance shipment by air transport of type "O" blood in cold storage. Doctors returning from military service at the end of the war had become accustomed to referring to a blood transfusion unit, as well as an IV unit, as "a Baxter."

TRANSFUSO VAC SYSTEM

Dr. Naurice Nesset at Baxter became keenly interested in advances in blood therapy as an opportunity to build on technologies the company had already begun to master. Through a field sales representative, Eben "Bud" Erickson, he met with Dr. Warren B. Cooksey of Henry Ford Hospital in Detroit. Erickson's role was an early example of how important a committed medical sales representative can be in relating development to market and patient needs. This kind of role would be emulated down through the years by many Baxter sales representatives. Cooksey began to consult with Baxter, and the company acquired the rights to his blood system in development, the "Cooksey Set." Then Nesset became aware of the work reported in 1936 by Dr. John Elliott, chief of laboratory services at the hospital in Salisbury, North Carolina, and later captain in the U.S. Navy, on blood plasma and sera.[2]

On October 5, 1938, Nesset filed patent applications for blood transfusion devices, and on June 26, 1939, the company signed a royalty agreement with Elliott covering some of his ideas that were incorporated in Transfuso Vac device design.[3]

During this early period, Nesset also worked closely with Mary Sproul of the American National Red Cross and maintained contact with the Mayo Clinic, which expressed interest in Baxter's promising blood work.

The Transfuso Vac solution that resulted from this work was a completely closed system under vacuum, containing sodium citrate to prevent blood coagulation, with specially designed valve and filter devices.

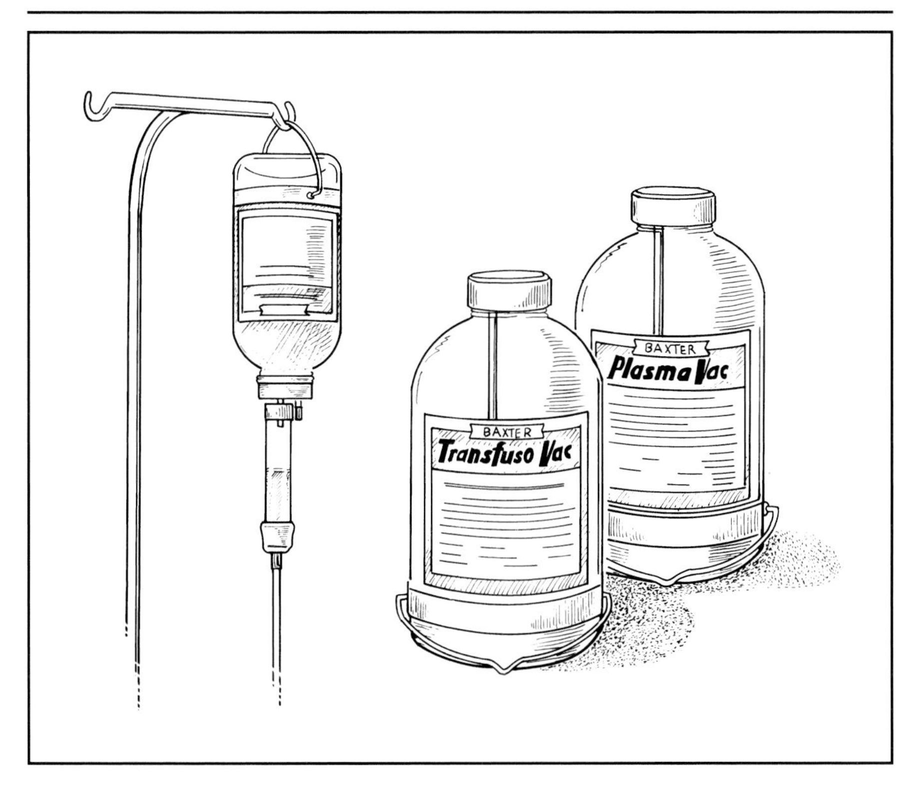

The Transfuso Vac and Plasma-Vac: *These two products were most important in establishing the reputation built by Baxter for blood product storage and administration. There were several accessories to facilitate use of this equipment during the donation and ultimate administration process.*

The Transfuso Vac apparatus is an example of the product line extension and specialty niche approach that Baxter would later make a central part of its corporate strategy. Customer acceptance was slow to build (except in the military), in part because of problems with the reuse of rubber tubing sets. The advantage was that limited market size probably discouraged entry by a number of potential competitors. Transfuso Vac development paved the way for Baxter's entry into the business of blood products and blood components. The acquisition of Hyland Laboratories in 1952 and of Fenwal Laboratories in 1959 strengthened and broadened the company's leadership in blood therapy, which continues to the present time.

TRANSFUSO VAC SYSTEM MANUFACTURING PROBLEMS

There were a host of system and product problems to be overcome, in addition to patient reactions to sodium citrate, pyrogenicity, air embolisms, nonsterile equipment, and febrile reactions caused by finely divided sulfur used to cure rubber tubing. The Transfuso Vac, like the Vacoliter, was part of a complex system, and the company had to progressively address systems problems such as needles, filtration, and specifications for refrigerated storage.

Lab workers using pipettes drew samples from test batches of Transfuso Vac containers.

For the container itself, creating a rubber stopper for a larger opening (53 mm) than that of the Vacoliter solution container, and having to meet very different patient administration requirements, proved to be vexing problems. The original stainless steel "Scalborn" valve wasn't completely satisfactory, and methods for drawing and measuring container vacuum were difficult. Cleaning the container valve for reuse was also a major challenge. Ed Nawoj remembered, "It took almost two years to engineer this whole process and develop a technique for measuring container vacuum to 29.0 after sterilization."

THE PLASMA-VAC CONTAINER FOLLOWS IN 1941

While these manufacturing and engineering problems were progressively resolved, the Plasma-Vac container was introduced in 1941 for separation, storage, and administration of blood plasma. While the U.S. military had initial reservations about blood storage and administration devices because of their earlier experience with other equipment, Baxter blood and plasma equipment soon was in wide use in both the European and Pacific theaters of operation, yielding enormous human benefits.

GLENVIEW GEARS UP FOR WARTIME PRODUCTION

By the early 1940s, a $350,000 plant expansion had increased Glenview space to 70,000 square feet. The plant began to operate on a seven-day, three-shift basis. Soldiers worked the third shift in the early years and then were replaced by civilian women who flooded the work force as the war went on. In the European theater of operations alone, one-third of a million transfusions of whole blood were used, half of those flown from the United States.[4] Setting up IV solution production laboratories close to combat theaters was considered by the military and discussed with Baxter Laboratories. Considering the stringent, sterile conditions in which solutions must be produced, it's fortunate that the idea was never implemented.

By war's end, Baxter Laboratories had shipped 1.2 million Transfuso Vac and Plasma-Vac container units and 4.3 million IV solution units to the military. Military sales for the war period totaled $6 million by April 1945. This was a tremendous growth in volume since non-military sales were growing concurrently.

The College Point, New York, plant closed in 1943, and in 1945 a plant dedicated solely to military requirements opened in Ellenville, New York. It operated for a very brief time.

Dr. Paul Lazar, an M.D. dermatologist affiliated with Highland Park Hospital in Illinois, was born in Ellenville in 1922 and lived there until he went away to school at Northwestern University. He attended New York Medical School and interned at Michael Reese Hospital in Chicago.

Ellenville was a town of 3500 people in 1945. Dr. Lazar recalled Baxter's acquisition of space in the old Sunray Brewery building, which was to be used for fractionation of blood during the war. Baxter employed about fifty people. Lazar was often in the building because his father had a handkerchief factory there. He still remembers

Aboard a WWII hospital vessel, a wounded soldier is being prepped for intravenous plasma by the triage team.

the smell of Pepsi Cola throughout the building, including the Baxter space, from the Pepsi Cola bottler also located in the building.

Figure 1 shows the company's revenues and profits for the war years.[5]

BAXTER SALES AND EARNINGS
1941 - 1945

Year	$ Net Sales	$ Net Income (Before Taxes)	$ Net Income (After Taxes)
1941	1,168,000	251,000	156,000
1942	1,950,000	433,000	162,000
1943	2,770,000	558,000	176,000
1944	2,990,000	597,000	191,000
1945	4,082,000	382,000	176,000

Figure 1

WORLD WAR II ADVANCES IN MEDICAL AND HEALTH CARE PRACTICE

More significant by far than the wartime surge in demand for lifesaving Baxter products were the profound and lasting effects of war experience on medical knowledge and practice. Despite the remarkable development in the thirties of safe commercial IV solutions, many doctors remained concerned about them because of their prior experience with patient reactions to hospital solutions and because of the time they had to spend overseeing this procedure.

As many of these same doctors were drawn into military service, their experience with commercial solutions broadened and their confidence grew. This was not due solely to treating battlefield injuries. In induction centers where military recruits were processed, there were outbreaks of meningitis and other infectious diseases. One doctor, recalling the progress of these years, spoke about the "miraculous recovery of a desperately ill patient" after injection with sulfa in solution (sulfa was used for direct application to open wounds).[6]

Wartime stresses developed in the civilian health care system as well. Workers migrated to war production centers like Detroit, where Henry Ford and Harper Hospitals had been forced to reduce available beds because of medical staff shortages.[7] Perhaps such stresses caused civilian hospitals to become receptive to the rapid advances being made in both intravenous and blood therapy.

In 1941, Congress passed the Lanham Act to provide capital support to health care centers and hospitals in defense production areas. In 1943, the Federal Emergency Maternity and Infant Care Program (EMIC) was launched through the states. It provided direct, cost-based payments for obstetrics and pediatric care for military families, responding to the number of babies being born in substandard conditions. In 1946, when the program was terminated, one out of every seven U.S. births was covered under EMIC.[8]

The war years must include reference to the milestone British discovery of penicillin. In June 1942, there was only enough penicillin available to treat ten patients. The wartime U.S. Office of Scientific Research and Development and its Committee on Medical Research coordinated penicillin development with the result that penicillin treatment of military casualties began in April 1943. In the summer of 1945, penicillin was close to full availability for the general population.[9] Just as the discovery of penicillin remains one of the milestones of British science, the extraordinary speed of getting the product into volume manufacture is one of the outstanding achievements of the U.S. pharmaceutical industry.

The research emphasis which led to penicillin's success affected all aspects of medicine and clinical care, and broadened the understanding and application of Baxter's intravenous solutions as more difficult surgical procedures were undertaken.

Due to the important work of Dr. Douglas B. Kendrick and others, military specifications for intravenous solutions were developed.[10] Baxter's more than 20 solutions were the first to be approved in 1944.

The work of Dr. Kendrick and others also led to higher volume of intravenous solution use per patient and per procedure, approximating modern standards of IV therapy. For example, patients' intravenous caloric intake daily was increased from 200 to 1000, and recommended administration of solutions with a gall bladder operation increased from about one to six liters.

Important progress was also made by the military and by Baxter Laboratories in many components of the intravenous therapy system: needles, tubing (sets), as well as containers themselves. It was probably war experience that enabled Baxter, after the end of the war, to progressively and successfully introduce disposable plastic tubing and disposable solution containers. Cleaning tubing for set reuse and resharpening needles in combat-area conditions were not only difficult, they were risky. Availability of raw materials was also a factor in encouraging plastic use. At any rate, military experimentation with plastics was prophetic of later events as tubing sets, accessories, and containers themselves for IVs and blood products were converted to plastics. These developments would extend Baxter's technical leadership, increase its vertical integration, and build commercial market stability as these products became true "disposables."

The same kind of remarkable progress was demonstrated throughout the war with Baxter's blood transfusion and plasma equipment (Transfuso Vac and Plasma-Vac solution containers). Shortly before the onset of war and the introduction of Baxter equipment, doctors were just as anxious about blood transfusions as they were about intravenous injections. Until the introduction of the closed Transfuso Vac container system, transfusions took as long as six hours. The doctor had to be involved every step of the way, alert for patient febrile reactions, air embolisms, leaks and blood loss, hemolysis, and contamination.

That all began to change with the first drawing of blood for the Blood for Britain Project on August 16, 1940, the day the bombings of

London began. By January 17, 1941, when the project ended, 14,556 units of blood had been drawn and 5500 liters of plasma had been shipped to the United Kingdom.

The American Red Cross Donor Service was inaugurated on February 4, 1941, at the request of the U.S. Army and Navy. At the height of the program, 35 fixed centers and 63 mobile units were in operation, collecting an average of 110,000 pints of blood every week.[11] Dr. Falk's wife, Marian Citron Falk, became very actively involved in Red Cross wartime efforts.

An indication of the importance of these developments was that during World War II less than 5 percent of Americans wounded in battle died, while an estimated 10 percent of wounded Germans died between 1939 and 1943.[12] In Rosemary Stevens' book, *In Sickness and*

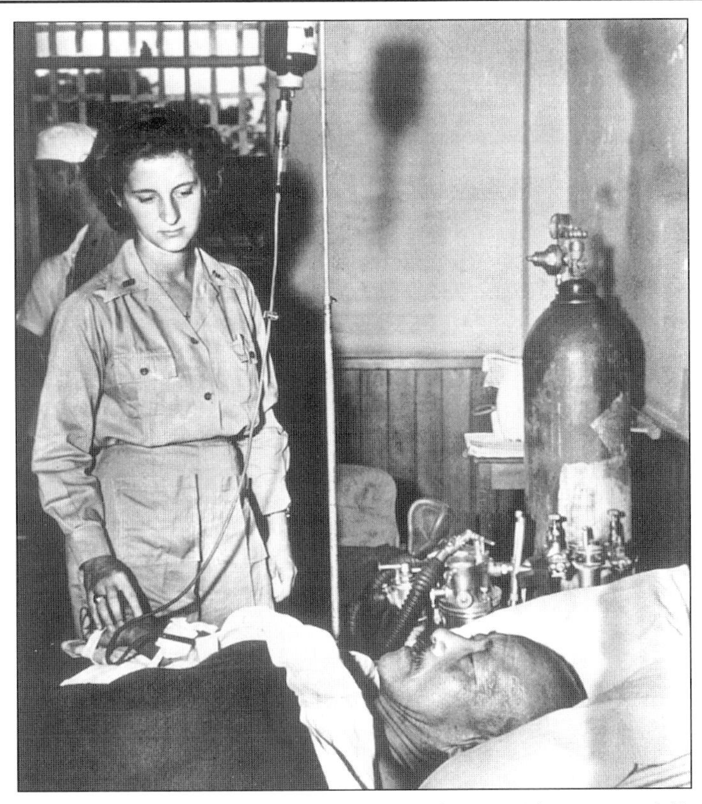

Tojo Hideki, the Prime Minister of Japan, after his suicide attempt following the surrender of Japan in WWII. He received blood and dialysis treatment, and recovered to stand trial as a war criminal.

in Wealth, frequently cited in this history, "resuscitation therapy (for the prevention and treatment of shock) and better blood replacement techniques, including the development of blood plasma supply" are cited second only to penicillin as outstanding medical successes of World War II.[13]

Dr. Kendrick's comprehensive book on the World War II blood program, cited here several times, is a rich source of further information about the dimensions and implications of Baxter's contributions. For example, he wrote,

> "The successful use of whole blood reached a high point in Okinawa (1945) . . . there were 40,000 casualties, and their treatment involved the use of approximately 40,000 pints of whole blood, 1:1. All the blood . . . was flown from the United States, a distance of 8,000 miles. With the dating period set at 21 days, it required careful timing. . . . There were two reasons why the operation was successful: first, the blood supply (distribution) from the United States to Okinawa via Guam was highly efficient. Second, the commanding general . . . assigned to a trained transfusion officer full responsibility for the supply, distribution, and correct use of all whole blood brought onto the island."[14]

At another point, he summarized the argument for a *separate* intravenous therapy service within the Armed Forces.

> "Intravenous therapy is a medical specialty, training in which is not provided in a routine medical education. The complexity of the problems involved in the manufacture, processing and preservation of blood, blood substitutes, and other parenteral fluids is little known to the average physician nor has he acquired the knowledge to design equipment and test it for efficiency in the collection and administration of these fluids."[15]

Both observations had clear implications for the Baxter Laboratories-American Hospital Supply relationship, which was coming to the forefront again as civilian market post-war planning began.

Kendrick, covering the Korean conflict as well, notes the infection of plasma supply with the hepatitis virus[16] during those hostilities—a portent of problems to come, with the threat of various infections in the nation's blood supply. Protection of the blood supply against preventable risk is another area where Baxter has made significant contributions.

HOMEFRONT DEVELOPMENTS

Not all the significant events of this period were directly related to the war. In 1943, Baxter Laboratories and American Hospital Supply began to renegotiate their distribution contract. Negotiations were acrimonious, leading to Foster McGaw's resignation that year from the Baxter board. A 32-year-old attorney with the firm of Dawson & Ooms, William B. Graham, became involved in those negotiations on behalf of Baxter, and his maturity and analytical skill attracted the attention of both Dr. Falk and Ed Snow, the Boise attorney.

When the revised contract was signed in 1944, it contained two new provisions of note. The first required a two-year notice of termination by either party, a stipulation that would grow in significance as future events unfolded. The second, Section 17, allowed Baxter for the first time to put its own technical service representatives in the field working with hospitals. This was designed to provide to the professionals using Baxter products direct technical support and to track application knowledge back to Baxter engineering and product development. The American Hospital Supply sales force sold a broad line and was more accustomed to dealing with hospital purchasing personnel rather than with medical staff. This contract modification served to heighten tensions between Baxter and its exclusive U.S. distributor.

PRELUDE TO BASIC MANAGEMENT CHANGE

In late 1942, after one of his monthly trips to the Baxter Laboratories Glenview facility, Dr. Falk sought out Snow back in Boise.

"Ed, I'm concerned about our control of all the things going on in Glenview, particularly about military requirements and coordination," he began. "It's helpful that Naurice Nesset has taken more responsibility for production as well as product development, quality, and engineering. But that still leaves a management void. Harry probably can't fill the void. What do you think ought to be done?"

"I've been waiting for you to raise that question," Snow answered. "Harry's made a lot of contributions as the business has taken root, but you and I both know he is not going to be the kind of general manager I think you're suggesting is needed. It's a difficult situation. Why not bring in an outside consultant to study it and make recommendations to you?"

Falk continued to think about this conversation and in early 1943 the management consulting firm of Booz Allen & Hamilton (which it appears may have concurrently been doing some work for American

Hospital Supply) was retained to conduct a comprehensive review of Glenview operations.

The two-hundred-page Booz Allen report dated July 31, 1943, was incisive. After noting Baxter's favorable attributes of "intensive employee loyalty," dedication to quality, clear leadership in parenteral therapy, and stringent technical standards, the report homed in on problems that needed to be solved: lack of "solidity" in the company; "underplanned and undercontrolled operations;" dependency on the single solutions product line; ineffective organization; and "overlapping management responsibilities," particularly between Nesset and Harry Falk. The report concluded that Baxter Laboratories should seek "common ownership" with American Hospital Supply Corporation through either a sale of Baxter to American or formation of a holding company which would own both Baxter and American.[17] That judgement produced an emphatic "No!" penciled in the margin by Ralph Falk.

One immediate and tangible result of the study was the retention of Booz Allen to recruit a manager from outside Baxter. A compromise had been reached on the consultant's recommendation because when Graham Evans was elected by the Baxter board on October 23, 1943, as "third vice president of the corporation at $10,000 per annum with duties of statistical, cost, and production analysis; profit analysis; and service in an advisory capacity as an economist"[18] he clearly was not a general manager and he reported to Harry Falk. Within a year it was clear this attempt to shore up the organization had been unsuccessful, although Evans' formal resignation didn't occur until December 31, 1945.

BEGINNING OF THE POSTWAR ERA

By August 1945, when World War II ended, Baxter's parenteral and blood products had proven their value and reliability in the most extreme conditions. The product line had broadened (see Figure 2). The company's attempt to strengthen its management direction and control had been unsuccessful. It was now entering war-end termination negotiations on military contracts that represented more than half its total volume.

1945 produced another landmark event, which would introduce a promising new era for Baxter.

BAXTER SOLUTIONS PRODUCTS IN LATE 1940s

TRAVENOL SOLUTIONS

1. normal saline
2. 5 percent sodium chloride
3. 2.5 percent dextrose in saline
4. 5 percent dextrose in saline
5. 10 percent dextrose in saline
6. distilled water
7. 5 percent dextrose in water
8. 10 percent dextrose in water
9. 20 percent dextrose in water
10. Lactate Ringer's
11. 5 percent dextrose in Lactate Ringer's
12. 10 percent dextrose in Lactate Ringer's
13. Ringer's Solution
14. 5 percent dextrose in Ringer's
15. 10 percent dextrose in Ringer's
16. 5.7 percent sodium sulphate
17. histamine in saline
18. histamine in 0.8 percent chloride solution
19. Darrow's Solution
20. one-sixth molar sodium r-lactate
21. 5 percent alcohol, 5 percent dextrose in saline
22. 5 percent alcohol, 5 percent dextrose in water
23. 10 percent alcohol, 5 percent dextrose in water

TRAVAMIN SOLUTIONS

Protein hydrolysate solutions in various combinations with salt and dextrose Travenol solutions.

TRINIDEX SOLUTIONS

B Group vitamin solutions again combined with salt and dextrose Travenol series.

TRAVERT SOLUTIONS

Solutions of invert sugar prepared by hydrolysis of sucrose.

Figure 2[19]

END NOTES

CHAPTER IV

1. Much of this material excerpted from Elmer L. De Gown, M.D., and Robert C. Harden, M.D., *Blood Transfusion* (Philadelphia: W. B. Saunders & Co., 1949).

2. De Gown and Harden, *Blood Transfusion*.

3. Baxter Laboratories, Inc. board minutes.

4. De Gown and Harden, *Blood Transfusion*.

5. Abstracted from Lehman Brothers prospectus for Baxter Laboratories' first public stock offering in 1951 and Baxter internal financial records.

6. Patrick McBride, Northwestern University interviews.

7. Rosemary Stevens, *In Sickness and In Wealth: American Hospitals in the Twentieth Century* (New York: Basic Books, 1989), 209.

8. ibid., 210-11.

9. ibid., 201-202.

10. Douglas B. Kendrick, *Blood Program in World War II* (Washington, D.C.: Medical Department, U.S. Army, 1964).

11. Stevens, *In Sickness and In Wealth* and historical records of the American Red Cross.

12. Stevens, *In Sickness and In Wealth*, 202.

13. ibid., 202.

14. Kendrick, *Blood Program in World War II*, xv-xvi.

15. ibid., 77.

16. ibid., xvi.

17. Booz Allen & Hamilton Management Report dated July 31, 1943.

18. Baxter Laboratories board minutes of October 23, 1943.

19. Origination and use of the Travenol name, which figure importantly in Baxter Laboratories' history, are discussed later.

PART TWO

FORMULATING A STRATEGY

By April 1945 Baxter had been in existence for almost 14 years. It had overcome most of the technical and application problems of Dr. Donald Baxter's original invention. It had pioneered another entry to the vital pathways of the human body through development of the Transfuso Vac container. Through both these efforts, the company had begun to accomplish Dr. Ralph Falk's principal objective in founding the enterprise: to contribute to marked improvement in hospital care of patients.

Baxter was still, however, a fragile business. The Booz Allen Hamilton Report in 1943 had as much as concluded that the only certain prospect for survival and growth lay in a combination with its larger distributor, American Hospital Supply Corporation. Baxter's total annual sales were about $4 million, and of that over half were military requirements now rapidly coming to an end. Even including military business, a year's total volume then was about one-tenth of Baxter's current *daily* volume. Size was not the inherent problem though. Despite the talent that had begun to be attracted in the late thirties and into the forties, the company's internal management was inadequate. Dr. Falk was unwilling to provide active management, preferring to remain in Boise. Harry Falk had proven unable to make the transition from entrepreneur to general manager.

The company hadn't developed a clear sense of long-term direction. It was being buffeted by outside events. A new leader and a strategy were urgently needed. With postwar adjustment already underway, time was short.

CHAPTER

V

EMERGENCE OF THE MODERN BAXTER

"There must be some way you can convince him to leave his law firm and join Baxter in a general management position. Both of us have talked with him for over a year now. You're sure he can do what needs to be done despite his lack of business experience. If you don't bring in someone you have complete confidence in, the problems in Glenview will continue, and the company won't be in a position to react to the opportunities the end of the war will bring. We both know what his concerns are. I think it's time to face up to them."

It was 1944, and in what had become a familiar refrain, Ed Snow was again making the case to Dr. Ralph Falk for recruiting William B. Graham to Baxter from the law firm of Dawson & Ooms. Not that the case needed to be made, and Falk said so.

"I agree with you, Ed. The obstacle is Harry's role in the business. Graham has made it clear that he won't consider an offer unless Harry's role is radically changed. I've been reluctant to meet that condition. Now it's time. I'll start talking with Harry and then open up discussions with Graham again."

BILL GRAHAM'S BACKGROUND

Who was this Bill Graham Dr. Falk and Snow were so determined to recruit? He was a 33-year-old attorney who had graduated from the University of Chicago with a B.S. in chemistry in 1932 and from the University of Chicago Law School in 1936. He had distinguished himself at Chicago: first in his graduating class, Phi Beta Kappa, and also elected to Sigma Xi, a scientific honor society usually reserved for chemistry graduate students. He also showed early some of the determination which was later to become one of his hallmarks. He found time to become the University of Chicago's handball champion. He was taking graduate chemistry courses before obtaining his undergraduate degree, and continued in graduate school intending to pursue a doctorate in chemistry. Despite the strong influence of the University of Chicago's Nobel Prize winners in chemistry at that time, he concurrently enrolled at night for one semester in the DePaul University Law School. He still found time to help his cousin, George McCabe, with Graham's father's law practice.

Graham's choice of the law, leading him to enroll full-time in the University of Chicago Law School from which he graduated cum laude, was influenced by McCabe, by his father, and perhaps by his father's untimely death while Graham was a junior in college.

Bill Graham

William Burden Graham was the only child of William and Elizabeth Burden Graham. He was born on the south side of Chicago on July 14, 1911. Both his parents were school teachers. His father later made a career change—studying for and being admitted to the Illinois Bar. Young Graham spent his childhood summers on farms owned by his parents in western Illinois' Bureau County. At one time, Ronald Reagan's family lived in a house owned by Graham's mother in the small town of Tampico. He attended elementary and secondary schools in Chicago.

Tampico then and now had a population of about 1,000. Graham's mother, one of eight children, and his father, from a family of twelve, had been born within four miles of each other in that area. Their farm was 400 acres with another 300 acres operated and owned with relatives. When Graham's grandfather died, he owned over 2,000 acres. Graham still has roots in that area, owning a 540-acre farm and a part interest in two other parcels of 120 and 80 acres. He continues even today to oversee the running of several Bureau County farms. That experience may have shaped his business thinking more than his colleagues ever realized.

After receiving his law degree and being admitted to the Illinois Bar, he joined the firm of Dyrenforth, Lee, Chritton & Wiles to practice patent law. When Horace Dawson left Dyrenforth Lee in 1940 to form Dawson & Ooms with the former commissioner of patents, Graham followed him. Dawson concentrated on larger clients (Armour, Bendix, General Mills), and turned some 60 smaller clients, including Baxter, over to Graham.

Graham married Edna Kanaley of Weedsport, New York, on June 15, 1940. She was one of four children, the daughter of an insurance executive who had moved his family to Chicago from upstate New York. The Grahams had four children: William, Elizabeth Anne, Margaret, and Robert. Edna Graham died in 1981. The Edna Kanaley Graduate School of Management at Xavier College, from which she was graduated, was named in her memory. On July 23, 1984, Graham was married to Catherine Van Duzer, Edna's first cousin and a bridesmaid in Bill and Edna Graham's wedding forty-four years earlier.

GRAHAM BECOMES VICE PRESIDENT AND MANAGER OF BAXTER

After counseling with Snow, Ralph Falk stepped up the discussions with Graham. He began to prepare Harry Falk for changes in his role. He even enlisted the aid of Horace Dawson, Graham's senior partner, telling him how important it was for Graham to take a management position in Baxter. Through these late 1944 negotiations, Graham was gracious but firm.

"It's uncomfortable for me to insist on these conditions because I like Harry," he said to Ralph Falk, "but I can't do the job reporting to Harry or even with him in a loosely defined top management role."

By the end of 1944 Ralph Falk and Graham had reached an agreement, which Graham confirmed in a personal letter to Falk.

Graham's title and position were spelled out. Harry Falk was to move to his horse ranch in California's San Fernando Valley, to be available from time to time for advice and counsel.

3930 Mobile Avenue
Chicago, Illinois
November 29, 1944

Dr. Ralph Falk
Drake Hotel
Chicago, Illinois

Dear Dr. Falk:

This letter is to supplement my other letter of this day regarding the possibility of my employment by Baxter Laboratories.

When in September, we agreed to disagree I told you, in response to your question, that if Harry should retire the situation then would be entirely different. The plan which we are now discussing contemplates, as I understand it, that Harry will be inactive and will live in California but, for the present at least, will retain the position of Executive Vice President of the company. Under this arrangement Harry would meet with you to discuss policy matters, would come to Glenview at regular intervals, and would attend Directors' meetings.

It is my understanding that Harry wishes to receive as compensation an amount which will decrease from year to year until the sum of $25,000 per year is reached.

Of course, your arrangement with Harry as to compensation is not of primary concern to me except as it might affect my own position. I would wish to feel certain that, if some portion of Harry's compensation should be disallowed as a corporate income tax deduction, he would not assume or reassign additional duties to justify for future years the compensation which had been disallowed. In other words I would want to feel sure that Harry wouldn't change his mind about inactivity after I had given up my law business and was working for Baxter Laboratories.

Although it is difficult to predict with accuracy what compensation will be considered reasonable, I do feel as a lawyer that it will be extremely difficult to justify compensation substantially in excess of $25,000 per year for this position. However, I feel that this is a matter that is in your own discretion and no primary concern of mine provided that it is clearly understood that the future allowance or disallowance of Harry's compensation would have no effect upon my position in the company.

Sincerely yours,

(signed)
William B. Graham

WBG/JOB

Dr. Falk never formally replied to or referred to Graham's letter. "I guess he was a little embarrassed over the issue of Harry's effect on the business," Graham said years later. Harry Falk accepted with delight the opportunity to play more of an advisory role while retaining his title as executive vice president and annual salary of $25,000. His interests were shifting to his ranch and the horses he raised there (on which he reportedly experimented with Baxter's drug compounds as they began to be developed in the late forties and early fifties).

This arrangement caused some awkwardness in Graham's original title of vice president and manager. That, however, did not prove to be a serious obstacle. Naurice Nesset probably had mixed feelings about the addition of Graham to the Baxter executive team. On balance though, it was a plus for Nesset to have Harry's influence reduced. Despite the potential rivalry and the differences about strategic issues that came later, Nesset and Graham respected each other and got along well. Graham would sometimes help Nesset load and cart potatoes from Nesset's small "gentleman's farm" off Route 53 outside Barrington to Glenview and then later, Morton Grove, where part of the crop was sold to Baxter employees.

On April 24, 1945, the Baxter Laboratories board resolved to employ Graham at a salary of $18,000 and, on August 10, 1945, as the war in the Pacific ended, he was elected to the Baxter board to replace Dawson.[1] A new Baxter era had begun.

WHAT GRAHAM ENCOUNTERED

Baxter Laboratories' commercial business, in the spring of 1945, was running at an annual rate of $1.6 million. Graham recalled,

"Baxter hadn't yet taken shape or been organized as a business. The books were five months late in closing, and one of the first things I had to do was bring in Maury Stans and the Alexander Grant accounting firm to help us clean that up.[2] The contract termination negotiations with the military had to be brought under control. We were out of expansion room at the Glenview site, and Harry Falk had already begun to deal on another five-acre parcel in Des Plaines which I was sure wouldn't be adequate. So I had to turn that around quickly."

Graham in one of the Baxter labs.

These are only a few of the short-term problems that crowded in on Graham. The long-term direction of the business still needed to be firmly established. He had no real experience dealing with these kinds of issues. There were at that time no other companies that might serve as appropriate models for Baxter, from whose successes and failures he could learn. There was no one within the company on whose experience and counsel he could draw. The closest possibility was Dr. Nesset, initially in parallel with Graham, with responsibility for production and research. However, Nesset was clearly more of a scientist than a businessman.

So Graham had to set about learning by trial and error, which may be the best management and business teacher—asking the right probing questions and assiduously mastering detail.

Some clear signs of the distinctive Graham management style began to emerge in that initial period. There was increased emphasis on executive and management councils and communication. A forward-looking employee profit-sharing plan was established in November 1945, linking employee interests to company performance and results. Strategic direction and investment were increasingly controlled at the top of the organization by Graham himself. How strategy was formulated and driven both initially in these early years and later on a continuing basis is an important and distinctive aspect of Baxter's history. The company was not a completely rounded entity in the forties and even the fifties, as long as American Hospital Supply continued as its exclusive domestic distributor for IV solutions. Development of Baxter strategy focused more intensively than was then typical on certain areas which developed into enduring competitive advantages: manufacturing technology and manufacturing cost, product development, applied research, financial strategy, and international market development.

Pharmaceutical companies, while generally larger than Baxter, offered the most relevant strategic models for comparison and possible emulation. Graham studied them in considerable depth. He concluded that the pharmaceutical firms were concentrating their management attention almost exclusively on the two functions of marketing and R&D. This was the beginning of the era when the pharmaceutical companies were vertically integrating and rapidly expanding their share of consumer expenditures for drugs and medicines. Bristol, for example, only had 40 detail men in 1954, and anti-infectives enabled it to expand from the position of a bulk supplier of drugs to an integrated company.[3] Prescriptions were 32 percent of all consumer purchases of medicines in 1929; 57 percent in 1949; and 83 percent by 1969.[4] These statistics, of course, also indicate the tightening grip of government regulation on drugs and other areas of health care. Baxter, and Graham specifically as the chairman of the Pharmaceutical Manufacturers Association, would get caught up in these forces in 1959 and 1960.

Graham also began the practice of communicating by monthly, or more frequent, management letters to Ralph Falk in Boise in the intervals between the latter's periodic visits to the Chicago area. These letters, several examples of which are included in the appendix, reported on operating and financial results and commented on key management decisions in progress.

In a letter dated October 12, 1949, Graham described to Falk an untoward event in the forward march of science and medicine.

> "It is now said that we have the highest priced guinea pigs in the pharmaceutical industry. Day before yesterday we obtained a new chemical which [we] have been checking as a possible constituent of a portion of the Piromen complex. Dr. Nesset and Dr. Byrne, medical director, tasted it and then brought it in to me to taste. Against my better judgement, I also tasted it. Ten minutes later Byrne and Nesset were laid out cold in the first aid room. Fortunately both of them recovered, although they spent the night in the first aid room. Apparently I took just the right amount because I did not get sick at all. We have now established a rule against testing new chemicals by tasting them.
>
> "We are still not sure what happened although it seems likely that the chemical is contaminated with a toxic amine since the injection of the material into rats produced sudden death. At any rate, everybody seems to be feeling all right by now and though it was not true at that time, the incident now seems rather humorous. After a half an hour or so when Naurice began to recover a bit he spent a great deal of time making a record for posterity. Ann [the company nurse] took notes of his feelings and reactions, and detailed blood studies were made at that same time. I think the prize of all the notes is one which reads, 'blood pressure 156/88—Dr. Burke [long-time company physician] says disregard (Nesset bequeathing estate at this point)'."

This was the likely beginning of Graham's strong interest in good shareholder communication, at which he continued to work hard for many years after Baxter made its first public stock offering in 1951. Baxter's commitment to shareholder value has continued to current times, shaping the landmark decisions made by Loucks in 1985, 1987, and the early 1990s, as this history was being readied to go to press.

END NOTES

CHAPTER V

1. Baxter board minutes, 1945.

2. Alexander Grant remained Baxter's outside auditor until 1986. Maurice Stans became managing partner of Glore Forgan William R. Staats, and then President Nixon's Secretary of Commerce.

3. Peter Temin, *Taking your Medicine: Drug Regulation in the U.S.* (Cambridge, Mass.: Harvard University Press, 1980), 75.

4. ibid., 75.

CHAPTER

VI

THRUSTING OUT IN NEW DIRECTIONS 1946-53

As the 14-year-old company struggled with its immediate problems, Baxter's long-term strategy began to take shape. Strategy is one of the major themes of this history, along with innovations in patient care, superior business and financial results, and manufacturing (and more recently, distribution) leadership. The principal individual elements of strategy, and how they developed over time, are described in succeeding chapters. A brief overview is provided here in order to set the context for later, more specific discussions of strategy.

CORPORATE STRATEGY IN THE 1940S

It was relatively uncommon in the 1940s, at least for pharmaceutical companies, to pursue a total or comprehensive strategy. The marketing concept, so called, was just taking hold in American industry. Corporate strategy as it's practiced today was relatively unknown then. Most strategies involved one or, at most, two, dimensions: R&D and sales in the case of pharmaceutical companies; materials and manufacturing for steel companies; marketing and distribution for consumer goods companies.

Baxter's approach to strategy developed differently, partly because of the character of its leadership and the determination of that leadership not to "follow the herd," but mostly because of constraints the company faced and because it was "distanced" from its principal markets by its exclusive distribution contracts. Its products were "specialties" in the narrow sense. It was by no means certain in the forties that either IV solutions or blood and plasma products could produce sufficient volume to build a robust, independent company.

ESSENCE OF BAXTER'S SUCCESSFUL STRATEGY

It is difficult to capture in a few paragraphs the gist of the company's strategy as it evolved and developed over time without oversimplifying the strategy itself and, more importantly, its flesh-and-blood leadership. Nevertheless, here are some of the major elements of Baxter's strategy. First, since the company didn't have a complete and integrated marketing and sales organization until the early sixties, the focus necessarily was on involving the whole organization—principally technology and manufacturing—directly in the needs of the customer. The customer was rigorously defined as the professional in specific fields of clinical medicine. That in turn led to an emphasis on "technical medical specialties," rather than supplies.

Baxter sought specialty market niches which it could open up and then grow into and dominate as the principal competitive force, leading to the "Hit 'em where they ain't" theme. The market niche approach proved to be the keystone of Baxter's successful strategy. It enabled the company to become the best cost producer in its chosen markets. It provided the profits and cash flow to reinvest in R&D and marketing. In order to be effective over time, though, the approach required a very high batting average in early identification of promising new niches, speed in opening up the niches, and then tenacity in defending them against latecomer "me too" competition. Consistent with that basic concept, the approach to customer service and support developed around technical and application specialists. When a full-fledged field sales force came into being later, it continued to emphasize specialization by medical practice area.

The company had to be able to move into a potential market quickly, sometimes on a "trial and error" basis. That required a flexible and fast-moving manufacturing system. That system was carefully planned and controlled. Product development, whether in IV solutions, blood therapy, dialysis, or diagnostics, was closely linked to manufacturing. A strategic financial approach to support long-term investments in manufacturing capacity while niche market volume increased had to be devised. The financial strategy emphasized keeping the cost of capital low and producing consistently superior earnings.

While Baxter products were all in hospital and clinical care areas, individual market niches were diverse. That explains why product names—Viaflex or Travenol (the latter also a part of the corporate name for a number of years)—were until recently better known than the corporate name itself. Integration of operations and central thrust were provided by manufacturing along with technology. That became even more important as Baxter pioneered use of medical-grade thermoplastics across its various product lines. As patient safety and efficacy for plastics were established and market acceptance grew, the shift away from glass and other materials to newer plastics allowed Baxter to achieve a substantial degree of vertical integration. Plastics had the effect of making Baxter's most important products true disposables, sharply expanding volume potential in many of its specialty market niches.

So while the company always kept a watchful eye on patient and medical needs and while it was aggressively opportunistic in regard to new opportunities, its strategy was developed "from the inside out" rather than "from the outside in." These factors led to an even balance among all the elements of corporate operation and, at the same time, to extremely tight corporate control.

STAGES OF STRATEGY DEVELOPMENT

The major elements of Baxter's overall strategy did not, of course, develop separately in specific time periods, but they are shown in that fashion here to provide a framework for the reader to follow as the company's development is described.

General Sequence of Baxter Strategy Development

1931-39	Single product (IV) commercialization
1940-45	"Survival" strategy
1946-49	Strategic experimentation
1946-56	Development of manufacturing and technology base
1947-59	Product diversification and market niche strategy
1950-65	Human resources/organization strategy
1951-70	Financial/investment strategy
1955-65	International strategy, stage 1
1962-64	Baxter's strategic response to the break with American Hospital; begins to recruit a new generation of managers
1965-74	Materials strategy: conversion to thermoplastics
1966-76	International strategy, stage 2
1972-78	Broadening the market for IV solutions and coping with rapid growth
1972-78	Regulatory strategy
1972-80	Management development and succession
1977-86	Alternate Site strategy, following patients to alternate care settings
1980-84	Strategic experimentation, as in the late 40s, to adapt to the changing health care environment
1985-89	Strategy on a larger scale: making the acquisition of, and merger with, American Hospital Supply work
1985-	Niche markets "go global"
1986-	Hospital penetration strategy
1987-	Strategic emphasis on services, systems, and processes
1993-	Three-part strategy: technology, investment in global leadership, and U.S. low-cost delivery of medical hospital products.

After the basics were in place, development of these various aspects of strategy proceeded more in "checkerboard" fashion than along a time line because the company was extraordinarily alert and responsive to external and internal opportunities. Indeed, in the late seventies and early eighties, Vern Loucks and other members of senior management would illustrate Baxter strategy with a grid or checkerboard, showing those therapy areas where the company already had a market and technical lead, and prioritizing other "cells" for market probes, full-scale "beach heads," or market "breakouts."

NICHES WHERE BAXTER DIDN'T FULLY ACHIEVE ITS GOALS . . . AT LEAST THE FIRST TIME AROUND

In the kind of niche strategy Baxter elected, there were bound to be misses as well as hits. There were several misses. For example, Baxter was an early entrant in the field of diagnostics, through Hyland Laboratories. The scientific leader of that effort was Dr. Roy Fisk. When he died in 1964, some of the early momentum was lost. According to Hyland President John Bacich, Fisk developed latex technology while experimenting with farm animals on his family ranch in Montana. Baxter continued to be an important factor in the diagnostics market first in radioimmunoactive assays, then through a joint venture with Genentech, and most recently since the 1985 merger with American Hospital Supply, which had built a major position in diagnostics. However, Baxter still has not achieved a commanding leadership position in diagnostics.

In artificial organs, including both the dialysis machine and the heart-lung oxygenator, Baxter may have defended its early leading technology for too long. When heart-lung technicians began to swing in favor of hard-shell technology, Baxter stuck to its soft-shell approach and saw its market lead slip away. It is just now being won back in the 1990s. And as dialysis technology shifted in the seventies to negative pressure and hollow fiber filtration, the company again found itself in the position of defending older technology. In that case Baxter was flexible enough to adapt to the new technology and then to improve on it, so its dominant position in all segments of dialysis was never lost. The current generation of Baxter senior management learned important lessons from these experiences.

During the sixties, Baxter also entered into a partnership with Zenith in the emerging field of medical electronics that was not successful. In part, this was because the technology Baxter and Zenith employed was not sufficiently advanced to provide a competitive advantage. The more basic reason, though, was that Baxter did not, in pursuing the goals of the partnership with Zenith, stay as close to the needs of the marketplace and the customer as it had in other areas.

Two observations about these examples are that in each case the difficulty was technology rather than strategy or management; and it's remarkable how the company persisted in the face of difficulties, and maintained or regained a leadership position—the heart-lung machine serving as a notable illustration.

STRATEGIC ISSUES

For a number of years, particularly in the seventies, there was a continuing question about how far the market niche strategy could carry the company. Apparently, it was Graham's opinion that it could take Baxter to $100 million in sales, and then later that it was appropriate to $250 million in sales. Certainly, Baxter's explosive growth during the seventies put stress and strain on the market niche strategy.

A DIFFERENT APPROACH

The years from the end of World War II through the cold war stalemate in Korea were busy ones for Baxter Laboratories and its new vice president. Graham recalled, "I wasn't consciously developing a new strategy. We were concentrating on several priority problems that had to be solved. One was our cost structure. Baxter didn't enjoy the manufacturing margins pharmaceutical houses did. We were paying two 'tolls' [licensing fees to Don Baxter and distributor discounts to American Hospital Supply]. Since our principal IV competitors were also manufacturing in high cost areas (Cutter in San Francisco and Abbott in Chicago), I thought a different approach would give us a competitive advantage.

"Also, we needed to get closer to the marketplace. That meant new products that didn't have to be sold exclusively by American Hospital. Third, what kinds of new products would be best? I didn't think we could risk going head-to-head with the pharmaceutical companies. They were increasing their R&D investments and the price of entry was stiff. We had to develop a new product flow on a pay-as-you-go basis because I was determined to keep reinvesting in our IV leadership position. Small specialty niches filled the bill . . . particularly where immediate profit potential didn't draw a crowd and where disposable product characteristics would make it possible to achieve steady sales growth."

So out of these three necessities a Baxter strategy began to emerge.

MOVE TO MORTON GROVE—1945 TO 1947

Shortly after Graham joined Baxter, he took direct responsibility for selecting a new location for the company's headquarters and principal laboratory. Harry Falk's plan to move to a five-acre site in Des Plaines was scrapped. With the help of Ed Nawoj, Graham identified a 20-acre site in nearby Morton Grove (the former George Pullman estate). Construction of the $1.6 million, 142,000 square-foot facility began in 1946. Financing was a combination of retained earnings and a $750,000 15-year, 4 percent mortgage. Baxter pushed its borrowing capacity quite aggressively in order to finance the much larger facility. The move to Morton Grove was completed in August 1947. Baxter remained in that facility for almost 30 years until the construction of the present Deerfield headquarters. Understandably, many memories of Baxter achievements and people are associated with Morton Grove and its small company atmosphere. After the move to Deerfield, the Morton Grove facility was used as a research laboratory and distribution center. It was sold in 1988.

Anecdotes are still told about the small company Morton Grove atmosphere. Loucks remembered a bell signaling the beginning and end of morning and afternoon coffee breaks, when all employees gathered in the small company cafeteria. The practice promoted a sense of cohesiveness, and elements of it continued into Deerfield.

There was a small putting green in Morton Grove visible from the cafeteria and some executive offices. Loucks also remembered that one morning Graham glanced out and saw a young manager on the green slowly practicing his putting. He said to Loucks, who was his assistant, "You better do something about that." Within days the putting green was gone, and not too long after so was the unfortunate manager.

IMPROVEMENTS IN SOLUTIONS PRODUCTS—1946 TO 1948 AND BEYOND

One of Baxter's drives, then as now, was continued enhancement of established products. Solutions products expanded to four major lines: Travenol solution, the original saline and dextrose combination; Travamin protein hydrolysate; Trinidex solution, containing B

Morton Grove headquarters, 1947.

group vitamins; and Travert solutions of invert sugar. As described in the next section, Travenol was to become a major brand identification for Baxter. Before the forties were over, a separate division was formed to sell diversified products independently of both Don Baxter and American Hospital Supply. Later, Don Baxter and American Hospital would object strenuously to the use of the Travenol name in Baxter Laboratories' intravenous solutions product labeling.

Equally important, Plexitron expendable plastic solution sets were introduced. Not only did they eliminate the problems associated with cleaning and reuse of rubber tubing, they also advanced Baxter's product and market strategy. Work was proceeding too on a lighter-weight, "one-way" glass solutions container.

Plastic tubing sets (administration sets) were a major advance in hospital labor-saving, convenience, and sterility in patient use. From Baxter's vantage point, this began its pioneering work in plastics materials and manufacturing technology for medical use, work which continues at this time. In the forties and fifties, there were many concerns and obstacles concerning biocompatibility of thermoplastics that needed to be overcome. Introduction of Plexitron solution sets also was an important step forward in professional product dispos-

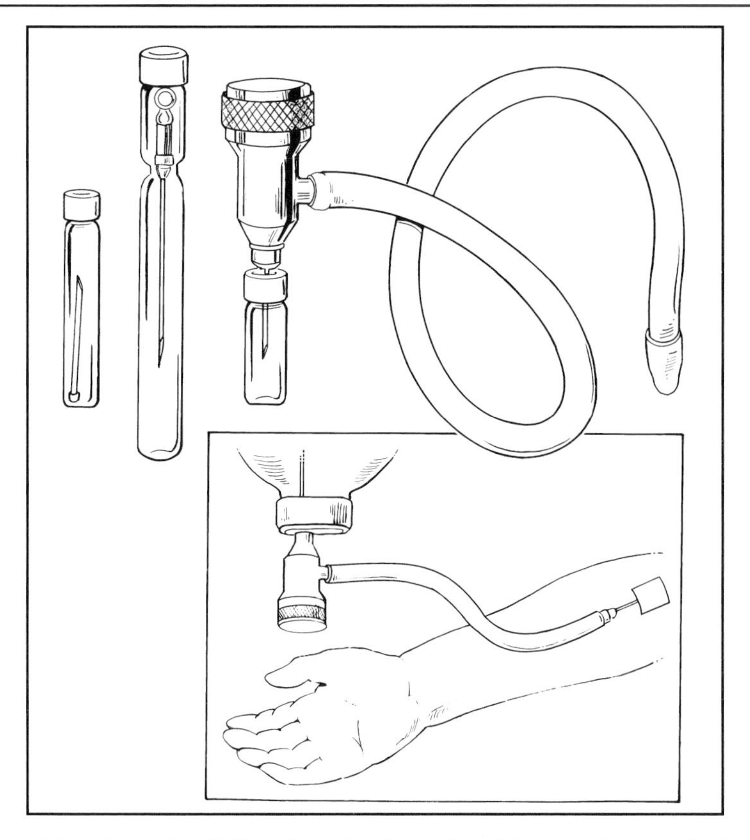

Early Tubing Sets for Collection: *To obtain blood from a donor and store it in an evacuated container such as a Transfuso Vac, these tubing sets with attached needles were made available by Baxter. Vacuum in the container facilitated withdrawal of whole blood from the patient's vein. Glass vials surrounding the needle protected sterilized surfaces until shortly before use.*

ability, one of the keystones of the strategy taking shape in Graham's mind.

TRAVENOL—CREATION OF A PROFESSIONAL BRAND—1947 TO 1949

In the late forties, as mentioned earlier, Baxter introduced an important new trade name, Travenol. This move was an important step in the company's developing strategy for several reasons: Travenol would be the identification for Baxter's new products, reducing

Baxter reliance on solutions and blood containers; it would be used to label solutions as well as nonsolutions products sold nationally, including Don Baxter's protected territory of eleven western states; and it was insurance against possible threats to long-term use of the Baxter name.

Horace Dawson, Graham's former law firm colleague, had explored trade names using the root, "Trav," from "intravenous" in the late thirties, at a time when Harry Falk was unsuccessfully pursuing diversification through a vehicle named Falk Laboratories, Inc.

Graham revived that brand name development work. Ben Bannister, manager of traffic and distribution, came up with the name, "Travenous." Graham described his objectives, "We were looking for a 'synthetic' name. Kodak was our model. Looking ahead, we had to have a name we could use around the world . . . particularly considering the ill-advised things Don Baxter was doing to assign rights to the Baxter name to third parties in other countries not covered by our agreement. Ben Bannister's suggestion was modified to 'Travenol.' We had problems with the name in several countries, notably Germany and South Africa—with Chesebrough-Ponds, which were ultimately resolved."

The beginning of a Travenol sales division took shape in 1949. The familiar Travenol logo, the "reclining B" or "mortar-and-pestle" symbol was added much later in 1962. The Travenol name and associated symbol became one of the most widely recognized professional "marks" in hospitals in the United States and many other countries. So much so that when a corporate name change was considered in the early sixties, Travenol was the leading choice to replace the Baxter name. At the same time, shortly after Dr. Ralph Falk's death, the suggestion was made that the company be renamed the Graham Corporation. Graham firmly squelched that idea. The corporate name was formally changed in 1976 to Baxter Travenol Laboratories, Inc. At the time, this was expected to be a transitional step to renaming the company Travenol Laboratories, Inc. That would have resolved continuing concerns about diverse rights to the Baxter name. The plan was abandoned when the company acquired, it was believed at the time, all rights to the Baxter name from American Hospital Supply Corporation in 1983.

Long before any of these events, though, the most immediate effect of the new Travenol name was to produce a vehement objection from Don Baxter, Inc., particularly when the new name was added to IV solution labels. American Hospital Supply weighed in shortly thereafter with its objections to the Travenol name.[1]

CUTTER SOLUTIONS RECALL—1947

In late summer 1947, as a portent of later events profoundly affecting the intravenous business and intravenous technology, Cutter Laboratories experienced an IV product recall.[2] Cutter executives got on the phone to seek Baxter support in replacing their hospital customers' inventories. Graham immediately agreed to provide product at cost plus 10 percent.

Air shipment was essential to this time-urgent operation, and at times Baxter's volume requirements exceeded the total capacity of the fledgling air transport industry. Initially, Bannister and his small staff were on the phones all night trying to book more commercial space with airline personnel suspicious of the calls as some kind of hoax. The cost of air shipment climbed past the value of the product being moved. By the time the operation reached its peak, Baxter had eighteen semis standing by at Chicago's Midway Airport waiting for available air carrier space.

LANDMARK TRADEMARK LITIGATION—1947 TO 1949

In 1947, not long after passage of the Lanham Trademark Act, Don Baxter, Inc. filed for exclusive rights to the Baxter trademark in all 48 states, a complete reversal of the terms of the original 1931 agreement between the two companies. Dawson, Graham's former partner, filed an opposing claim and was able to show that Don Baxter did not "control" the Baxter Laboratories product and its quality. The court ruled in Baxter Laboratories' favor. This may still be the only time when "parallel" ownership of a trade name, Dr. Donald E. Baxter's name, was granted to two separate companies, which by now had become competitors. The management of Don Baxter at the time certainly weren't very happy about it. Trademark rights were continued in the respective U.S. territories of the two companies as well as in countries around the world per the original 1931 agreement. Settlement regarding effects of the joint registration of the Baxter name on foreign antitrust problems wasn't finalized until 1951. The contest over the Baxter name was taking on the characteristics of a protracted chess match, and was far from over.

SELECTION OF CLEVELAND, MISSISSIPPI, MANUFACTURING SITE HERALDS NEW BAXTER MANUFACTURING STRATEGY—1949

The 1949 Baxter annual meeting formally ratified management's decision to locate a major manufacturing plant in Mississippi's Delta country. This was an immensely successful move. Before the initial facility was completed and operating, an addition was already approved and underway.

It was the first step in a comprehensive, long-term manufacturing strategy which would shape the character of the company in many ways. Paying at the high end of prevailing wage rates in the inner Delta area of plentiful labor supply would still yield a competitive advantage. The likelihood of union organization would be reduced. Plants would be relatively small and "focused," but still flexible enough so that new products could be accommodated and manufacturing volumes shifted. All plants would be integrated in a single system. Perhaps most important were the capital costs. Baxter shareholders ratified the continuing expansion in Cleveland, Mississippi, at the annual meeting on May 1, 1951, where the terms were recorded as "a fifteen-year lease at 6.66 percent of construction cost plus eight successive ten-year options and an additional three-year option at a rent of $500 per year." Issuance of industrial revenue bonds in connection with the Cleveland facility was a Baxter and a medical industry first. Also, on March 12, 1951, the board approved a second new southern plant in Greenville, Kentucky, which was not destined to be as long-lived as Cleveland.[3]

The company's manufacturing strategy was the first element to emerge in a comprehensive strategy that remained consistent and highly effective into the 1990s.

Not that the strategy emerged suddenly. Characteristically, Graham analyzed southern U.S. locations for Baxter plants (and Mississippi specifically) in an intensive manner before making a decision. He, Dr. Naurice Nesset, and Nawoj made many visits to Cleveland. They developed a cooperative working relationship with state and local officials. Nawoj, who was to be the "driver" of Baxter manufacturing for many years, until he retired as a senior vice president in 1982, says that Graham even gave thought to relocating corporate headquarters from the Chicago area to Florida with the idea that Florida might provide an edge in recruiting scientists.

The Cleveland plant began manufacturing Transfuso Vac containers and vacuum solution containers in 1950. It was the beginning of a long and happy relationship with the community of Cleveland, the state of Mississippi, and most particularly with employees there. The Cleveland work force developed solid manufacturing and quality control skills and progressively showed extraordinary loyalty to Baxter. As time went on, seniority levels steadily mounted in Cleveland, in part because of pride employees felt in the success of the

A production line for filling glass containers with solution.

operation, and also because of the superior long-term growth of their profit sharing accounts.

A key element of Baxter's developing strategy was to share company gains with employees, principally through the forward-looking 1945 profit-sharing plan. How well the ambitious objective of providing all employees with a secure, comfortable retirement, independent of their other resources and Social Security, was met for Cleveland and other employees throughout the company is illustrated in Figure 3 (next page).

The philosophy about employee participation in the growth of the company and the increasing value of its common stock was another keystone of Baxter's strategies. It provided motivation and a sense of belonging for all employees regardless of their location or position and it tied long-term rewards to company performance. It served as a continuing reminder of the company's concern for and commitment to its employees.

At the same time, the distinctive Baxter approach to management organization was becoming clear. You will remember management consultant Booz Allen Hamilton's comments about the Baxter organization in 1943, prior to Graham joining the company, and which in fact were a principal stimulus for Dr. Falk to work so hard to recruit Graham. By this time, those historical weaknesses had been overcome by an organization that was strongly functional, had clear lines of authority, relied on strong people (the Graham "good man theory"), and emphasized team work but allowed lots of room for indi-

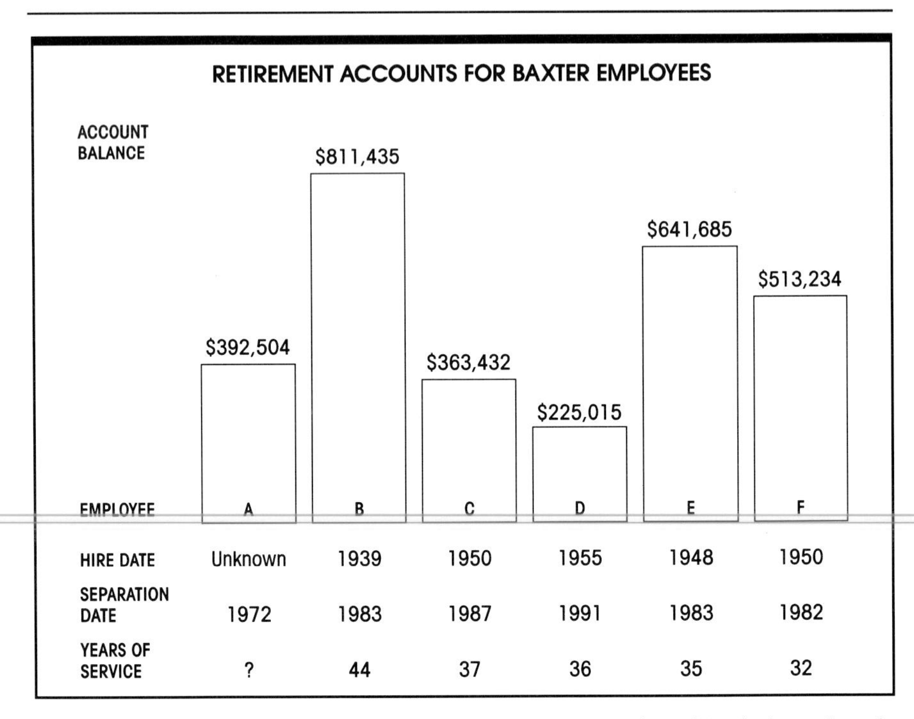

Figure 3: *For the reader's information, the employees selected include an hourly maintenance worker, two manufacturing employees in Cleveland, a laboratory chemist, and two administrative employees. Comparing account amounts with employee annual earnings and then converting dollar amounts to current levels would make the data even more dramatic.*[4]

vidual initiative. The functional orientation continued as a major organizational characteristic until the 1980s.

Several distinctive elements of the Cleveland siting and planning process still stand out even after all these years. Graham summarized, "We were the first national company to venture into the deep Delta under Mississippi's 'Balance Agriculture With Industry' (BAWI) program. There was risk in being first, so we worked hard on picking the site that might pave the way for other southern plants. Mississippi Industrial Revenue Bonds[5], under which we repaid only principal, were a powerful financial inducement—and certainly contributed to the way we developed our financial strategy—but we weighed all the considerations. Most important, the Cleveland decision gave us the kind of leverage we needed in our Chicago cost and labor union situation. There was a union struggle over Cleveland with representatives moving there for eight months for an organizing campaign. We won. And because our concept was 'parallel manufacturing,' we accomplished all this without layoffs or take-aways in Morton Grove."

Another action Baxter took in Cleveland was to "seed" the new facility with top manufacturing and technical people from headquarters. Owen Fess moved to Cleveland as manufacturing superintendent. Ralph Falk II, who had joined the company in 1948 after receiving his MBA from the University of Michigan, was assigned to a management position in Cleveland. Dick Von Drasek, who joined Baxter in 1944 and whose mother was a Glenview employee, was named the bottling plant foreman. Olin Taylor, who was hired locally, became one of the most respected personnel and industrial relations managers throughout the company as the Cleveland facility began to grow. Later, Art Baumann was relocated to Cleveland from Morton Grove to become plant manager. Don Madsen also did a tour there.

Two examples of this significant contribution to manufacturing strategy were Von Drasek and Madsen. Von Drasek very much wanted to go to the Cleveland plant when it opened. In March 1950 he was relocated, the only Morton Grove assistant foreman so selected. In mid-1951 he moved to the new Greenville, Kentucky, plant as assistant superintendent with Madsen. He then returned to Cleveland for almost six more years, becoming assistant superintendent with Baumann. Shortly after Baumann was reassigned to Puerto Rico, Von Drasek was asked to move to Canada in March 1958.

Nawoj telephoned the Thursday Von Drasek got to Canada to say he was coming up from Morton Grove to meet with him the following Tuesday. When Nawoj arrived he immediately removed the Canadian production manager and expanded Von Drasek's responsibilities. His responsibilities continued to expand over the many years he stayed in Canada. In 1978 he was assigned to the Thetford Plant in the United Kingdom, where he worked seven days a week for a year to overcome manufacturing problems there. He returned in 1979 to the North Cove, North Carolina plant, by then the flagship U.S. facility. He took global responsibility in 1983 for a major materials and manufacturing innovation project (Equinox) at Baxter's technical campus at Round Lake, Illinois. Von Drasek retired in 1990 after a 46-year Baxter career. He died in 1993.

Madsen's manufacturing track with the company was even more peripatetic. Trained as a chemist, he joined the company in the laboratory in 1946 after three-and-a-half years in the Air Force. Clearly, Graham believed in recruiting potential manufacturing managers with a chemistry background. He followed this preference successfully with Nawoj and Madsen, and later with others such as Jim Taylor and Bob Rain. After Madsen moved out of the laboratory into Nawoj's manufacturing organization, the whirlwind began for him. He was sent to South Africa in 1949 to start the 40/60 Baxter joint venture there with Saphar Laboratories (Keagram Pty. Ltd.).[6] This business continues to prosper, but Baxter withdrew from it on September 30, 1986, because of anti-apartheid pressures and the fact that as a minority partner the company was not in control of local management response to political conditions there. In fact, this is one of several instances over Baxter's history where the company had to withdraw or limit its contributions to life-saving patient care because of political conditions. (The Philippines is another such example that occurred during the same general time period.)

Baxter's investment in South Africa was $25,000 worth of surplus manufacturing equipment for producing intravenous solutions. Madsen returned to Cleveland, Mississippi, in the summer of 1950. From 1954 to 1960 he was in Brussels starting European manufacturing operations.

Madsen described the period of early international expansion. "Both South Africa and Europe were initially defensive moves. Most countries were not going to import IVs and pay for them in dollars. Graham's timing was good. By the time we started manufacturing in Belgium we had had a distribution relationship with A. B. Christaens that dated back to 1933. But Bill Graham said no more joint ventures. Don Baxter was beginning to manufacture in Trieste, Italy, through a licensee about that same time. However, their strategy was not as clear and far-reaching as ours."

Madsen moved to the Kingstree, South Carolina plant, which initially manufactured solutions, then blood products and Wallerstein chemicals, from 1960 to 1967. In 1970 he was given responsibility for the Wallerstein business.

At the time of Nawoj's retirement in 1983 Madsen became a corporate officer, and went on to head worldwide manufacturing for Baxter as senior vice president before retiring in 1986 after forty years.

MANUFACTURING STRATEGY

The key elements of Baxter's manufacturing strategy as it emerged very quickly in the late forties and early fifties were:

- Early location of facilities in areas where there was a ready labor supply, with Baxter paying above local prevailing wage and benefit levels.
- Innovative financing of manufacturing expansion, first through Industrial Revenue Bonds in Mississippi; soon after and well ahead of others (under Section 936) in Puerto Rico, where Baxter remains today one of the island's largest manufacturing employers; and then in a number of other locations around the world.
- A vision of manufacturing as a total, integrated system with "parallelism" built in; even though individual plants developed in very different ways with lead roles as focused "wet" (solutions) or "dry" facilities; pilot plants; and parts and material producers.
- Tight central control of every detail of process, quality, technology, and logistics throughout the manufacturing network by means of what Madsen called "Ed Nawoj's system of 'checkers'."
- Development and rotation of a manufacturing cadre, typically from technical ranks.
- Close attention to every aspect of manufacturing technology, including the development of proprietary materials and equipment in such critical areas as compounding, heat-sealing, extrusion, blow molding, and sterilization.
- Keeping manufacturing units relatively small even as Baxter began to grow rapidly.
- Using manufacturing as the base for country-by-country international expansion (made necessary in part by the nature of the business).

The view of manufacturing as a total system and emphasis on manufacturing and product technology were very innovative for that time and surprisingly consistent with today's view of manufacturing and technology in an era of global competition.

ORGANIZATION AND PERSONNEL STRATEGY

Graham's values and beliefs regarding people, management, and organization can be inferred from the development of manufacturing strategy as it has been described. Some of these guiding values can be traced back to Dr. Falk.

By the late 1940s and the early 1950s a strong management team was developing. It included Nesset, of course; Nawoj; Joe Rau, the controller; Ted Gewecke; Wayne Brandon; and Jack Knowlton, who became general counsel. Other strong scientists in chemistry and immunology were being recruited to the Baxter organization: Dr. Leonard Ginger, Dan Borgen, Dr. Nicholas Kartinos, and Dr. Harry Fevold, among them.

Graham subordinates from those days refer to the Graham "good man theory of management." That is, select individuals with a high level of general intelligence and a similarly high level of energy and drive, and provide them ample room and "rope" to grow into their jobs.

Motivation was high because of the many growth challenges and the growing importance of such programs as profit sharing invested in Baxter stock. Graham's philosophy from the beginning was to get managers and other employees to think and behave as owners rather than employees.

Part of Graham's agreement to join the company in 1945 permitted him to acquire stock from Ralph Falk. He invested $10,000, and learned later to his regret that Dr. Falk would have sold him considerably more. The cost basis for that 1945 stock translated into today's shares was $.0088, representing a gain at the end of 1990 of over 3,000 percent. Yet when stock was offered to the key management group named earlier, Graham had to do some "arm-twisting" to get them to act on the opportunity.

Later, after a forward-looking employee stock purchase plan was set up, the company would "guarantee" the price of employee-purchased common stock at one of those rare points in time when it was falling because of the "wind-down" of the Korean Conflict. Stock options were introduced in 1955.[7]

In spite of these positive factors, there were some personnel issues in Glenview and then in Morton Grove. The Chemical Workers Union had represented employees since World War II. In part, this was due to Harry Falk's management approach. Also contributing was the tough approach to direct supervision characteristic of that day. John Storner, the Glenview plant superintendent, and Posey Hutchins, the tube and needle department foreman, ruled "by fear." Storner used to watch the washroom for malingerers. One worker named Therrier left his boots standing in a lavatory stall, crawled out the window, and went back to work so that the watching Storner would have his bluff called.

Neither Glenview or Morton Grove were ever "closed shops," but concern about Teamsters Union influence caused Baxter to avoid operating its own "private cartage," (which could have given a boost to overall manufacturing strategy) for a number of years.

Baxter's management was not explicitly opposed to unions, but the manufacturing strategy that was being pursued did not favor their expansion. The relationship between the Chemical Workers Union and Baxter in Glenview and then Morton Grove remained uneasy. In 1957 an election failed by seven votes to remove the union. In 1958 the union was overwhelmingly defeated and ousted. The following year, 1959, the union in Canada, the Operating Engineers, was ousted as well. From that time to this, Baxter has operated in North America essentially without third-party representation, and organizing efforts have been generally unsuccessful. Of course, in other countries where union representation is a part of the "social contract," the company has been supportive and cooperative. Lincoln R. Dowell and Bill Treacy, both of whom were intensively involved in Baxter labor relations during this formative period of the fifties, recall that the company was principally concerned about the effects of union-restrictive work practices on rapidly changing and improving products and manufacturing processes. Also, management was sincerely committed to blazing new trails in employee relations and benefits, and felt it could best do that without formal bargaining. The credibility that Graham (and later, Loucks and other executives such as Madsen) commanded with employees at every organization level supported that position.

PHARMACEUTICAL/NONPHARMACEUTICAL PRODUCT STRATEGY

Graham concluded early that head-to-head competition with pharmaceutical companies was not in Baxter's interest. Nonetheless, at this stage, Baxter introduced some pharmaceutical products. Piromen, an injectable pyrogen that Dr. Ginger worked on under Dr. Nesset's direction, was introduced in 1949. An injectable polysaccharide developed from earlier distillation "baffling" to remove pyrogens from IV solutions, Piromen injections became popular with allergists and dermatologists. Baxter later removed it from the market when the U.S. Food & Drug Administration required more data to demonstrate patient benefits and a Baxter-commissioned Arthur D. Little study raised questions about whether continued participation in this particular market was consistent with the company's leadership position in other areas.

Work on Synthroid [levothyroxine sodium] and Choloxin [dextrothyroxine sodium], two other pharmaceutical products, followed.

Synthroid [injection or tablets] was a thyroid drug already described. Choloxin tablets were a medicine for reduction of serum cholesterol, following Baxter's early recognition of the health significance of elevated cholesterol levels. It may have come too early because the health care community did not mount aggressive public education, prevention, and treatment efforts for high cholesterol and lipid (triglyceride) levels until much later.

In 1955 the Incert additive vial system was introduced with Urevert solution (a decompressant to reverse brain-swelling). The system of "piggy-back" administration of drugs through IV infusion would become another important avenue of innovation for Baxter. While Baxter assumed from the start that drug products which competed directly with emerging pharmaceutical firms and their much larger R&D budgets, or which played follow-the-leader, were not its best diversification avenue, the direction of developing drugs was held open as one viable alternative. Nesset was committed to that kind of research, and the company was building relevant R&D talent. It wasn't until after Nesset resigned in 1955 to lead the expansion of Chicago's Lutheran General Hospital that further product development in pharmaceuticals was de-emphasized.

1950: RELATIONSHIP WITH DON BAXTER, INC. IS FRACTURED

By 1949 Ralph Falk was so concerned about payment of royalties on unpatented products to Don Baxter that he and Snow initiated negotiations with Emory Beardsley, president of Don Baxter, to reduce or eliminate them. The negotiations became more and more acrimonious. Snow was the "heavy" in the dispute, and Falk then approached Graham to take Snow's place at the bargaining table. Graham politely declined the invitation as inappropriate at that stage. Whether a change of the personalities involved would have altered the course of subsequent events, there is no way of knowing.

As the chasm widened between the two companies, Foster McGaw was working behind the scenes with Beardsley and Dr. Baxter's widow, Delia Baxter. In early 1950, McGaw telephoned Graham to announce with considerable satisfaction that American Hospital Supply had reached an agreement to purchase Don Baxter.

On its face, this was a violation of the original 1931 agreement between Don Baxter and Baxter (then DBIP) giving the latter first right of purchase. Baxter promptly went to court to ask that the acquisition of Don Baxter be stopped. American Hospital had, however, bought assets rather than the company itself, in an attempt to get around the 1931 first-purchase provision. The litigation dragged on. It was finally settled in 1951. American Hospital Supply got to keep Don Baxter Laboratories' name and existing territorial rights were reinforced. Most important the royalties to be paid by Baxter were phased down and then eliminated. American continued to distribute Baxter products in the eastern states. McGaw proceeded to build the Pharmaseal division around Don Baxter, just as Graham had earlier, in 1949, launched the Travenol division. These events further eroded what goodwill had existed among these several strong-willed individuals.

BAXTER LABORATORIES PUBLIC STOCK OFFERING IN 1951

In a prospectus dated December 10, 1951, Baxter offered 100,000 shares of $1 par value common stock to the public and 25,000 shares to employees at $17 a share. Lehman Brothers managed the offering, and the stock began to trade on the over-the-counter market. Frank Manheim of Lehman went on to play a key role in later crucial Baxter acquisitions: Wallerstein in 1957 and Fenwal in 1959.

Ralph Falk agonized briefly about the public offering reducing his ownership interest to less than 50 percent. Prior to the public sale, there was an internal share split of 65:1.[8]

EFFECTS OF KOREAN CONFLICT: 1950 TO 1953

On June 25, 1950, the Republic of South Korea was suddenly invaded by North Korea. For the second time in less than a decade, Baxter had to adapt to a sudden surge in military demand for its products followed by just as sudden a collapse of that demand. "If there ever was a need to validate Bill Graham's management strengths," Ralph Falk II said, "the 'ramp-up' for Korea and the turn around afterwards certainly did so."

Once again, Baxter products played a vital battlefield role. Pilot quantities of a new plastic solutions container were tested during the Korean Conflict at the U.S. Army's Walter Reed Hospital. Perfected versions of these containers would revolutionize the commercial IV business when introduced about 20 years later in 1969/70. In the meantime, blood was shipped to Korean battle areas in glass bottles. Just as in World War II, agitation of the containers caused some damage to blood cells.

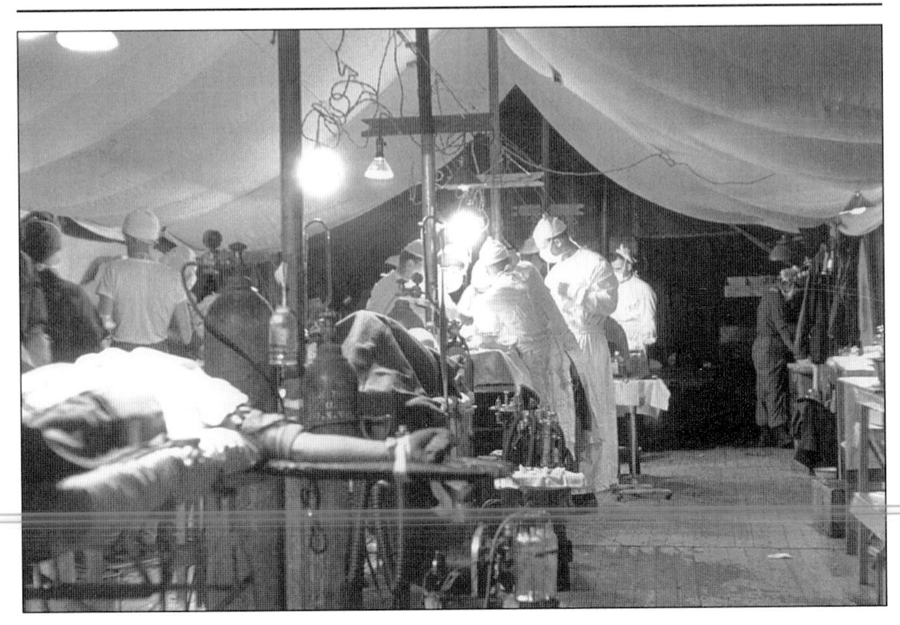

MASH units working with glass containers for blood plasma and IV solutions.

The adjustment for Baxter after the Panmunjom Truce in mid-1953 was a hard one. Sales in 1954 fell. Profits sagged. Baxter stock fell from its 1951/52 offering level of 17 to near 10. Hassles with American Hospital Supply over pricing and discount structure for large hospital customers in competitive situations were becoming more frequent.

"Before the end of the Korean Conflict," Graham recalled, "we planned and planned, and looked at all the possible ways to reduce costs. That exercise really helped us strengthen our planning system as we grew. But I concluded then that any costs we cut would trade away future growth and profit opportunities." In less than a year the company was turned around and headed for a long period of dramatic growth.

BAXTER MAKES FIRST ACQUISITION IN 1952

Stung, no doubt, by McGaw's acquisition of Don Baxter, and with diversification still a primary goal, Graham acquired Hyland Laboratories in 1952. Baxter's OTC traded stock was used to make the acquisition. Baxter board minutes recorded the transaction for 11,889 common shares and 3,206 new preferred shares. Hyland's valuation was shown as $599,991.50. For the prior ten months Hyland's sales had been $1.7 million, yielding net profits of $107,000 after taxes.[9]

Hyland had been formed in 1935 as the Convalescent Serum Center on Sunset Boulevard in Los Angeles by Dr. C.M. Hyland, pathologist and director of clinical laboratories for Los Angeles' Children's Hospital. In the early 1950s the expanded operation relocated to Glendale, where Don Baxter, Inc., also began.

At the time of the acquisition, Dr. Hyland was still involved, but he had brought in Preston Snow and Fred Marquart from Cutter to run the company. Graham knew both of them from the American Pharmaceutical Manufacturers Association, and when the financial problems of Hyland proved insoluble, Snow called Graham to suggest a deal.

Hyland was a leader in the businesses of whole blood and plasma. Later, after the acquisition, Hyland produced anti-hemophiliac factor (AHF), mumps hyperimmune globulin, albumin in saline, and a variety of blood bank, coagulation, and biochemical test products. The real "kicker" in the Hyland product line became its early position in blood fractions and in what would prove to be one of health care's most profitable growth segments: diagnostics.

Marquart continued with Baxter for a number of years and played a pivotal role in the successful integration of Fenwal after the acquisition of that Massachusetts company in 1959.

To an extent, the Hyland acquisition met the tests to which other Baxter developments and acquisitions were generally subjected; that is, to extend the "latticework" of relevant technology (in this case, blood fractions) and to gain a foothold in promising new markets (diagnostics).

In 1952, however, Graham had very basic criteria in mind. "Given the situation with Don Baxter and American Hospital Supply, we wanted to buy a company with headquarters on the west coast. The company had to have its own sales force, including ability to sell into Don Baxter's western territory . . . and last, it should expand the diversification efforts we'd had underway since 1945-46 in protein hydrolysate, invert sugar, and amino acid for solutions, and more recently in other products not sold through American Hospital Supply, such as Piromen, Choloxin [dextrothyroxine sodium], and Synthroid [levothyroxine sodium]."

GRAHAM BECOMES BAXTER PRESIDENT IN 1953

On July 9, 1953, a little over eight years after joining Baxter Laboratories, Bill Graham was elected president. Records of that time show compensation of the key officers: Ralph Falk, Chairman $65,000; W.B. Graham, president $45,000; Naurice Nesset, vice president $40,000; and Harry Falk $30,000.[10] Harry Falk's compensation was a shade above the $25,000 level set out in Graham's "employment" letter to Dr. Ralph Falk eight years earlier.

Election of Graham had long been expected and was a "non-event" except in two respects. First, it led ultimately to the resignation of Dr. Nesset (effective June 30, 1955), who had a different R&D and diversification vision than did Graham. Second, it left absolutely no doubt as to who was calling the shots for Baxter.

FINANCIAL RESULTS DURING PERIOD OF EXPERIMENTATION AND CHANGE

Sales and profits continued to grow in a steady fashion during this time, interrupted, as noted earlier, by the post-Korean Conflict adjustment. Figure 4 summarizes that data.

BAXTER SALES AND EARNINGS
1946 - 1954

Year	$ Net Sales	$ Net Income (After Taxes)	$ Net Earnings Per Common Share
1946	2,763,000	303,000	0.62
1947	3,976,000	308,000	0.62
1948	6,326,000	693,000	1.40
1949	7,104,000	633,000	1.27
1950	9,875,000	875,000	1.75
1951	11,307,000	705,000	1.41
1952	16,190,000	865,000	1.65
1953	17,064,000	667,000	1.24
1954	14,793,000	535,000	1.02

Figure 4

THE HOSPITAL ENVIRONMENT

Hospitals and health care were concurrently experiencing growth and change. These were due in part to the Hill-Burton Act (1946) and the report of the Commission on Hospital Care (1947).[11] A larger influence, of course, was population and economic growth after the war. Hill-Burton provided federal funding for hospital construction. Both Hill-Burton and the 1947 commission report stimulated many state hospital planning studies. The program of the Joint Committee on Accreditation of Hospitals began in 1952.[12]

In 1946, there were 4,444 U.S. hospitals. By 1964, there were 5,407.[13] General hospital admissions grew 32 percent from 1941 to 1946 and another 26 percent from 1946 to 1952.[14] The average size of hospitals remained relatively small: only 9.2 percent of hospitals had more than 300 beds in 1946; 6.9 percent in 1955.[15]

The emphasis in the fifties was still on short-term care. In 1957/58 there "were more hospital patients admitted for hemorrhoids than heart disease; more for hernia repair than cancer."[16] Surgeries on the increase were hernia procedures, hemorrhoidectomies, gall bladders, and hysterectomies.

U.S. hospitals increased their employment from 500,000 in 1946 to 1,000,000 by 1960, and doubled that again by 1970. Throughout the 1950s, voluntary hospitals kept a 70 percent share of general, short-term patient admissions. Hospitals expanded the number of specialty residencies from 10,000 in 1945 to 25,000 by 1955.[17]

From a larger perspective, per capita health care expenditures rose from $29 in 1929 (3.5 percent of GNP) to $82 in 1950 (4.2 percent of GNP). More important, in the same time period the government portion of health care expenditures doubled from 13.6 to 27.2 percent.[18] The drive for health care reimbursement was intensifying. By 1960, 63 percent of all nongovernmental health expenditures were being paid by Blue Cross or other insurance plans.[19] Combined total insurance benefits for all kinds of care rose from $772 million in 1948 to $8.7 billion in 1964.[20]

Meanwhile, the number of family and general practice physicians as a percentage of the total was falling precipitously, from 83.5 percent of all physicians in 1931 to 77.7 percent in 1940; to 67.3 percent in 1949; and to 38.4 percent by 1961. Not surprisingly, given those statistics, hospital outpatient care began to grow in the mid-fifties.[21]

Clearly, there was no shortage of market niches and alternative strategic directions that the emerging Baxter might elect to pursue.

JUST ANOTHER STORY OF A SMALL COMPANY STRUGGLING FOR SURVIVAL?

Baxter's course of action at this stage was unique because it began early to look beyond immediate problems to seek a long-term strategy. From the start, it sought an *integrated* strategy, not one focused on or limited to sales and marketing. The only strategic model that was somewhat relevant was the pharmaceutical companies of that era. The company elected not to emulate that model, although it did continue its work on pharmaceutical product development that had begun earlier. This was a period of broad and rapid advance in patient care and clinical medicine, and Baxter, small as it then was, chose to pursue opportunities for technical leadership.

The elements of an integrated strategy that began to emerge building first on the basic "people values" which Dr. Falk established and Bill Graham then nurtured, were:

- A primary emphasis on manufacturing systems and manufacturing costs
- A deliberate effort to develop and then dominate new specialty market niches, which the company's rapidly-developing manufacturing system supported
- Initial concepts for financing the investments in product and market development, which were further refined and advanced in the fifties

MILESTONES

1940—1949

1940	Expansion of Canadian manufacturing facilities.
1941	Introduction of Plasma-Vac.
1943	Booz Allen & Hamilton management study, followed by hiring of Graham Evans.
1944	Baxter solutions first to be approved under U.S. Military specifications.
1944	Renegotiation of AHSC contract, adding two significant new clauses.
1945	Graham joins Baxter in April, and later in the year replaces Dawson on the board.
1945	Ellenville, N.Y. (west of Poughkeepsie) plant closes after brief military production using uniformed personnel. Baxter retains College Point, N.Y. facility (contiguous to what is now LaGuardia Airport).
1945	Baxter employee profit-sharing trust is initiated.
1946/47	Baxter "disposable" IV sets quickly begin to replace reusable rubber tubing in commercial markets.
1946/48	Baxter expands solutions product line with protein hydrolysate, invert sugar, and amino acids.
1947	Move of headquarters and laboratory from Glenview to Morton Grove.
1947	Cutter solutions recall.

1948	Internal stock split prior to first public offering.
1947/49	Trademark dispute with Don Baxter, Inc.
1949	Introduction of Piromen injectable.
1949	Work begins on Cleveland, Mississippi, plant.
1949	Don Madsen assigned to South Africa to open joint venture facility there.
1949	Sales exceed $7 million in 1949.

END NOTES

CHAPTER VI

1. Rights to the Baxter name did become an issue in the U.S. and other countries. There was also some risk then of the name taking on a generic meaning since hospital personnel sometimes referred to any commercial solution as "a Baxter"; it's easy to understand why. Recent historical work for the nation's oldest prepaid health plan, Kaiser, uncovered container shards marked Don Baxter Inc., Chicago, Illinois, at the Contractors General Hospital in southern California where the plan began in the very early thirties. Stephen A. Gilford, letter to Les Jacobson of Baxter, October 3, 1990.

2. The Cutter solutions recall came about eight years before it had to recall its polio vaccine product. *The New York Times,* November 25, 1990, Sunday Magazine, p. 61.

3. Baxter board minutes, 1949-51.

4. Baxter profit sharing trust records. Employee names and social security numbers have not been published to safeguard confidentiality. In later years, as Baxter common stock price increases slowed, profit sharing balances for individual employees also fell to more typical rates of growth. In 1985, when Baxter adopted a defined benefit pension plan retroactive to 1961, long-term employees benefited from a "double hit" in long-term benefits. That additional benefit is *not* included in these calculations.

5. Chapter 241, Laws of the State of Mississippi of 1944 under the authority of the Mississippi Agriculture and Industrial Board. Under this law municipalities have the power, the right and the authority to issue the bonds of the municipality for the purpose of acquiring land and constructing a manufacturing facility and to lease or rent such land and buildings to such manufacturing industry found suitable to the needs of the municipality.

6. The joint venture with Saphar Laboratories Ltd. (also Keatings Pharmacy) was approved at the Baxter annual meeting, 29 March 1948.

7. Baxter board minutes.

8. Baxter Laboratories Stockholder Records.

9. Baxter board minutes of 23 June 1952.

10. Baxter board minutes 1953.

11. Rosemary Stevens, *In Sickness and In Wealth: American Hospitals in the Twentieth Century* (New York: Basic Books, 1989), 213-220.

12. ibid., 247.

13. William G. Rothstein, *American Medical Schools and the Practice of Medicine* (New York: Oxford University Press, 1987), 208.

14. Stevens, *In Sickness and In Wealth*, 213, 220.

15. ibid., 230.

16. ibid., 231.

17. ibid., 231.

18. Rothstein, *American Medical Schools*, 184.

19. Stevens, *In Sickness and In Wealth*, 258.

20. ibid.

21. Rothstein, *American Medical Schools*, 201, 213.

CHAPTER

VII

LAUNCHING A NEW STRATEGIC ERA: 1955–62

By 1955, William Graham had been president for two years, a Baxter officer and director for ten. The post-Korean Conflict transition had been successfully navigated. The concepts and general direction of Baxter's strategic organization, personnel, and benefits programs were largely in place and ready to be built upon. As an illustration, by this time the company already had a "semi-retirement" plan under which employees could work part-time after retirement to supplement company profit-sharing and social security benefits (an approach some leading corporations are just now discovering in the very different employment market of the 1990s).

The beginning of a long, and in many respects still unparalleled, period of growth gave Graham the opportunity to exercise his talent for identifying and attracting smart people with strong drive and orientation to achieving results.

Raymond D. Oddi, a Northwestern graduate and Gold Medal Winner in the Illinois CPA Examination, returned from Korean military service and joined Baxter in January 1954. He moved through a variety of accounting and financial assignments before becoming a corporate officer, senior vice president, and chief financial officer. He also worked for about eight years, from the late sixties through the mid-seventies, as assistant to the CEO, which gave him broad management perspective. Oddi's pleasant and mild manner made him very effective in the tough role of "substitute CEO," which Graham acknowledges is one of the ways he used Oddi to focus in on specific problems. By his retirement in 1986 after 32 years, Oddi had built a much respected financial organization.

Shortly after, in 1956, Lincoln R. Dowell was recruited to develop the Baxter employee relations function. An Illinois Institute of Technology graduate, Dowell had been home office personnel manager for Allstate Insurance Company. He describes how, after initial interviews at Baxter, he asked the Allstate investment manager for an opinion. "If it was my career, I'd forget about Baxter," was the reply. "It's a small company which makes a commodity product. It's sugar and water in a simple delivery system. Furthermore, they have a powerful distributor who's three times their size, and who'll probably gobble them up one of these days." Dowell was impressed enough by Graham's leadership and vision for Baxter that he accepted the position despite this less-than-ringing endorsement. Dowell recalls that he became so sure during the interviewing process the future of the company was sufficiently dependent on the president's continued leadership that he had the temerity to ask Graham what the chances were that the latter might be recruited away to run a larger company. Graham answered that he was totally committed to Baxter's success and that it was unlikely another company was going to come looking for him anyway.

After Dowell's early work in employee relations, he went on to help Graham develop a corporate communication function. Together they decided to project what they called a "quiet public posture" for the company through some challenging times—the Kefauver Hearings on drug industry pricing, the public battle with American Hospital Supply, and the rapid spread of investment interest in the young company by analysts like Mary Wrenn of Merrill Lynch. Baxter let performance speak louder than words. The company never overstated or overpromised. Dowell would recommend to Graham one or two accomplishments or developments the company wanted to emphasize, but even these were low-keyed.[1]

This aspect of the company's integrated strategy seems to have attracted less attention perhaps than others. Baxter's approach to communications evolved naturally out of Graham's personal leadership and communication style, and then was further influenced by Vern Loucks' personal communication flair. It was also shaped by two early communication challenges: the Morton Grove employee vote on union decertification in 1958 and, in a larger national arena, the 1960 to 1962 Kefauver U.S. Senate hearings on the pharmaceutical industry.

Dowell was centrally involved in both of these challenges. He recalled, "The 1958 employee vote on whether there should continue to be a union at the Morton Grove plant was critical. It's true that persistent attempts by the International Chemical Workers Union to organize our newer Cleveland, Mississippi plant had been unsuccessful. Still, a 'pro-company' vote at our home location would make it much more difficult for the union to organize other locations as our manufacturing system continued to grow.

"Bill Treacy [2] and I recognized early that one of our strongest assets in the contest was high employee regard for Bill Graham. The general employee feeling was if anything went wrong in Baxter it would be fixed as soon as Bill Graham found out about it. So we built our communications campaign on employee letters and bulletins from Bill and speeches by him at key points.

"To be natural for him, communication had to hew to some key criteria. First, there was absolutely no hyperbole. He insisted on a standard of credibility that looked ahead to the long-term rather than considered just the moment. Promises and commitments made were to be delivered on, without exception. Second, there was no truculence in our campaign despite the fact that truculence then characterized many management-labor conflicts and some had exploded into 'causes célèbres.' Even in those days Bill's manner was mild (a characteristic occasionally some would misread to their subsequent regret). We didn't attack the union, but questioned its applicability to our situation. Consequently, third, we waged a very quiet battle and did everything we could to keep it from becoming a noisy war. The campaign succeeded. Morton Grove employees voted overwhelmingly 'no union'."

Dowell paused before going on to the second early communications challenge. It was the 1960-62 U.S. Senate hearings on pricing in the prescription drug industry—the "Kefauver investigation." These hearings followed hard on the heels of Senator Estes Kefauver's widely watched televised hearings on organized crime and its alleged links to organized labor. The television-viewing public was transfixed by scenes of a succession of shadowy mob and labor figures being skewered by Senate committee members, an aggressive approach Mr. Kefauver apparently planned to carry forward with drug industry witnesses.

"The experience is still timely and relevant," Dowell went on. "Senator David Pryor is now reviving the issue of prescription pricing.[3] Back in those days, the Pharmaceutical Manufacturers Association (PMA) had just been formed from two predecessor organizations. Bill Graham was the second chairman, first chairman-elect of the PMA. The industry had concentrated on direct communication with ethical health professionals and had seen no pressing need for media and public relations.

"Bill's chairmanship and my heading the PMA public relations committee gave us an excellent vantage point from which to observe and learn. When Bill assigned me internal Baxter P.R. responsibility, we simply built on the PMA experience as well as the earlier Morton Grove union campaign. As he described the emerging communications strategy in a speech to the Public Relations Society of America, 'We learned that one must have documented facts if one is to present his story effectively. We learned that only the story which is available at the right time and place will get a hearing. We learned that the simple story will often get a hearing where the complex one will not'."

From these straightforward beginnings the company's communications strategy took shape, remaining relatively consistent from that day to this.

Recruitment of solid scientists picked up speed. Dr. Harry Fevold, who had worked as part of the Link Group at the University of Wisconsin, was already director of research under Dr. Naurice Nesset. Dr. Leonard Ginger, with a solid background in synthetic organic chemistry, was the lead bench scientist. Ginger, who joined Baxter in 1949, did the original Piromen injectable work, and Synthroid [levothyroxine sodium] was also his concept. He was a graduate of Northwestern, held an M.S. from the University of Chicago, and a Ph.D. from Yale. He had been with Merck and the Manhattan Project earlier. Dr. Nicholas Kartinos joined Baxter during this same period (1953). Dr. Robert Herwick, a lawyer, M.D., Ph.D. pharmacologist, and former director of medical affairs for the F.D.A., became medical director, replacing Dr. Byrne. Herwick played a key role in the most significant Baxter product development of the 1950s—kidney dialysis. The hiring pattern at Baxter was to seek scientists (and others) with excellent academic credentials, successful experience in leading organizations, and in many cases, a combination of disciplines.

When Nesset's resignation became effective in 1955, and Ginger replaced him and became an officer, the company's R&D orientation shifted more toward synthetic chemistry.

The Baxter philosophy for attracting and rewarding key people was refined at this time, as were the legends about Graham as a hard bargainer. The philosophy was that salaries should be "in the market ballpark," but not necessarily top dollar. Long-term incentives should be at top levels based on actual company performance. As for the legends, they can be illustrated by the 1958 recruitment of Jim Ammon. The first of a long line of Harvard Business School graduates to be recruited by Baxter, Ammon said, "I was contacted by Herbert Halbrecht, an agency then upgrading to retainer executive search. After interviews in Morton Grove, I decided I really wanted the job as assistant to the president. I felt, though, at the appropriate point I had to point out I was being offered 10 percent less than my base and bonus at Chrysler. Bill Graham's friendly blue eyes turned to steel. 'Well Jim,' he answered, 'if you don't want the job, I know two other men who would give their eyeteeth for it.'"

Ammon took the job and served as director of marketing, then treasurer, and vice president for corporate development before retiring in 1972.

THE MOST BASIC BUSINESS PROBLEM STILL LOOMS

While Baxter progressively resolved its operating problems, the overriding business issue grew more vexing. Following the 1950 American Hospital Supply acquisition of Don Baxter, Foster McGaw alternated between pressure on and overtures to Baxter to consider becoming a part of American Hospital. Late in 1950, he made a concerted effort which was rebuffed. Also, after American's acquisition of Don Baxter, he raised continuing objection to Baxter's use of the Travenol trademark on solutions.

After the 1950 rebuff, McGaw continued to test the Morton Grove waters for receptivity to a business combination through a variety of emissaries, even including Frank Manheim of Lehman Brothers, who had been close to Graham since the initial Baxter public stock offering in 1951. Given that the length of the difficult relationship among Ralph Falk, Don Baxter, and Foster McGaw now spanned more than 20 years, McGaw's persistence must have set some kind of record.

IV solutions' pricing became more competitive by the mid-fifties. Baxter-American jockeying began to take a toll in the hospital market. American lost some big accounts to Abbott and opted not to rebid others, claiming the discount structure didn't permit meeting competition. Baxter reacted by negotiating adjusted terms and discounts and by taking direct responsibility for hospital accounts when volume exceeded 50,000 liters, giving past business development credit to the distributor. Reducing American Hospital discounts and commissions soured the two companies' relationship further. In Morton Grove, there was suspicion that the pricing "crunch" was, in large part, another McGaw stratagem to tighten the screws on Baxter. Whatever the true facts, Baxter's solutions market leadership slipped.

As the conflict of goals and personalities continued unabated, Baxter management became more convinced than ever that Baxter's number one strategic priority had to be direct access to the market (not just in the United States, but in other countries where Harry Falk had signed exclusive distribution agreements). However, the time had to be right because of high investment costs of going direct, as well as for other reasons—and it wasn't right yet.

BAXTER MOMENTUM BEGINS TO BUILD—LAUNCHING A RECORD-SETTING ERA OF TWENTY-NINE YEARS

Early on, Baxter established a tradition of quiet understatement about its accomplishments. The tradition was followed in the mid to late fifties in contests with unions in Morton Grove and Cleveland, Mississippi. It was confirmed in the late fifties and early sixties by the approach to earnings projections as Baxter common stock began to attract wider notice due in part to favorable attention by analysts such as Mary Wrenn of Merrill Lynch. Its value was demonstrated conclusively during the battle with American Hospital Supply (1962-64) and still later during the introduction of Viaflex. Baxter's financial performance record for almost three decades beginning in 1955 (with a base year of 1954) is truly remarkable. For 29 years through 1983 Baxter's earnings per share (EPS) grew at a compound annual rate of about 20 percent. EPS data for this period is summarized in in Figures 5 and 6, which follow.[4]

Research of Baxter internal financial data, Fortune 500, and New York Stock Exchange reports, and Value Line analyses suggests that no other leading public corporation has matched this record of consistent superior earnings for so long a period of time. We compared Baxter's performance with that of all public companies, including other health care companies, and found none that came close to this record. In fact, very few other companies remained on the top list for EPS growth rate for the entire three decades analyzed. Baxter's staying power in that regard was unique.

Baxter's durable EPS growth record itself can be divided into three parts, as shown in Figure 6: a small company "lift-off" phase from about 1954 to 1962, fueled in large part by innovation; a strategic "break-out" phase where the company overcame its major strategic obstacle, strengthened its presence in other countries, and innovation continued from 1962 to 1971; and from 1971 to 1980 a growth investment phase where strong product market positions had to be defended while innovation became more dependent on synergies among various therapies and technologies. As this period of superior financial performance continued, Baxter faced the ever more difficult challenge of meeting or exceeding the high standards and expectations it had created.

COMPOUND ANNUAL GROWTH IN EARNINGS PER SHARE (EPS) 1954 to 1983	
Company	Growth Rate
Baxter	20.0%
Bristol-Myers	15.6
Johnson & Johnson	13.6
Smith Kline Beckman	13.2
Eli Lilly	12.9
Abbott	12.6
Merck and Company	12.5
Pfizer, Inc.	10.5
Sterling Drug	9.8

Figure 5

This record was produced by a number of different management decisions and actions. Most notable among them were Baxter management's early decision to pursue the objective of consistent and predictable earnings growth. Hand-in-hand with that was the product marketing philosophy that Graham called "hitting lots of solid singles." As Baxter was successful in hitting those singles, there was a multiplier effect. Since the company was deliberately seeking to hit into gaps (market niches), it could, in many instances, increase its operating margins. And those growing net profits were diversified over a progressively broader product base.

Baxter's aggressive manufacturing cost management contributed to both share-of-market gains and earnings growth. And another important contributing factor was creativity in financial management on the part of a number of people including Graham, Ammon, Oddi,

BAXTER COMPOUND ANNUAL EARNINGS PER SHARE (EPS) Growth Rate		
1954 - 1983	29 years	20.0 %
1964 - 1983	20 years	21.3
1969 - 1983	15 years	19.8
1974 - 1983	10 years	20.7

Figure 6

and later many others. The company managed its cost of capital astutely and, for many of these years, enjoyed a favorable tax rate (despite punctiliously observing the tax code). Cost of capital was as favorable as it was because of Baxter's steadily increasing common stock multiple, among other things. Taking advantage of industrial revenue bonds to defray the cost of rapid manufacturing expansion, (already described for the Cleveland, Mississippi plant) was another method employed. Locating manufacturing facilities in tax-sheltered areas such as Puerto Rico (described a little later in this chapter) and, after that, in Ireland, was still another contributor.

Beyond cost of capital, favorable labor rates, employee dedication and loyalty, careful choice of new plant manufacturing sites, training of new manufacturing employees, painstaking attention to every detail of new plant start-up and "break-in," as well as generally excellent employee relations were other important factors. And throughout the late fifties and much of the sixties, the company used convertible subordinated debentures (CSDs) to its great advantage. Baxter was able to obtain extremely favorable interest rates and typically retired debentures rather than allowing them to be converted. In those days this type of security carried about a 4 percent interest rate and commanded as much as a 25 percent premium over straight stock. Therefore, not only did the company benefit from use of CSD instruments, bondholders also did very well. Another example of how Baxter, very early in its growth, began to seek approaches that would provide benefits to multiple stakeholders is the investment of employee profit-sharing funds in Baxter stock, mentioned earlier.

Baxter board minutes show a steady flow of debenture sale and repurchase over a long period. On February 24, 1967, one such issue received an "A" rating, the first such rating obtained since a Food Machinery Corporation issue six years earlier. Somewhat later, Baxter would be one of the first American companies to tap the Eurobond market.

1983 wasn't the end of Baxter's superior financial performance. There was, however, a pause as the company adjusted its strategy to basic shifts in the U.S. health care system, its economics, and other changes.

UNIQUE BAXTER STRATEGY DEVELOPS IN SUCCESSIVE STAGES

Baxter's comprehensive strategy developed in stages over a period of time. Once developed, it remained in place—always being modified and adapted—until 1983. In some respects, it is still guiding the company today. How the strategy shifted after 1983 is an interesting later part of the story.

The first stage was "direction-setting" in the late forties and early fifties. Graham had two basic alternative directions to consider. One was the model of the successful pharmaceutical companies of that day. The other was moving more in the direction of Baxter's distributor, American Hospital Supply, or combining with American, for which McGaw continued to press. Graham chose neither, but instead elected a "contrarian" strategy of pursuing hospital and clinical care specialties, the markets for which had to be created out of whole cloth. Many of these specialties (solutions, blood therapy, dialysis, and the heart-lung oxygenator) were needs which large hospitals and teaching institutions had met internally in some fashion. Baxter had to convince the hospital that an outside supplier could do it better and that patients would be better served that way.

The second stage in strategy development (beginning in the 1940s) was to build Baxter's core competence in manufacturing and technology. In retrospect, this may appear to be out of proper sequence since the company's marketing direction was still to be clearly established. However, Baxter was very much a "supplier" at that time, and it was isolated from its principal markets in the United States by its larger distributor, American Hospital, and in other countries by exclusive distributors as well. This was, in fact, the major strategic issue, causing Baxter's strategy to be initially largely defensive.

Third came the difficult stage of deciding marketing approach and product development priorities (1947-57). What gradually emerged here was a *combination* of some of the more effective attributes of the pharmaceutical business, on the one hand, and the hospital supply business on the other, thus creating a whole new industry segment. There were primary-product market areas—IV solutions, blood products, and artificial organs (initially, the artificial kidney);and secondary ones—drugs such as Piromen, Synthroid tablets, and Choloxin tablets; enzymes; and electronic products (initially, the Zenith Defibrillator and patient monitoring equipment). In primary product areas, Baxter itself undertook all of the development, application work, and investment. These took years of persistence and of surmounting obstacles. The solutions business required about 15 years to mature and solidify (1931-46); the blood business took longer (1939-59); and the artificial kidney (hemodialysis) took eight years (1956-64). Baxter sometimes took a different approach, seeking out small companies that had already partially developed a market

Dextrose solutions underwent stringent quality testing to ensure reliability of the product. In 1959, this woman conducted the final analysis testing before shipping solutions to the Armed Forces.

niche and a beginning technology position (Hyland and Fenwal, for example).

To deal with the problem of isolation from its user-customers, Baxter began to build a field sales support organization (the Medical Service Representatives) and some marketing elements long before the company became a fully independent marketer in 1962, when the tie to American Hospital Supply was broken. Therefore, many of the specific marketing decisions made in this period (1952-62) were to diversify and hedge against the central relationships with American Hospital and Don Baxter. For example, Travenol-labeled products and the market's recognition of the Travenol name were being emphasized. Medical sales representatives (MSRs) were given incentives to sell these products. Still, it took years before Baxter made a dent in Don Baxter's western territory. Graham said, "We made a lot of mistakes as we began to get started in marketing."

Still, when the company did emerge as an independent marketer, it quickly proved itself to be a formidable "sales machine" (as some Baxter alumni describe it). Sales effectiveness was due principally to small specialized sales teams with excellent product, technical, and application knowledge and strong professional relationships within the hospital customer organization. A Baxter alumnus said, "At that time Baxter hired salesmen and tried to make gentlemen out of them. Abbott hired gentlemen and tried to make them salesmen. And American Hospital Supply took young people out of college and taught them the 'McGaw Gospel' of customer service."

Out of this marketing experience evolved a Baxter philosophy of early niche dominance, accompanied by a drive for strong sales growth and appropriate pricing action. As the number of separate market niches grew, there was a question of whether Baxter could maintain its technical leadership and investment commitment in all of them. It entered the field of medical electronics early with Zenith technology that was perhaps already outdated, and it failed to support for long enough its first pioneering work in bubble oxygenators (the artificial heart-lung). That's part of the price of the marketing strategy Baxter elected. Managing these many emerging niches meant catching not just the first wave, but also the second and third waves, and also making a deliberate effort to obsolete one's own product technology. Growing success makes it more and more difficult to do that across a broad front of specialized patient therapies and technologies. As time went on, this would become a strategic issue for Baxter.

Still another element in the marketing approach was concentration on product disposability at a time when this aspect of design had generally not been considered for the kinds of medical products Baxter offered. Not only did this increase convenience for doctors and nurses, and ensure sterility of equipment and increased safety for the patient, it also increased market stability and consistency for Baxter.

The fourth stage in strategy development (1955-60) was the articulation of a financial and investment approach, which was particularly effective, and which made possible the pursuit of all these many initiatives concurrently.

Fifth was the long-term approach for stimulating and rewarding innovation, not just in R&D and product planning, but throughout the whole organization and across all business functions. This was emphasized not just internally within the organization itself, but through timely exploitation of appropriate technology from outside as well. During the period from 1955 to 1970 particularly, the Baxter organization developed an enviable record of innovation across diverse technologies and medical therapies.

The sixth stage was early development of an international strategy, from 1954 when manufacturing in Brussels was begun, to 1959 when an international division was first created. That strategy called for Baxter to establish its presence in each country where it chose to operate through manufacturing rather than by exporting. This was a risky and high investment-cost approach at the time. The high product value and low gross shipping weight of pharmaceuticals made it possible for the drug companies to be successful exporters. That approach, however, would certainly not have worked for Baxter shipping bulky solutions. Jim Tobin recalled old-timers who would quote Graham, "You can't ship water over water." So Baxter set out to take one country at a time, establish the necessary in-country relationships, pick one or more of its products where market dominance could be established, obtain regulatory approvals, and establish a manufacturing presence there. Once that cycle was complete, Baxter would move on to repeat the cycle in another country—almost like the successful American "island-hopping" Pacific campaign in World War II. Typically, no local competitor in a medical specialty could match Baxter's overall R&D resources. The strategy was preemptive because, in most cases, the single-country specialty market would not support a second investment by a competitor.

All of these elements of strategy were driven by necessity. Still, taken together, they represent an extraordinary strategic undertaking, and in each of them, Baxter did an outstanding job of balancing long-term and short-term considerations, as demonstrated by its 29-year financial record. Long-term consistency is most directly attributable to Baxter's skill in spotting and developing specialty-market niches: "hitting lots of singles."

The recent summary report of the Massachusetts Institute of Technology Commission on Industrial Productivity had this commentary on strategy and time horizons:

> "It is no great insight to say that successful business planners have to pay attention to both the long-term and the short-term consequences of their decisions. There are many cases where a firm has hung on too long or given up too soon.[5] . . . Competitive success . . . is rarely the result of overnight breakthroughs; rather it is built on years

of effort, years spent testing, adjusting, improving, refining, and in the process accumulating detailed technical knowledge of products and production techniques. Often progress also involves the parallel development and eventual synthesis of several different technologies.[6] Surprises are inevitable, and they are not always pleasant ones. Firms engaged in such development must expect to enter technological cul-de-sacs from time to time. The successful firms . . . are those with the conviction and the stamina to stay the course in spite of risks and mishaps."[7]

This 1989-90 commentary on America's industrial competitiveness could have been written about Baxter's strategy through the fifties. And interestingly, hospital and health care markets in the United States have thus far generally escaped the ravages of international competition that other domestic industries have suffered.

FINANCIAL MANEUVER IN 1956-57 AVERTS THREAT OF AMERICAN HOSPITAL SUPPLY TAKEOVER

During these years, Baxter certainly wasn't spending a lot of executive hours on the stages of strategy development. The issues confronting Baxter were immediate, and there were still risks threatening the company's long-term survival. It wasn't until 1964 that those principal risks and constraints were overcome and Baxter could confidently look ahead to the future with a solid strategic foundation in place. In 1956, unpleasant reality intruded again.

"Bill, Foster McGaw has got things stirred up again. He's convinced Harry we should sell the company to American now. Young Ralph is leaning in that direction too. I have to tell you between the two of them I'm reconsidering my own position. I want to get together in Chicago this week to decide what we should do." It was mid-August 1956. Dr. Falk was on the telephone from Boise with Graham in Morton Grove.

"Has your position changed at all on this issue?" he asked Graham. "This thing has heated up to the point where everyone, particularly Foster McGaw, is counting the votes and telling me where everyone stands. Where do you stand?"

Graham replied, "Ralph, my position hasn't changed. I'm still against selling the company to American Hospital or any form of combination with American. What's going on is that Foster is applying some old-fashioned business pressure. He's trying to show us that American can influence the market in a way that will drive the value of Baxter down. Sounds like he's already got Harry convinced that's going to happen. What we have to do is apply some counter-pressure. I may have just the way to do that."

MIDWAY AIRPORT MEETING

A few days later, on August 18, 1956, a meeting was held at a Midway Airport motel. Ralph Falk was en route to New York. Harry Falk came to Chicago from California. Bill Graham was joined by Ralph Falk II, and Everett Travis (a Robert Heller consultant who, by this time, had developed a continuing working relationship with Baxter and Graham).

The atmosphere was tense. Personal agendas bubbled beneath the American Hospital Supply business issue. Harry Falk was in poor health (he would die not long after, on October 9, 1956, following surgery). It's quite likely that his health contributed to his concern about a possible decline in Baxter's value. To some others in the motel meeting room the pressure from McGaw and American perhaps held out the hope of an easier and safer path for Baxter to travel. Graham saw a substantial risk of his vision of Baxter as an independent health care leader slipping away.

Harry Falk led the charge. "If we don't react to this latest expression of interest by Foster, the company could be worth less a couple of years from now than it is today. There seems to be a lot of price pressure in the marketplace, isn't there, Bill?" he asked, looking across the table at Graham. Falk continued, "In the past when Foster has gotten down to specifics, his terms have been fair. He sees an important role for Baxter and our people in any combined organization. If we can't get agreement around the table that this is the thing to do, at least let's agree it's worth exploring."

The last thought brought some nods of agreement. Dr. Falk asked Graham what his position was. "I'm against our business direction being decided by someone else," Graham answered. "We have better alternatives, and we should give them a chance to work."

After an hour of discussion Falk wrapped it up. "Well, Bill, if you're firmly opposed, then we're not going to pursue discussions with Foster McGaw and American. The matter is closed."

The acquisition of a company named Wallerstein turned out to be the workable alternative Graham was talking about. There is hardly any evidence today of Wallerstein's impact on Baxter markets or technology. Yet Graham contended that Wallerstein may have been the most important acquisition Baxter made—until 1985.

Wallerstein was a Staten Island, New York, producer of enzymes for food, brewing, and industrial use. In 1956, Leo Wallerstein approached Lehman Brothers and Frank Manheim, who had managed Baxter's first public stock offering in 1951, to find a buyer for the company. Manheim talked to Graham about the company then. Graham didn't see any connection to health care and turned him down.

Lehman Brothers was able to sell Wallerstein's food segment to Corn Products (now CPC International) for almost as much as Leo Wallerstein wanted for the whole business. There were no takers for the rest of the business, however, so Lehman put together an investment banking syndicate to buy and hold the rest of it.

Under the pressure of the events leading to the Midway Airport meeting, Graham began to think about what Manheim had told him about Wallerstein's numbers. What Manheim had said was that for a modest investment Baxter could substantially increase its volume and about double its profits. Graham reasoned that the change in Baxter's financial condition would alter McGaw's view of its supplier's vulnerability. He called Manheim. No, Wallerstein had not yet been sold, Manheim said, but a major Milwaukee malt company, Froedert Grain and Malting, had signed a letter of intent. The company's board was meeting that week to ratify the deal. Graham told Manheim his level of interest in Wallerstein had gone way up and asked to be kept informed.

By the weekend following the Midway meeting, the Froedert board had reversed their management and nixed the Wallerstein deal. Baxter quickly went to work with Manheim's help and reached a business agreement with the investment banking syndicate. On February 14, 1957, Wallerstein became a wholly owned subsidiary of Baxter. The purchase was financed by a loan from Equitable and by convertible debentures. Part of the debenture offering was retired before the end of 1957. The acquisition did come close to doubling Baxter's profits over two years. Market and pricing pressures exerted by American Hospital Supply began to ease. It would be the last time McGaw attempted to gain direct control of Baxter. Now, he began to move in a different strategic direction. Wallerstein was an early example of a take-over defense that became familiar later in the 1980s.

PHARMACEUTICAL MANUFACTURERS ASSOCIATION AND THE KEFAUVER HEARINGS

Graham became involved early in the American Pharmaceutical Manufacturers Association (1947). APMA provided him an opportunity to test and develop Baxter strategic direction in an arena of typically larger companies with substantially greater resources.

In 1958 Graham was elected president of the APMA, which merged in 1959 to form the Pharmaceutical Manufacturers Association (PMA). George Smith of Johnson & Johnson was the first PMA chairman, Graham the second (1960-61). The recognition of his leadership was rather remarkable since Baxter's annual sales were still less than $30 million. PMA leadership responsibility placed him center stage when Senator Estes Kefauver[8] held hearings on the drug industry, its pricing policies and profit levels. This was one of the early Congressional hearings projected beyond Capitol Hill to a national television audience. The "sound byte" (in today's terms) the committee tried to convey to the public was that of an industry piling unconscionable margins on top of minimal product raw material costs. Graham countered with a Baxter example, "Look, if that's the picture the committee wants to paint, maybe there's a better example than drug products which take years and cost hundreds of thousands of dollars to develop. My own small company provides for medical use a product on which we have a 625,000 percent markup on materials and a 7.1 percent profit. That's distilled water of the very highest purity." He proceeded to illustrate how fallacious this whole line of reasoning was.

Graham remained involved in this activity for almost four years. All in all, the industry probably gave as good as it got. An effective industry counteroffensive was also launched beyond the congressional context. This experience significantly influenced how Graham went about

Senator Estes Kefauver, left, and Senate GOP Leader Everett Dirksen of Illinois, right argue about the need for businesses to disclose trade secrets during the hearings.

developing Baxter strategy, and also probably had an impact on his thinking about government regulation and public affairs.

An amusing incident occurred when the industry had Dr. Vannevar Bush, a Nobel Prize-winning scientist from MIT, testify before the committee on the prime importance of R&D investments in our free enterprise system. Dr. Bush was much respected and he was an eloquent spokesman for R&D. Under Graham's questioning, he made a number of telling points for the industry's position. Representative Emanuel Celler[9] was glancing at his watch and thinking about gaveling the hearings to a close for the day so he could catch his late afternoon train to New York City.

Then one of the committee's key aides, an attorney named Johnson, leaned in to insert a question about marketing. It turned out that Dr. Bush didn't think much of marketing at all. He launched into a long tirade about how advertising and selling were a waste of the consumer's money and how, if you left it up to him, cars would be sold without advertising or dealer showrooms. The intelligent consumer could buy automobiles from their product specification sheets. Representative Celler leaned back with a smile and, for the moment, forgot his train to New York. This was just what the pharmaceutical industry needed to hear from its own witness, and just in time for the evening news. Graham was fuming, but there was no way to stop Dr. Bush.

PUERTO RICO

Not long after Baxter's twenty-fifth anniversary in 1956, and the establishment of a Baxter lectureship at the American College of Surgeons to commemorate it, came another significant Baxter milestone. It was the opening of the first Puerto Rican manufacturing plant at Hato Rey, outside San Juan, in February 1958. Why was this step so significant? Primarily, it was, like the Cleveland, Mississippi expansion before it, a giant step forward in establishing a far-flung, integrated, and flexible manufacturing system. Second, it substantially strengthened the company's position as the "best-cost" producer for its major markets. And third, it tested and expanded Baxter's planning capacity.

In the mid-fifties, Teodoro Moscosco made a personal appeal to Graham to start a Baxter manufacturing operation in Puerto Rico. Moscosco, one of the great men of Puerto Rican politics, was a colleague of Governor Munoz-Marin and head of the Economic

Development Administration. This agency, known better by its Spanish nickname, *Fomento,* was responsible for administering the "Operation Bootstrap" program to increase employment in Puerto Rico by attracting new manufacturing operations.

The tax advantage was obvious (Puerto Rico would grant Baxter a 100 percent exemption from income and other taxes), and there was an ample labor supply at rates below those found on the mainland. Yet the decision was a difficult one. Language would be a problem, public utilities on the island could be unreliable, shipping costs would be high, inventories would have to be increased, and the shipping industry was prone to strikes.

The planning of the Puerto Rico start-up took more than five years.[10] Graham himself, Ed Nawoj, Milt Ray of the law department, Oddi, and many others planned at successively more detailed levels and made countless visits to Puerto Rico to work with Fomento in order to ensure success. There were U.S. mainland plant "loading" and capacity issues, industrial relations considerations, logistics questions, and concerns about training the local Puerto Rican labor force, as well as core financial and tax issues to be resolved.

Baxter would not have entered Puerto Rico without a substantial tax incentive[11]. There were, however, strategic considerations and decisions that led to the initial manufacturing entry and which made the Puerto Rican base extremely effective as it rapidly expanded. There was an ample labor supply there, and the Commonwealth government was cooperative and supportive. At the same time, however, there was concern about how health care professionals in the mainland United States would feel about the quality of products manufactured there. So Baxter emphasized its name as the manufacturer. Graham chose not to use the parent corporation, Baxter of Delaware, as the vehicle for Puerto Rico. Instead, Baxter used a sequence of corporations incorporated in different states. Maryland was the first. This carefully crafted decision produced a number of important benefits. First, it sequenced the tax privileges for each individual manufacturing facility on a time-phased basis. Second, it allowed the parent company to bring cash home as successive corporations were liquidated. Payment of dividends, on the other hand, would have been fully taxable. Third, if "anticompetitive" or other suits had ever been brought, they would have had to be pursued in and through a number of different states. And based on this early experience, company management became adept at using various forms of legal organization to serve operating needs. By the early eighties, the parent Baxter organization was operating and managing through a network of over 60 subsidiary corporations.

Once the decision was made to manufacture in Puerto Rico, the company didn't take the approach of other medical products and pharmaceutical companies at the time, which Graham described as "a tableting machine, five operators, and away we go." Baxter planned and carried out a substantial entry that was good for the economy of the Commonwealth and for the labor force there, as well as for the company. That presence has now grown to plants from the western end of the island to an island off its eastern tip (Culebra), and a work force of about 6,000, which has made Baxter one of the largest private employers on the island. The beginning initially did not appear that promising to the Puerto Rico Industrial Development Company[12] because Baxter's first building in the Hato Rey industrial subdivision was only 12,300 square feet (with additions), employed 29 people, and was budgeted to produce $1 million worth of product in its first full year.

Subsequently, Baxter and the IRS had a protracted negotiation about the way the company allocated operating profits between Puerto Rico and the mainland United States. The standard applied by the IRS was fair for other medical and pharmaceutical companies. However, as already pointed out, Baxter operated very differently, with an integrated manufacturing and technical organization on the island to justify larger profits allocable to Puerto Rico. The company ultimately prevailed on this basis.

Puerto Rico is another example of a Baxter strategic undertaking that had a modest beginning, but grew steadily over many years because of the soundness of the original concept and painstaking implementation. Baxter operations there confirmed what the Cleveland, Mississippi facility had already begun to show—that its manufacturing management and systems could successfully operate production facilities in just about any kind of remote location. A twenty-fifth anniversary celebration of Baxter's Hato Rey beginning was held at the Condado Beach Hotel in 1983. It was attended by many officials of the Commonwealth government, including some Fomento staff who had worked with the company for several years before the actual opening; also by Art Baumann, who had been responsible for island operations for many years; by Jack Knowlton, who was general counsel when Hato Rey began; and by Jim Taylor, then island vice president for operations. Marsh Abbey, corporate general counsel at the time, was the principal speaker. And in the audience were four of the original nine Puerto Rican employees (the original nine had quickly expanded to 29 as manufacturing "ramped up"). Those four were still employed with Baxter 25 years later.

PRODUCT DIVERSIFICATION CONTINUES THROUGH ACQUISITION

Baxter made two acquisitions in 1959. Early that year, Flint Eaton was acquired. Fenwal was acquired just before year-end in December 1959. Because Fenwal was such a critical building-block in Baxter's marketing and technology development, it is the subject of a later chapter.

Flint Eaton was a Decatur, Illinois company founded in 1897, whose principal products at the time were Choline, for treatment of "fatty invasion of the liver," and Ferrolip, therapeutic iron for anemia. The company had 40 sales representatives, some calling on the wholesale drug trade. Wholesale drug channels were another avenue Baxter wanted to explore as a move away from distribution through American Hospital Supply.

Actually, the most significant products associated with the Flint name were Synthroid [levothyroxine sodium], which Baxter had developed prior to the acquisition of Flint Eaton and chose to sell through the division, and Travase [sutilains ointment], a product for debridement of tissue damaged by burns or ulceration, also an internal Baxter development based on Wallerstein's enzyme technology.

Three of the acquisitions of the 1950s—Hyland, Flint Eaton, and Fenwal—established a strategic approach that was to be followed for years to come. That was to seek small acquisitions whose technology was still being developed or which provided a sales channel complementary to Baxter's. Their share of market and profitability were not significant considerations. Wallerstein was the exception because it had been, as already described, a "take-over defense" in response to a specific challenge.

STOCK PERFORMANCE AND STOCK SPLITS

Baxter stock recovery, following the company's adjustment after the Korean Conflict, attracted more investors and analysts intrigued with the company's long-term potential. In 1959, Baxter split its common stock two-for-one. This followed an initial 60:1 internal split long before the first public offering (1945), and a 65:1 split as a part of the 1951 public offering. The 1959 2:1 split would be the first of seven such splits between that year and 1983. Baxter common stock was on its way to a long period of sustained superior performance.

STEADY BAXTER SALES AND PROFIT GROWTH SUPPORTS BRIGHT OUTLOOK FOR STOCK VALUE

Figure 7 shows Baxter sales and earnings for the period covered in this chapter.

BAXTER SALES AND EARNINGS 1950 TO 1962

Year	$ Net Sales	$ Net Income (After Taxes)
1950	9,875,000	875,000
1951	11,307,000	705,000
1952	16,190,000	865,000
1953	17,064,000	667,000
1954	14,793,000	535,000
1955	12,045,000	571,000
1956	13,147,000	622,000
1957	23,783,000	1,062,000
1958	25,057,000	1,394,000
1959	29,154,000	1,835,000
1960	33,775,000	2,142,000
1961	37,562,000	2,518,000
1962	42,319,000	2,845,000

Figure 7

DEATH OF DR. FALK

Dr. Ralph Falk died of cancer on November 2, 1960. He was 76 years old (but reported as 74 years old) and had been associated with the growth of Baxter for almost 30 years. When he and Graham met and talked last, not long before Dr. Falk's death, he said to the man who now ran the company he'd founded, "Let's not talk about the business, Bill. I feel fortunate it's in such good hands." Instead, they discussed Dr. Falk's health and other matters. Dr. Falk also told Graham then that he wanted him to be a trustee for the

Falk Testamentary Trusts. Graham agreed. The physician at the Mayo Clinic had just told Falk that the average life expectancy was 60 days for 28 cases of liver metastasis under treatment at Mayo, cases which were similar to Dr. Falk's. Falk had always been a realist in his business judgment as well as in his medical practice.

He was survived by his widow, Marian Citron Falk, who served as a Baxter director and then as honorary director until her death in December 1990; by a son, Ralph II; and a daughter, Carol. His brother Harry had died in October 1956 after a short illness.

Dr. Ralph Falk

The passing of the company's founder, whose ethical values and dedication to meeting medical and patient needs made a lasting imprint on Baxter, left a void. The direction of the company, however, had been in Graham's hands for some time.

Upon the death of his father, Ralph Falk II assumed the title of chairman, and Graham became CEO. Ralph Falk II had joined the company in 1948. He served as a director after his father's death until his retirement from the board in 1992, and continues as an honorary director. He quoted his father as saying that his wisdom in spotting and attracting Bill Graham alone entitled him to all the returns he had earned from the company.

1961—ANOTHER MILESTONE

In 1961 Baxter was listed on the New York Stock Exchange. The market for Baxter's common stock was broadening. In the late fifties, Graham had begun to spend an increasing part of his time on the road addressing and answering the questions of security analysts.[13]

Bill Graham stood with the president of the New York Stock Exchange, Keith Funston (r), for the first day of trading of Baxter stocks on the NYSE.

THE 1950s SEE MANY NEW PATHS ALONG BAXTER'S CENTRAL STRATEGIC ROADWAY

The period of the fifties in Baxter's history was described earlier as a time of thrusting out in different directions. Most of these new directions have now been sketched out in this chapter. It was a diverse set of paths for a company whose annual sales averaged about $20 million during that decade, and therefore the directions and required investments were closely controlled by Graham himself.

The multiple paths included:

- drugs (Synthroid [levothyroxine sodium], Piromen [injectable pyrogen], Choloxin [dextrothyroxine sodium])
- "piggyback" drugs (drugs added to intravenous solutions, beginning with Urevert solutions)
- diagnostics (from the 1952 Hyland acquisition)
- enzymes (from the Wallerstein acquisition) contributing to two medical products: Travase [sutilains ointment] and, later, Discase (Chymopapain injections)
- alternative distribution and sales channels
- international expansion (marked by the creation of the International Division in 1959)

and most notably,

- artificial organs, with initial work on both the artificial kidney and the bubble oxygenator starting in 1956

Yet none of these impeded progress along the main strategic roadway. The last of them, in fact, became an important part of the main roadway. And in the sixties, all of these initiatives became more closely linked together in a way that contributed to growth and technology leadership.

The underlying basic thrust of the fifties was continued improvement of solutions and blood products. In solutions, Baxter was losing market share because of problems with American Hospital Supply. Its technical leadership, however, continued to increase. The solutions product line was broadened: amino acids and fat emulsions were added. A lighter, one-way glass bottle was introduced. Progress was made with roller clamps, vein access products, and other tubing set accessories. Also important, Baxter plastic tubing sets were perfected in the early fifties and began to dominate the market. Not only did these offer patient and doctor benefits (because reusable tubing was a principal source of infections and pyrogens), its work in plastics made Baxter a leader in the field of materials biocompatibility, which had applications in kidney dialysis and heart-lung work as well as in solutions themselves. Substitution of plastics for glass and rubber contributed to the company's strategic goal of product disposability. The internal work in plastics compounding, equipment development, extrusion, and molding advanced another strategic goal for greater vertical integration. David Bellamy, one of the central figures over many years in Baxter's successful conversion to plastics, points out still another consideration. "When Baxter's international sales began to grow," he said, "Bill Graham was very concerned about the quality and reliability of glass supply in other countries. Plastics gave us a solution." So in the fifties and sixties, just as Dustin Hoffman was told in the movie *The Graduate,* the future was plastics.

In blood products, Baxter introduced the "stand-up" plastic Cube-Pak, and work was proceeding on plastic blood donor and administration sets. Because of the greater complexity of blood containers in manufacture, sterilization, and actual use, compared with solutions, many obstacles still lay ahead for the use of new materials in this therapy. The market resisted these innovations for a long time. Some of the other early market entrants (Abbott, particularly) found the blood products business difficult and unattractive, and soon de-emphasized it. Baxter, on the other hand, had by this time become expert in creating totally new markets where none had existed before.

Artificial organs (first the kidney and then the heart-lung machine) were shortly to emerge as a third force in Baxter's primary strategic thrust, together with IV solutions and blood products. Because of their great importance to Baxter and to clinical medicine, they are discussed in the next chapter.

THEN . . . SHOCK WAVES IN 1962

In 1962 a series of rapid-fire events occurred which, while not unanticipated, still produced one of the most dramatic periods in all of Baxter's history, posed grave risks for the company, and riveted management attention on the management requirements they created from 1962 to 1964. Those events are described shortly.

MILESTONES

1950-1961

1950	Outbreak of Korean hostilities.
1950	Expansion of Baxter's Cleveland, Mississippi plant.
1950	Foster McGaw again attempts to persuade Baxter Laboratories to become a part of American Hospital Supply.
1950	American Hospital Supply acquires the assets of Don Baxter, Inc. and later builds the Pharmaseal division around it.
1951	Baxter's first public stock offering.
1951	Legal action resolved in regard to Don Baxter Inc., Baxter royalty payments phased out, and new ten-year Baxter-American contract signed.
1951	Greenville, Kentucky, plant opened.
1952	Baxter acquires Hyland Laboratories (formerly Convalescent Serum Center, founded 1935).
1953	Graham elected president.
1954	End of Korean Conflict brings a "mini-replay" of downturn following World War II.
1955	Resignation of Dr. Naurice Nesset.
1956	Commercial development of artificial kidney machine.
1956	Midway meeting.

1956	Death of Harry Falk.
1957	Acquisition of Wallerstein.
1958	Hato Rey, Puerto Rico, facility begins production.
1959	2:1 Baxter common stock split.
1959	Baxter acquisition of Flint Eaton.
1959	Baxter acquisition of Fenwal.
1960	Kefauver hearings; Graham PMA leadership.
1960	Death of Dr. Falk; Graham becomes CEO and Ralph Falk II Chairman.
1961	Baxter stock listed on New York Stock Exchange; May 15 first trading day.
1961	Kefauver-Celler Drug Industry Legislation.

END NOTES

CHAPTER VIII

1. Oddi and Dowell, together with Graham, directed the planning, research, and preparation of this history.

2. Dowell had taken over labor relations responsibility from Bill Treacy in 1956 when the latter left the company to start a labor law practice. Treacy continued to work with Baxter as an outside advisor for some years.

3. The reference is to 1991 speeches by Senator David Pryor, Democrat of Arkansas.

4. Basic earnings per share data was provided by Value Line Inc., New York, NY 10017.

5. One example of this is American Hospital Supply's entry into the artificial kidney business. They got into the business late, chose to focus on hardware rather than software (i.e. "disposables"), and exited before Medicare funding for long-term dialysis was approved in 1973.

6. This kind of synergy was important in Baxter's growth and development, particularly in the late fifties and sixties, culminating in a remarkable product success in 1970.

7. Michael L. Dertouzos, Richard K. Lester, and Robert M. Solow, *Made in America: Regaining the Productive Edge* (New York: Harper Perennial in cooperation with MIT Press, 1990), 53-54.

8. U.S. Senator from Tennessee, 1949-63.

9. Emanuel Celler became an elected member of the 68th Congress from New York on March 4, 1923, and served in 24 succeeding congresses until January 3, 1973.

10. Appendix Exhibit. Reproduces a 1951 letter from Bill Graham to Dr. Falk reporting on the status of the Puerto Rican analysis at that very early stage. Other letters of the time are also included.

11. Section 936 of the Internal Revenue Code, successor to section 931 of the 1954 Internal Revenue Code. Exemption from taxation in the Commonwealth of Puerto Rico was by specific grant.

12. Pridco letter to Baxter, 19 September 1957, following the Commonwealth governor's approval of May 1957.

13. Because Graham's remarks to security analysts from 1959 to 1962 provide an opportunity to analyze his strategic thinking at that time, some key points are briefly excerpted in the Appendix.

CHAPTER

VIII

THIRD MAJOR DEVELOPMENT BY BAXTER CHANGES FOREVER THE LIVES OF KIDNEY DISEASE PATIENTS

In September 1964, Bennett Kivel went home to Melrose, Massachusetts. Not only did he return home, soon after, he went back to work as a senior engineer at Avco Corporation in Everett, Massachusetts. Dr. Kivel was then 34 years old. He was the first end-stage renal disease patient sent home on *family-administered*, long-term kidney dialysis from Dr. John Merrill's program at Brigham Hospital in Boston.[1] He lived almost another 20 years. Shortly before his death at age 54 in 1983, he said, "I think I've lived long enough now to have used more of Baxter's dialysis products than anyone else."

In many respects, the heroine of this story is Debbie Kivel, his wife. She willingly accepted the responsibilities and uncertainties this new treatment approach posed.[2] Still in the same Melrose home they lived in then, she says that Dr. Hampers, director of dialysis facilities at Peter Bent Brigham Hospital at that time,[3] didn't offer the option of her husband continuing dialysis center treatment. So there was no real alternative to home-based treatment.

Kivel lived for the objective of seeing his two sons, then four and six, graduate from college. That objective was accomplished. Avco was a supportive employer, making transportation and other arrangements for him. For three years the Kivels had to pay for their own dialysis supplies, the policy on reimbursement for dialysis treatment remaining an issue until 1973. Kivel was on dialysis for a total of 18 years, 10 of them on home dialysis from 1964 to 1974. He received a kidney transplant in 1974.

Kivel's return to his Melrose home was truly a landmark event. There are now over 300,000 individuals in 27 countries around the world who are alive and leading better lives because of long-term kidney dialysis of one kind or another, the commercial equipment for treatment all pioneered by Baxter. This and subsequent landmark events in long-term dialysis all flowed from a single meeting at Baxter's Morton Grove headquarters in the summer of 1954.

BACKGROUND OF KIDNEY DIALYSIS

Just as with Baxter's earlier two breakthroughs in intravenous and blood therapy, knowledge of the principles and potential applications of dialysis was not new. In this instance, it went all the way back to the Romans and their hot baths for "vividiffusion." Dialysis means separation of large from small molecules in solution by selective diffusion through a semipermeable membrane.[4] Kidney dialysis is the removal of waste materials and toxins from the bloodstream when kidney function is lost or impaired.

What was needed in the mid-fifties as Baxter began to get involved was a simple, practical, and "controllable" way to put the known principles to work, and then gradually to expand the boundaries of clinical need that could be served. Others had already tried and lost patience. However, this was exactly the kind of medical niche Baxter sought and the kind of challenge it had already proven it could successfully meet.

JUNE 1954 MORTON GROVE MEETING

These events were set in motion by a meeting in early June 1954 of Dr. Willem Johann Kolff and Dr. Robert Herwick at Baxter's Morton Grove headquarters. Dr. Kolff had come to Chicago from Cleveland, Ohio, to meet with another health care company. When those discussions proved to be fruitless, he called Baxter on short notice and arranged a meeting with Herwick for the mid-afternoon.

Dr. Kolff was born in Leiden, the Netherlands, in 1911, a few months before Bill Graham's birth in Chicago. Kolff attended the University of Leiden (1930-38) and the University of Groningen Medical School. He was both an M.D. and a Ph.D. in pharmacology. Dr. Herwick was also an M.D. and Ph.D. in pharmacology, and a lawyer as well, and had served as director of medical affairs for the F.D.A. before joining Baxter. Kolff received the Landsteiner Medal for establishing a Netherlands blood bank in 1942.[5] Pertinent to these developments, he continued his work on kidney dialysis during the Nazi occupation of his native country. He dialyzed 14 patients before one—a 68-year-old housewife named Sophie Schafstadt—survived.[6]

After the war Kolff came to the United States, where he became a naturalized citizen in 1956. In 1947 he demonstrated his "orange-juice can" dialysis machine (so-called because he built it from available components under Nazi occupation) at Mount Sinai Hospital in New York and then at Peter Bent Brigham Hospital in Boston.

Dr. Kolff stands with the Kolff-Brigham artificial kidney machine.

Westinghouse had earlier contracted with George Jernstedt of Pittsburgh to produce a modified version of the Alwall Kidney.[7] Only three of the machines were produced before the project was abandoned. Allis Chalmers also began to produce artificial kidneys based generally on Kolff principles. Fourteen Allis Chalmers devices were shipped before this effort too was terminated in the early fifties for lack of market response and market potential.[8]

Kolff was seeking a manufacturer to "commercialize" the artificial kidney. Of course, Dr. Kolff's view of the work and time required for successful commercialization was quite different from the views of manufacturers with whom he had talked. Nothing unusual about that. No doubt, though, the difference in view was an obstacle to Kolff negotiating the kind of agreement he wanted. He had had lengthy negotiations with one company, Mead Johnson, that failed when the management committee turned down the favorable recommendation of its product development committee. No volume potential now or in the foreseeable future, they said. That morning in the

Chicago area, another health care manufacturer (Abbott Laboratories) had turned Kolff down flat. "At least they didn't waste a lot of my time," Kolff thought to himself as he drove to Morton Grove to see Dr. Herwick without much optimism about the likely outcome. "Why should Baxter react any differently than the people with whom I've already talked?" he asked himself. "I'm not even sure they have the resources to do what needs to be done."

Baxter did, however, prove to be different, starting with Dr. Herwick. Herwick's educational background was similar to Kolff's. They established a relationship quickly and naturally. Then Herwick got to the point much more quickly than Kolff expected. "What long-term medical needs do you see the artificial kidney serving? Why haven't others who tried to commercialize the device succeeded? What kind of agreement do you want with us?"

Kolff hesitated before responding to Herwick's rapid-fire questions. Finally he said, "There is already medical need for dialysis for poisoning and trauma victims, and in conjunction with kidney transplant programs, as well as for research. Others failed because they weren't close enough to the medical needs. What I want is an agreement with someone committed to producing a commercial machine as quickly as possible. Once the right machine is available, other applications will perhaps develop."

Dialysis seemed to be a good fit with Baxter's niche strategy and Herwick was intrigued. "Let's see if Bill Graham is available," he suggested. "If he is, I'm sure he'd want to meet you. You'll find out he makes decisions quickly." A few minutes later they were in Graham's office. After listening to Kolff intently, Graham said, "Dr. Kolff, I can tell you right now we are interested in developing and manufacturing your machine. Give us 48 hours and we'll be back to you with a firm answer and a proposed working relationship."

Twenty-four hours later Herwick called Kolff at the Cleveland Clinic, where he headed the new department of artificial organs, and told him Baxter would like to proceed. "You can count on dialyzer development commanding the highest priority in Baxter, with Graham personally driving it," he added.

Graham, years later, recalled these 1954 discussions and decisions. "I wish I could say we immediately foresaw the entire future for chronic dialysis. We didn't. I did see an important medical need and a specialized market niche for Baxter. I also had a sense that there was a good fit with the technologies we were developing. But you have to remember that in 1954 the main issues we were dealing with were the decline in government demand for Baxter products following the end of the Korean Conflict and our continuing difficulties with American Hospital Supply." While the potential of dialysis was certainly consistent with Baxter's developing strategy, betting on this unproven technology that no one else was giving any chance of success illustrates how focused Graham was on the long term. The risk was particularly bold considering the time it was taken, with both the post-Korean Conflict adjustment and Baxter-American Hospital Supply jousting in the solutions marketplace.

BAXTER DEVELOPMENT TEAM STARTS WORK

Soon after the Morton Grove meeting with Dr. Kolff, a Baxter development team went to work. There was a lot to do. The Kolff kidney had not been designed either for manufacture or for simple operator use. Dr. Kolff's understandable impatience made him difficult to work with.

Ted Gewecke played a key role since much of the manufacturing was to be contracted out. Maytag was the first choice to manufacture the machine, which resembled a home washing machine. Maytag declined, and that part of the work was out-sourced to Groen Manufacturing in Elk Grove, Illinois. Cy Broman did a substantial amount of the Baxter engineering work. And Graham and Herwick remained actively involved.

There was a lot going on in the field of kidney research. The first successful live kidney transplant was performed at Brigham Hospital in 1954. The dialysis treatment center, begun within Brigham by Dr. Merrill, was gaining knowledge and experience, and began to exercise influence on medical thinking in other leading centers around the country, such as Georgetown University.[9] The Brigham dialysis program was designed specifically to support the kidney transplant program begun by Dr. Merrill and Dr. Joseph Murray in 1951[10] and for other short-term treatment. Grant support was provided by the Hartford Foundation, but it was limited to research and there was no funding provision for patient care. Dr. George Thorn, head of Brigham Hospital and an endocrinologist with a continuing interest in kidney disease, had done important research on the "crush syndrome." (During the Battle of Britain in the early 1940s, many bombing victims suffered crushed or damaged kidneys from building collapses and other related causes, hence "crush syndrome"). Dr. Thorn and others gained new insights into kidney function and treatment through study of this trauma. He reflected the attitude of the early fifties towards dialysis when he described treating a professor at Harvard College, "We were dialyzing him because he was trying to finish writing a book. When he got the book done, he said to us, 'That's it, gentlemen. I don't want you to bring the equipment over here again.'"[11]

There were still patient problems even with short-term hemodialysis: the "disequilibrium syndrome" and problems of arterial and venous access. Early experiments with peritoneal dialysis (1962) were plagued by problems of fibrosis, pain, protein loss, and infection.[12] More basic than any of these difficulties, though, was the fact that nearly all of the medical pioneers in this work were firmly and conclusively opposed to long-term or chronic dialysis.

NEW PRODUCT INTRODUCTION

In 1956, almost two years after the product development effort was launched, Baxter announced the UA 10 Twin-Coil artificial kidney.[13] The kidney was priced at $975. The Sigmamotor Pump was another $210, and disposable kidney coils were $59 each. Continuing pricing of dialyzer equipment and supplies as the market grew is a strategic subject to be returned to at a later point.

MARKET REACTION TO THE BAXTER UA-10

Hospital reaction to the commercial dialyzer was a yawn. Baxter *gave* a machine to Passavant Hospital in Chicago. It wasn't used. Another was donated to Michael Reese Hospital. Nothing happened there either.

Baxter plugged along in the face of disappointing results. Graham said of this period, "Two of the most common marketing mistakes are sticking with a market too long and not sticking with it long enough. At times, we made them both. In the case of dialysis, I did have doubts a couple of times about how long to stick with our original decision to proceed.

"There were two factors that kept the program moving ahead during this difficult time. The first and most important was Baxter's basic commitment to meeting medical needs. The second was that dialysis investment costs were relatively small.

"The company shipped 123 tank units from 1956 to 1959, many of them, it turned out, never uncrated by hospitals receiving them. Patients with temporary renal shutdown continued to be the primary recipients of treatment, and they required relatively little new investment in equipment and supplies."[14]

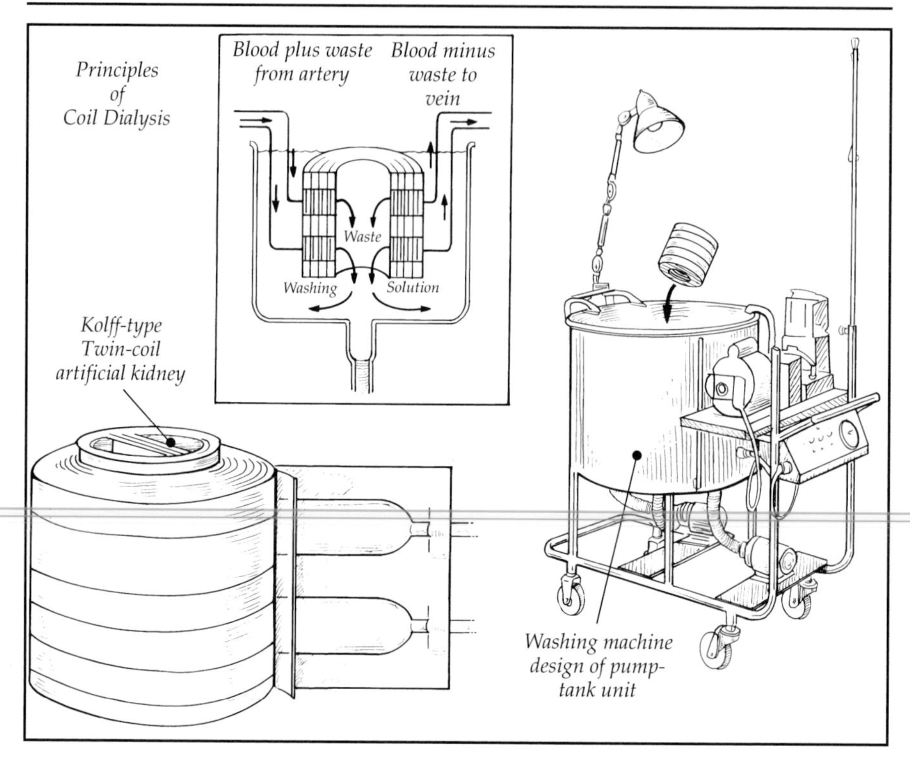

The Kidney Machine: *This picture illustrates the UA-10 apparatus which was the first generally commercially available dialyzer equipped with a disposable membrane circuit. The coil dialyzer was the result of Baxter engineering developments designed to manufacture and market a dialysis apparatus, following the general principles brought to light by Dr. Kolff. The coil was immersed in a large dialysis bath which was changed every two hours during a six-hour process. Recirculating and drainage pumps moved dialysis bath fluid. New solution was introduced through the top of the open tub.*

Seeking ways to spur interest, Graham and Howard Janneck of Baxter suggested to Merrill that his program at Brigham be expanded so that more patients could be treated on a chronic basis using Baxter's twin coil machine. An unrestricted grant of $75,000 was made by Baxter to help demonstrate that chronic hemodialysis was feasible. That grant was then renewed for two more years. Merrill and his colleagues decided to experiment with sending patients home with Baxter equipment so that the limited funding would cover treatment of more patients. This was clearly a turning point for chronic hemodialysis and for home dialysis.

At the same time, the Baxter dialysis organization was growing in capability. George Newport was marketing manager. Bob Skyles was the first dedicated sales representative. A key figure in the eventual success of dialysis was Janneck, who joined Baxter in Texas in 1956, relocated to Morton Grove in 1958, and was named the first general manager of the artificial organs division in 1962.

Don Joseph became president of the renal (dialysis) business in 1981 and still holds that position. Joseph, a graduate of Xavier University in Cincinnati with an MBA from that same institution, joined Baxter from the U.S. Public Health Service in 1966 and became the Louisville IV sales representative. After becoming a west coast regional sales manager, he was brought into headquarters by Vern Loucks as an assistant and manager of market development in 1972. He says he was stunned when Loucks told him he was being assigned next to AO (artificial organs) as Janneck's director of marketing in 1973. He would have preferred to get back into what he considered the "mainline"—that is, IV solutions.

Joseph recalled Janneck, "Howard always wore a very dark suit, brandished a long cigarette holder, and had snow white hair. We called him the penguin. He was a great salesman. He was close to Dr. Merrill, Dr. Cooley, and Dr. DeBakey. He deserves a lot of credit. Just before he left in early 1973, he had built the AO business to about $20 million—$15 million in dialysis and $5 million in oxygenators. Granted, in the later years he didn't pick up quickly on the trend to hollow fibers in dialysis. When McKinsey did a market share study showing our lead would be threatened and when Cordis Dow was making hay with hollow fibers, he fought McKinsey's conclusions. Still that $20 million business that Janneck led was the kernel that grew into what is now almost a $1 billion worldwide business."

A breakthrough of another kind occurred on March 9, 1960. Dr. Belding Scribner of the University of Washington (who had become interested in dialysis in 1953 at Merrill's urging) and his associate, Wayne Quinton, completed development of a new, permanent blood vessel access device which was implanted in a chronic dialysis patient—Clyde Shields.[15] The Scribner shunt overcame a major obstacle to chronic dialysis.[16] It allowed continuing venous access without the problems of vein collapse and other complications. Scribner opened the first center in the United States devoted to chronic dialysis care. The center had 12 beds at the University of Washington Hospital. With these developments, chronic dialysis

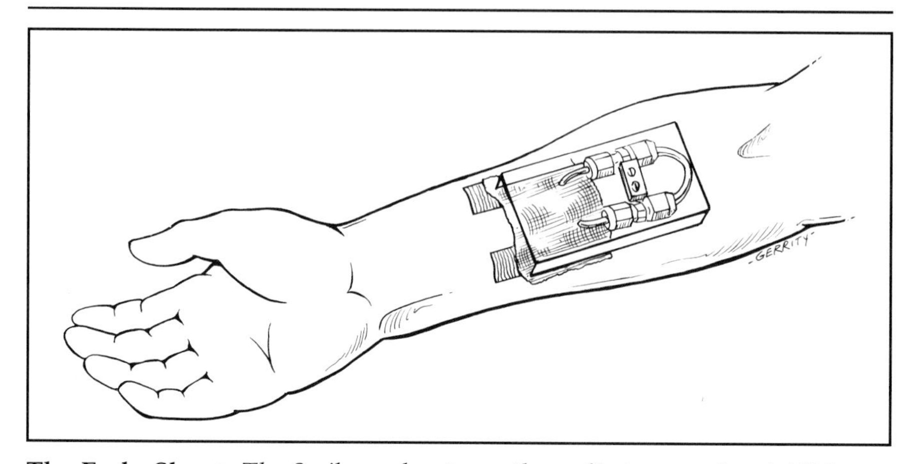

The Early Shunt: *The Scribner shunt was the earliest means to establish vascular access for chronic dialysis. It was a connection between an artery and a vein in the forearm which provided a blood pathway that could be connected relatively easily to facilitate dialysis. By this means and with subsequent improvements a chronic dialysis program for patients in persistent renal failure could be initiated and sustained.*

became a viable alternative to kidney transplantation and home care began to emerge as a preferred option to deal with the serious cost and reimbursement problems of long-term dialysis.

And so in 1964, Kivel was able to go home. Just a month later, Scribner trained a high-school-age patient for home dialysis.[17]

In 1961, five years after introduction of the commercial artificial kidney and seven years after the Morton Grove meeting with Dr. Kolff, the dialysis unit finally met its sales and profit objectives. Also in 1961, reflecting confidence in Baxter's niche strategy and broader application of this technology, an artificial organ division was formed.

STILL A LONG, STEEP ROAD FOR CHRONIC DIALYSIS

Even though the 1962 to 1964 period marked the beginning of a promising era for dialysis, and imitators began to follow Baxter as they had with other Baxter innovations, many hurdles remained.

In 1962, the science advisory board of the National Kidney Foundation at Princeton vigorously debated the approach to be taken to dialysis centers. A recommendation was adopted in 1963 for the Public Health Service to open several research-oriented centers. Later still, the Veterans Administration began to open dialysis centers that were subsequently the subject of a favorable evaluation of chronic dialysis outcomes (the Gottschalk Report).

Some states (Rhode Island, for example) moved early to cover dialysis reimbursement under existing disability laws. Debate about national reimbursement in the U.S. Congress moved slowly despite support by Senator Henry Jackson of Washington, among others. Advocates on the Hill began to lament the fact that Great Britain was moving ahead more rapidly with a national dialysis program than was the United States.

"RIPPLE EFFECT" OF THE ARTIFICIAL KIDNEY

Nonetheless, dialysis had already begun to have a remarkable impact. It was one of the very first "high-tech" maintenance therapies benefiting hundreds of thousands of individuals. It raised profound questions about medical cost and reimbursement. Through work at Peter Bent Brigham Hospital and other centers, this program created new knowledge about tissue typing and rejection, organ harvesting, biocompatibility of various materials, control of blood clotting time, and blood oxygenation—a key factor in open heart surgery. Baxter's contribution in that area is discussed later.[18]

Baxter made significant progress in several technologies as a result of its involvement in kidney dialysis and began to pull them together in what would now be called core competencies.[19]

Through its commercialization of the artificial kidney, Baxter created a whole new health care segment in this and other countries: the operation of dialysis centers. In the United States alone, there are now about 2,000 dialysis centers, each treating an average of 80 patients (with a broad size range of centers). Annual revenues of these centers approach $3.9 billion (160,000 patients x $22,000 per annum, plus $2500 per patient professional fees).

Having made possible the creation of such a large new medical enterprise, and having already begun to benefit from "backward integration," did Baxter seriously consider "forward integration" into the direct operation of dialysis centers? There was some consideration of that possibility. Dr. Gene Schupak, who ran the dialysis program at New York's Mount Sinai Hospital and went on to form the largest dialysis service company in the country, did have business discussions with Baxter. Janneck strongly supported the idea of participating in Dr. Schupak's business venture. Graham, however, overrode Janneck, taking the position that Baxter would not compete directly with its hospital and doctor customers. Later, Baxter would be tangentially involved in the hemodialysis center business in some other countries outside the United States, but more for market development than competitive reasons.[20]

Baxter's creation of a new therapy and the emergence of a new kind of service entity to provide that therapy posed strategic issues for the company—not unlike some of the issues it continues to face in the early 1990s. Baxter had always, from the start, been committed to patient care. Here were patients turning to sources outside hospitals for life-sustaining care. Why not provide it directly? Furthermore, Schupak's and Gus Hampers' dialysis venture, which became National Medical Care (NMC), the country's largest direct provider, would sometimes beat Baxter in bids on Baxter's own supplies. This was a cause for concern among nonprofit providers and other nephrologists. Why not integrate forward? Baxter had already proved it could successfully integrate backward. Joseph says the subject came up over and over again, but Graham always opposed competing with the company's own customers.

In the 1980s and 1990s patients were, in much larger numbers and for a variety of therapies, moving to alternate care sites from hospitals, because of new technology and, most of all, cost pressures. Again, this posed strategic issues for Baxter because of the company's long and close involvement with hospitals. These later events led to a replay of the same strategic conflict on a much larger stage culminating in a critical decision by Loucks in May 1992.

A HIGH POINT IN BAXTER INNOVATION

Baxter's contribution to worldwide acceptance of chronic dialysis and the enduring human benefits it produced is certainly a high point in Baxter's history. The 1961-62 period, when medical acceptance of dialysis as a "high tech" maintenance therapy began to occur, also happened to be the midpoint of the company's history to date. It demonstrated, conclusively, the merits of the company's focused niche development and marketing strategy. This notable achievement helped draw further favorable investment attention to the still small enterprise.

With the initial dialysis development completed, medical mastery of the human body's vital fluids and their internal "distribution system" had been asserted—through parenteral and blood therapy, and now through dialysis. It was remarkable progress and a series of remarkable contributions, considering where clinical care had been in the 1930s at the beginning of Baxter's history.

There would be continuing advances in dialysis as well as in other therapies where Baxter was the pioneer and leader. By now, the framework for innovation was clearly established, and the company's value system, philosophy, and methodology for seeking out and filling unmet medical needs were well understood throughout the company and in many parts of the health care and hospital communities.

Dialysis technology led directly to machine support of open heart surgery, which was born at about this same time (midsummer 1957). Surely, open heart surgery is the most dramatic symbol of twentieth century medical advances. Baxter's Dr. Robert K. Ausman, who participated in the pioneering open heart work at the University of Minnesota, said of that time, "Crossing the boundary of the human heart was not only joyful. It opened up unimagined medical vistas." Relevant to Baxter's early participation in open heart surgery through its artificial heart-lung, Ausman went on to say, "Not everyone understands that the medical profession is a spouse, mistress, and companion all in one. There is a lot of love involved. People who work with doctors have to understand that, particularly when you're pushing the frontiers. Baxter understood better than anyone else. That's why the caring they put into this development[21] they got back many times over."[22]

With the addition of dialysis to the product line, too, came a quickening of Baxter's internal technical integration. Advances in materials (thermoplastics and others), flow control, sterilization and "closed systems," RF sealing, administration sets, and vein access devices began to cycle back and forth among the individual products and development projects. The manufacturing system which had been launched in 1949 with the planning of the Cleveland, Mississippi facility aided the technology transfer process greatly.

This integration and synergy did not depend initially on Baxter sales and marketing to the same extent as it might have in other companies for many reasons, the first one being the exclusive U.S. distribution contract with American Hospital Supply for intravenous solutions. With dialysis outside the AHS distribution relationship, Baxter did become adept in quickly fielding small teams of sales specialists to penetrate market niches and then to defend them against latecomers. Indeed, the company was already using such specialists (called medical service representatives) to support and augment

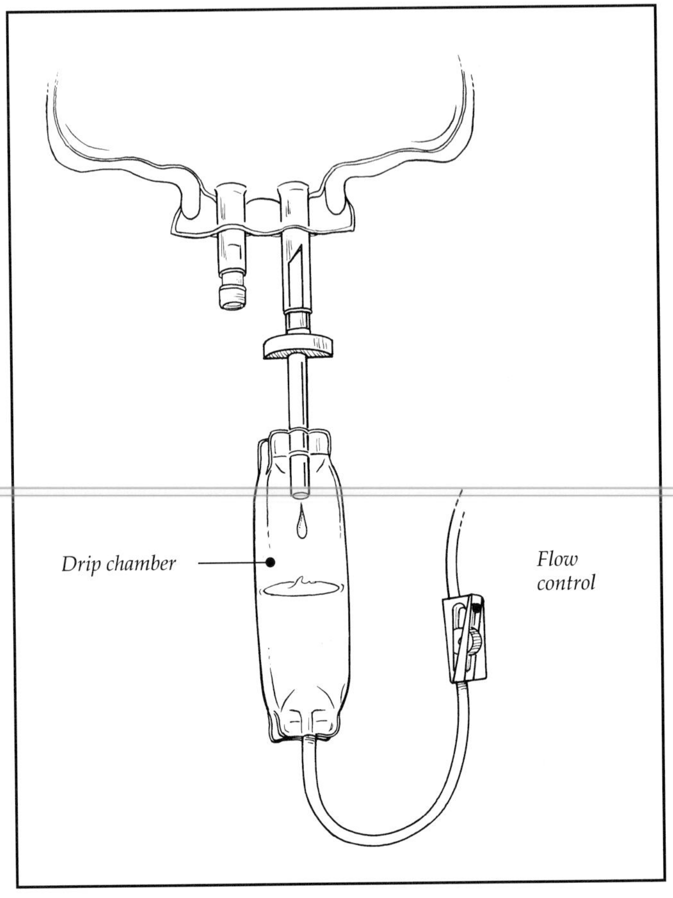

IV Flow Control: *To create a system that would regulate precisely the quantity of liquids being introduced to the patient, Baxter designers combined the use of gravity with a drip chamber and a simple constricting wheel on the IV tube to increase or decrease the carrying capacity of the tube.*

American Hospital's distribution of the more mature IV product line. A little later, these specialists would be called upon for real yeoman service.

Despite the lift provided by dialysis, however, underlying problems persisted. Baxter was losing domestic IV market share to Abbott because of Baxter-American disagreements over pricing, discounts, and hospital account control.[23] Sales of diversified products were still small. For example, the total 1961 revenue budget for dialysis was $250,000. Intravenous products were still the engine pulling the train.

INNOVATIONS IN DIALYSIS MERIT FURTHER STUDY AND COMMENT

Technology and innovation have long been popular management topics. In recent years, they've become more so with the suggestion that these may be the most serious chinks in America's competitive armor. Literature on the subject tends to keep focusing on the same developments: the transistor and then the chip (large scale integration); computing and communication technology; new materials and new material properties; in medicine, early developments such as penicillin and tetracycline, and more recently, biotechnology.

Dialysis is just as remarkable a series of developments in its own right, not just those dialysis developments already described, but others that still lay ahead. It's remarkable because of the human benefits, the size of the market created, the social policy and cost issues raised, the fact that a global market quickly resulted, and because of the broad effects on other areas of medical technology and clinical care.

Furthermore, here is an American company doing immensely effective "commercialization" without an elaborate formal R&D structure and based upon initial research conducted in Europe as well as in the United States. That's a very different picture than is usually painted for us today where companies outside the United States do the commercializing and adapt technical breakthroughs to market needs. Innovations in dialysis, and indeed other advances in extracorporeal technology that followed, warrant more examination than this history can provide.

END NOTES

CHAPTER VIII

1. *Family-administered* is the key phrase here. The Merrill group had an earlier patient (1963) in Framingham, Massachusetts, where the medical team went into the home to administer treatment, and concurrently Dr. B. H. Scribner, at the University of Washington, was beginning to experiment with home maintenance of patients.

2. In the case of an earlier Peter Bent Brigham patient recommended for home dialysis, the spouse flatly refused to accept the responsibility.

3. Constantine Hampers, M.D. and Eugene Schupak, M.D., *Long-term Hemodialysis* (New York: Grune and Stratton, 1967). The Kivel case is referred to in this text. Dr. Schupak is another of the leading dialysis pioneers.

   Dr. Kivel was diagnosed with myeloid metaplasia while a graduate student at Yale. Mrs. Kivel (telephone interview, July 1993) still remembers how brutally direct Dr. Hampers was about their limited options and the unaffordable costs associated with them. After coming home in time for Rosh Hashanah in 1964, he lived on dialysis for 18 years, through a difficult transplant in 1972 until his death. A movie feature *Rendezvous with Life*, captures more of the story of this courageous couple.

4. *The American Heritage Dictionary* (Boston: Houghton Mifflin).

5. It was perhaps through his blood banking work that Kolff became aware of Baxter.

6. Patrick McBride, *The Genesis of the Artificial Kidney* (Deerfield, Illinois: Baxter, 1987), 12.

7. ibid. Dr. Nils Alwall of Sweden developed a vertical drum kidney in the mid forties. In addition to designing the first "negative-pressure device," he described the first cannula for patient vein access (1948) and opened Sweden's first dialysis treatment center (1950).

8. ibid.

9. ibid.

10. Dr. Joseph Murray received the Nobel Prize for Medicine in 1990 for organ transplant work begun in 1954.

11. From an interview with Dr. Thorn in April 1990.

12. Hampers and Schupak, *Long-term Hemodialysis*, 2, 9.

13. McBride, *Genesis of the Artificial Kidney*, 43.

14. ibid., 47.

15. ibid., 50.

16. Earlier work had been done in 1959 with a polyvinyl cannula at the Brooke Army Center. Hampers and Schupak, *Long-term Hemodialysis*, 2.

17. ibid., 62-3.

18. McBride. Unpublished paper, 29 October 1990.

19. Gary Hamel and C.K. Prahalad, "The Core Competence of the Corporation," in *Harvard Business Review* May/June 1990.

20. About thirty years later, and more than one year after Baxter spun out its alternate site business to separate public ownership, that company, Caremark International, Inc., made its first dialysis center acquisition—illustrating how strategic issues recur.

21. The development referred to here is the bubble oxygenator, discussed later.

22. Dr. Robert K. Ausman, interview, 1 June 1990.

23. Baxter continued to maintain its IV market lead in U.S. government and international segments. While IMS data for the time showed Abbott's domestic, nongovernment share growing very rapidly at Baxter's expense, those familiar with solutions market activity then say that IMS data was skewed to the west coast—the only part of the United States where Don Baxter (by now part of American Hospital Supply) commanded a strong position.

CHAPTER

IX

STILL ANOTHER BREAKTHROUGH . . . AIDED BY ONE OF BAXTER'S MOST SIGNIFICANT ACQUISITIONS

In 1956, Johnson & Johnson acquired a 50 percent interest in Fenwal Laboratories, Inc.—a small subsidiary of Fenwal, Inc., in Framingham, Massachusetts. Fenwal, Inc. had been formed by Dr. Carl Walter and a man named Fenn to develop a temperature control business based on a new thermostat design by a third principal in the venture, Fred Turenne. Dr. Walter had long been interested in the potential of plastic blood bags. On January 3, 1950, Fenwal Laboratories was incorporated as a wholly-owned subsidiary of Fenwal, Inc. Dick Sellars, J & J vice chairman, became intrigued with the Fenwal plastic blood bag. He thought there might be potential for Fenwal's plastic packaging outside the medical field for a number of consumer products; motor oil was the example he used most frequently. Fenwal, on the other hand, certainly stood to benefit from J & J's marketing muscle. Its course of product and market development over six years had proven tortuous. Fenwal had not yet turned a profit. However, joint ownership was to prove signally unsatisfactory, particularly for Johnson & Johnson. The transaction with Johnson & Johnson was complicated, which may have led to some of the problems. Fenwal, Inc. sold 50 percent of Fenwal Laboratories to J & J and 50 percent to Dr. Carl Walter and Ed Poitras.[1] Marketing rights were assigned 100 percent to J & J. The Fenwal Building, in Framingham, was owned by the Mellon Street Trust.

BAXTER'S EARLIER WORK IN THERMOPLASTICS FOR MEDICAL APPLICATIONS

Earlier, Baxter had begun to move aggressively on medical applications for plastics before other manufacturers had learned enough about plastics formulation and biocompatibility to do so. The earliest example was the IV tubing administration sets introduced soon after World War II. By the early 1950s, Ed Nawoj and others were hard at work on plastics compounding, manufacturing processes and equipment, and necessary laboratory research. About the time work started on the artificial kidney in 1956, Baxter was successfully experimenting with plastics extrusion.[2] Stories tell how Nawoj sought to hire just about every plastics engineer with superior manufacturing experience who was available in the Chicago market and put those he signed to work on another development project.

CONTINUING BAXTER LEADERSHIP IN BLOOD THERAPY

Concurrently, Baxter was steadily expanding its blood products leadership. Introduction of the Transfuso Vac container in 1939 and Plasma-Vac container in 1941 had led to wide recognition of and reliance on Baxter blood containers in World War II. The 1952 acquisition of Hyland broadened Baxter's commitment and capability in this area. And Hyland's business in liquid plasma, blood fractions and sera was now making it a major Fenwal customer.

In 1957, just after Fenwal and J & J got together, Baxter introduced the plastic Cube-Pak unit blood container on an experimental basis. The Cube-Pak unit was a plastic bag within a folding cardboard package designed to stand up and permit easier handling as the bag was filled. Mounting the square container in a blood centrifuge, however, proved to be a problem. Baxter continued to market the product for some time after the bugs were eliminated from the Fenwal container.

FENWAL PRODUCT DEVELOPMENT

The initial Fenwal product concept ultimately proved to be sound. Indeed, it has become one of the most durable product designs in clinical care history. The concept was a flexible packaging system which, because it was closed, protected blood better, gave it longer useful life, and guarded against the danger of air embolisms. It overcame the problem of glass bottle breakage and provided through connecting bags in series—"doubles," "triples," and "quadruples"—a superior way to separate blood into its components for processing and therapy.

Market penetration, however, was slow and difficult. Fenwal Laboratories continued to experience technical and material problems up to the mid-fifties. Cutter and Abbott both entered the market with limited success. At one point later Baxter sued Cutter for product infringement. Cutter countersued, alleging restraint of trade in this market, and Abbott joined in Cutter's action. The suit was settled at

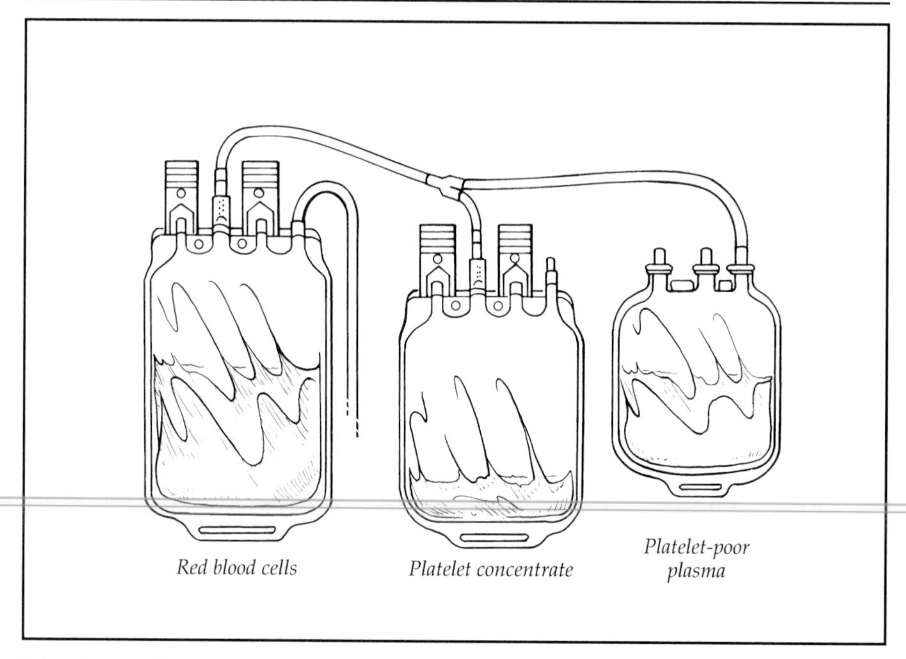

The Fenwal Multiple Blood-Pack System: *By arranging several polyvinyl blood collection containers in sequence and sealing them together with a no leak technology, the Fenwal system provided a completely closed environment from the moment of blood donation to the time of transfusion. This important feature minimized the risk of contamination and infection and facilitated safe blood storage, thus leading to successful blood banks.*

nominal cost. "Leakers" continued to be a vexing problem in the early Fenwal system.

Much earlier, Frank Wandell, Fenwal Laboratories general manager, had persuaded the company to file a new drug application (NDA) with the Food & Drug Administration based on the mixing of blood with ACD[3] even though application and approval weren't formally required then. That decision proved to be a wise and farsighted one.

Fenwal Laboratories wasn't as close to customer needs as Baxter had been in its earlier innovations. For example, it took some time before Fenwal realized that to compete with and supplant the established glass bottle market, it would have to offer a recipient tube that would work with both the glass and plastic systems. There was apparently some confusion and annoyance about the payment of royalties on Fenwal Laboratories products because of the division of ownership among J & J and Dr. Walter and Poitras, and J & J's sole marketing rights.[4]

A basic reason for these technical and market difficulties was that Fenwal tried to act like an operating company when in reality it was still in a development phase. Cash flow probably would not have allowed any other strategy.

PRODUCT CHAMPION: DAVID BELLAMY

David Bellamy joined Fenwal Laboratories soon after its formation and not long after his graduation from Yale with a degree in physics in 1949. The medical business was in his blood; his father worked for Wilmot Castle, an early manufacturer of sterilizers.[5] Bellamy learned electronics in the Marine Corps at the Naval Research Laboratory. That would come in handy because dielectric sealing was one of the continuing blood bag fabrication problems.

Bellamy recalled those early developmental years, "I was hired as the project engineer to make the Fenwal concept work. I arrived in Ashland[6] with broom, bucket, and mop to clean the place up. . . . Carl Walter taught me all about pyrogens. The bag design was very complex. Originally we didn't have ACD anticoagulant in the bag; we had an ion exchange column above the bag. . . . Eventually I got 12 complete systems made. I was so proud of them. That Wednesday, Walter came out to Ashland, cut them up with scissors, and showed me what was wrong with them. The next run I took to the autoclave, where they blew up. We were having to run an autoclave designed for 15 psi at 30 psi. . . . We got past a lot of those problems by 1953. Then we had trouble with mold growth, pasteurization, and in vivo red cell survival. . . . To clear some of those up, we had to switch to a new plastic compound from Ellay Rubber. Business was slow to develop. . . . We got an early order from the American Red Cross and then had order fulfillment problems. They had difficulty using the product so they soured on us. Eventually, the breakthrough we hoped for came at Walter Reed Hospital and then at San Antonio."

J & J RELATIONSHIP

Fenwal, Inc. sold a 50 percent interest in Fenwal Laboratories to Johnson & Johnson in 1956 because at the monthly volume of $80,000 (about $1 million a year) Fenwal still wasn't profitable, and the owners weren't willing to risk more of their own capital.

J & J first tried to sell the product by allocating 10 percent of the time and effort of its Ethicon Division general sales force. It didn't work. It was like a replay, in some respects, of the Baxter-American Hospital Supply relationship with the contest of strong wills between Fenwal and Johnson & Johnson management and also a conflict between the general-line versus specialized sales force approach.

Then the Ethicon Division brought in John Kimbell from the Texas territory, where he'd done a good job with Fenwal, to set up a small, specialized product sales force. The situation improved somewhat. Kimbell later joined Baxter when it acquired Fenwal. He played a key role in several important product developments, and briefly served as Baxter's president from 1971 to 1974.

Pete Phildius joined Fenwal from American Hospital Supply on January 4, 1960, because he wanted to be with a small company and "didn't like selling American's 58,000 line items." He learned later that Fenwal had been acquired by what he then considered a big company—Baxter. Fenwal remained a very tough sell. Phildius explained, "We were selling bags for $1.22. Glass bottles were much lower—a loss leader. We used a bigger needle for bags, 15 gauge instead of 18 gauge. It hurt like hell. The phlebotomist hated it. The hospital had to buy all kinds of other equipment with the bag. The bag had to be weighed . . . the recipient had to juggle it to mix the anticoagulant.

"In other words, the buyer didn't like it because of cost. The phlebotomist said it was too hard to use. The blood donor said the needle hurts too much. The lab said the procedures were too complex . . . and the hospital floor said 'Not only is it hard to use, we don't like the gravity flow.'

"The only one it was good for was the patient recipient. For the patient, it eliminated air embolisms. It was kinder to red cells. It provided multiple paths and permitted blood separation without reentry."[7]

Not until after the Baxter acquisition did Fenwal begin to win the market over. The first significant hospital conversion after Baxter got involved was Columbia Presbyterian of New York City, an institution that has been a key barometer in acceptance and penetration of many hospital products. Once the blood bag system began to gain acceptance, the Fenwal name became synonymous with it, just as the Baxter name had become synonymous with advanced, reliable IV solutions.

Blood banks relied on glass bottles for blood storage for years; the switch to plastic was a slow conversion process for medical staff used to using the glass containers.

A description, from a clinical viewpoint, of how hospital conversions to the Fenwal system began to occur came from Dr. Robert K. Ausman, then at the University of Minnesota, "Newell Ziegler, a Ph.D. immunologist, ran the blood bank. Matching and cross-matching blood was a nightmare. The surgeon in those beginning days of open heart surgery was also the 'pump chief.' When we were 30 minutes from 'run time' we'd ask for blood. On this day the nurses were pushed a little hard. When we heard the crash at the elevator, we knew the blood had been destroyed. . . . The next day we had a staff meeting and decided to switch to Fenwal."

Slowly but surely, medical and patient needs were asserting themselves.

J & J LOSES PATIENCE

Dealing with the Fenwal entrepreneurs didn't get easier for J & J. Sellars knew Bill Graham from the Pharmaceutical Manufacturers Association. Periodically in 1958 and 1959, he would talk with Graham by telephone and at industry meetings about problems with Fenwal. He would then suggest obliquely that maybe Fenwal would be a better fit with Baxter than with Johnson & Johnson. Graham's response was always the same. "Dick, we might be interested in Fenwal, but only if we could get 100 percent of it. From what you tell me, getting 100 percent on realistic terms would be very difficult."

In early 1959, Sellars got much more direct. "Bill," he said in a phone conversation in April 1959, "we should talk about your acquiring our interest in Fenwal. We'll make it attractive for you." While Graham was thinking about that offer, Sellars called back with chagrin evident in his voice. "Forget what I said about Fenwal. Phil Hoffman[8] says I just don't know how to manage this relationship. He's going to take it over himself and show me how it ought to be done."

The next call came in June. "Phil Hoffman has had his chance to work the Fenwal relationship," Sellars said. "He's singing a different tune now. Are you ready to talk?"

BAXTER ACQUIRES FENWAL IN DECEMBER 1959

With Milt Ray of the Baxter law department handling the legal and contractual work, Graham personally took on the task of negotiating with both parties to acquire 100 percent of Fenwal.

After the groundwork was done, the deal was struck in one day of hard work at New York's Barclay Hotel. Graham was on one floor, the two Fenwal principals on another, and J & J representatives on a third. Graham shuttled back and forth between them in Henry Kissinger-like diplomacy. The tactic worked. Graham recalled, "So much antipathy had developed between them that neither wanted the other to get a good deal. The way we had to work that out was through the consideration paid to Carl Walters and Ed Poitras for the Fenwal building they owned independently. . . . It had to be a stock deal because of their tax considerations even though we preferred convertible debentures.[9] J & J didn't want Baxter stock on its books at the end of the 1960 tax year. They asked for an 'Oklahoma guarantee'[10] that we'd take that stock back at the transaction price before year end. We made money on that part of the deal too."

The total purchase price was $1.9 million. The return on investment has been immense over the years, not only in market leadership and profits but also in technical synergy with other Baxter product lines and in the quality of people who joined and stayed with Baxter as a result of the acquisition. Some of those who stayed on were Kimbell of J & J's Ethicon division and Phildius. Wandell, the Fenwal general manager, became a key Baxter figure until his retirement in 1985.[11] Dale Smith, the California sales representative for Fenwal,[12] went on to become a Baxter corporate officer and group vice president, leading the blood therapy business that in recent years has been experiencing another burst of technological innovation.

And then there's Bellamy, who in 1950 was a young man with a broom and mop in the old stone mill in Ashland, Massachusetts. Bellamy is still with Baxter more than 40 years later, and has contributed in one way or another to nearly every Baxter product innovation. For example, he obtained the patent on the all-important port design[13] for the blood container. As early as 1953, he persuaded Fenwal to experiment with plastic IV solutions containers. Years ahead of their commercial development, these plastic solutions containers were used on a limited experimental basis by the military in Korea. Interestingly, Fenwal blood containers themselves were not used in Korea.[14]

BAXTER BEGINS TO MAKE FENWAL A PROFITABLE COMMERCIAL BUSINESS, 1960

There were a number of problems to face up to. Most basic were certain Fenwal management attitudes. While the deal was still being finalized, one of the two Fenwal founders said to Fred Marquart, "You know you'll never be able to make a profit on this product. It's just not in the cards."[15]

Fenwal-Ethicon had achieved only about a 10 percent share of the total blood container market, which continued to be dominated by bottles. Most of Fenwal's share was concentrated in the large teaching hospitals and not widely spread across the marketplace. Fenwal had only about ten sales reps.

Phildius described the sales effort of 1960. "Our primary target in the hospitals was the surgeon and pathologist. If they wanted it, we'd train all the hospital personnel—nurses, anesthesiologists, lab personnel. We'd ask to put in a 60-day supply on a trial basis with memo billing of ancillary equipment. And we'd ask that all Baxter and Abbott blood bottles be sent back. Our margins were long and we didn't cut them to meet the prices of the solutions guys.

Obviously, there were a lot of hospital purchasing agents who didn't like us."

And, of course, hospitals were only one part of the market. Red Cross Centers and the government had to be converted concurrently as well. Phildius' comments point up still another issue. After the Fenwal acquisition, Baxter consciously decided to compete with itself. It was a blood bottle supplier but it also had the experimental Cube-Pak unit on the market, priced about 30 percent above Fenwal.

Baxter did several things to overcome the problems. First, Graham put the heat on directly and also through Kimbell to get market penetration. In one of the meetings to monitor Fenwal progress with Kimbell, Marquart, and Graham, one of the key sales reps was complaining about leakers.[16]

"I'm telling you right now," he said somewhat angrily, "my accounts will absolutely buy no more Fenwal product until the leaker problem is completely corrected."

Graham was even firmer in reply. "We will correct the problem, but in the meantime you'll keep selling. Sealing[17] is still more art than science, and the best way to work on these problems is with the product out in the marketplace in actual use. If you can't sign up for that, then maybe John Kimbell needs to make some changes."

It should be understood that the product, even then, was absolutely safe for patients. In fact, it was far superior to alternative products. The leakage problem was more of a "professional" concern than a patient risk.

Another decision was to have Fenwal report to Marquart at Hyland. The two subsidiaries were thus encouraged to work together on their product-line synergies. More importantly, Fenwal specialties were kept out of the main solutions sales channels through American Hospital Supply. Baxter didn't deemphasize its own competitive products until it was clear Fenwal was strongly established.

Fenwal continued to manufacture in Framingham, Massachusetts, for a period while Nawoj and his small manufacturing staff got progressively more involved. Then, all the tooling in Framingham was reproduced in Morton Grove, and shortly after that manufacturing was relocated to Cleveland, Mississippi, and later to other Baxter plants. Tight manufacturing control of the new subsidiary was established, but in accordance with a planned timetable.

Bellamy was asked soon after the acquisition to move from Massachusetts to Baxter's Illinois headquarters. He did without knowing exactly what his job would be or, indeed, how much he would be paid. After Bellamy had been in Morton Grove long enough to find his way around, he surfaced his concern about the mystery of his compensation with his direct superior. That individual said, "Hold on; let me call Nawoj."

Nawoj was interrupted in a meeting. He got on the phone with Bellamy and, according to Bellamy, settled the matter immediately and fairly.

COMPETITION IN THE BLOOD BUSINESS

Both Abbott Laboratories and Cutter Laboratories entered the blood container business early, in 1953 and 1954. Later, Cutter was acquired by Bayer. They exited the solutions business, but remained in blood products. Bellamy said of those competitive entries, "What they initially did was try to leapfrog Fenwal technology, and that was a mistake."

Abbott soon withdrew; the CEO told Graham he didn't like the business and found it more complex than its small size warranted. And indeed the blood business was then and is still a "fussy" kind of activity. Risks were always there, and the hepatitis virus and, more recently, the HIV virus responsible for AIDS have made the public painfully conscious of them. So the professionals in the business, a distinct breed of specialists, always had an eye for every small detail of processing safeguards. They worked with such processes as cryoprecipitation, heat treatment, and pasteurization. It shouldn't be surprising, therefore, that managers and scientists in the business today are leading Baxter into the new fields of biotechnology and adaptive immune therapy. They are pursuing the same market niche, "Hit 'em where they ain't" strategy that Graham espoused in the fifties and sixties.

The commercial blood business is today a changing market. For years, every developed country except the United States has had a national transfusion service. In 1991, because of AIDS and for other reasons, Red Cross blood collections were down 4 percent. Usage fell 1 to 2 percent. Through renewed emphasis on technology and innovation, however, Baxter is redefining the business in a way that will extend its leadership and enhance patient benefits.

Cutter remained a competitor to Baxter primarily because its major customer was its own network of blood collection centers serving its blood fractionation business. That company, because of its similar size and product-line overlap with Baxter in the fifties, provides an interesting strategic comparison, particularly since Cutter pursued a diametrically different strategy. Cutter took a "follow-the-leader" approach in solutions, blood containers, Salk polio vaccine,[18] and other areas, while Baxter stuck to its selective market niche strategy, seeking and generally achieving market leadership in each of its chosen niches. Very soon after this period, Cutter began to lag further and further behind Baxter in growth and overall financial performance.

PATIENCE, SYNERGY, FIRM GRASP OF MEDICAL NEED

The first lesson of Baxter's growing success at this point was its dedication to understanding and meeting specific medical needs. The Fenwal acquisition helped to develop that quality further. Baxter's patience with slowly developing markets had already been tested with solutions, the Transfuso Vac and Plasma-Vac, and most recently, with the artificial kidney. Patience would be useful with Fenwal products since both the Fenwal founders and Johnson & Johnson had run out of patience.

Fenwal brought technical synergy at just the right time. Baxter was already making great progress with thermoplastics—their biocompatibility, heat sealing, and adaptation for "access products."[19] The acquisition of Fenwal leveraged that. Because of Baxter's philosophy about innovation not being confined to any single compartment of the organization, Fenwal development affected many Baxter product lines and provided a new burst of creative energy. So commanding did Baxter's lead become in medical applications of thermoplastics that it's reported Abbott actually considered at one point buying plastic administration sets from its principal hospital competitor.

This synergy boost would contribute, more than ten years later, to another Baxter breakthrough in solutions products.

END NOTES

CHAPTER IX

1. The two founders of Fenwal Laboratories, Inc. were Dr. Carl Walter, M.D. of Peter Bent Brigham Hospital and Ed Poitras. Fenwal, Inc. originally owned 100 percent of the Fenwal Laboratories stock.

2. Wide film had application to artificial kidney disposable coils.

3. ACD (acidified citrate dextrose) is used to prevent blood from coagulating.

4. Patrick McBride, interview, January 1991.

5. Wilmot Castle was one of two sterilizer equipment manufacturers at that time. The other was Amsco, which also manufactured IV solutions.

6. Ashland, Massachusetts, was an old textile mill facility site where early development work was done. At that time, Fenwal, Inc. was also located in Ashland. The parent corporation later moved to Framingham.

7. Peter Phildius, interview, 21 May 1990. Phildius became head of the artificial organs business and a corporate officer of Baxter. Later, he ran the company's parenterals (IV) business. He left the company in October 1978.

8. Hoffman was the CEO of Johnson & Johnson.

9. As noted earlier, Baxter was creatively using convertible debentures as "equity," keeping capital costs low.

10. Johnson & Johnson's general counsel, John Gibson, asked for the "Oklahoma Guarantee," which translates into "If you don't keep your promise I get to call you a son of a bitch."

11. Frank Wandell died in 1990.

12. Dale Smith actually joined Fenwal in 1962, about two years after Baxter's acquisition.

13. Ports are the means of gaining access to the container while maintaining its integrity as a closed system.

14. Brig. Gen. Douglas B. Kendrick, *Blood Program in World WarII* (Washington, D.C.: Medical Department, U.S. Army, 1964).

15. Marquart was the head of Hyland to whom Fenwal reported after its acquisition. Marquart became a Baxter officer and director.

16. Containers developed leaks because of sealing problems or for other reasons in customer use.

17. Radio frequency (RF) sealing was a major process problem.

18 Cutter suffered a recall of its polio vaccine in 1955. 204 people were infected. Three quarters of those were paralyzed. Eleven died. *The New York Times,* Sunday Magazine, 25 Nov. 1990, p. 61. This followed the 1947 Cutter solutions recall.

19. "Access" here refers to both patient access through vein or artery and also access to an extracorporeal closed, sterile system.

PART THREE

GROWTH YEARS

The reader will have already noted that this history's five major parts don't divide exactly into calendar periods. They're intended only to break Baxter's sixty plus years into readable segments.

Part II, just concluded, ranged all the way forward to 1964, when Bennett Kivel went home to Melrose, Massachusetts, from the Peter Bent Brigham Hospital-Dr. John Merrill Dialysis Program. To the extent strategy formulation and development are ever completed—and they never are—the major elements of the company's direction were generally set by the mid to late fifties, a few years after William B. Graham became president. It was clear before 1960 that Baxter would not attempt to follow the pharmaceutical companies. By that time also the decision had been made not to venture into any kind of consumer product requiring advertising and brand development. Even the outlines of an international strategy were beginning to emerge by 1959.

The reason the account of Baxter strategy development in Part II continued as far forward as it did is that the technological developments represented by the work on the artificial kidney in 1956 and the beginning of a series of breakthroughs accelerated by the Fenwal acquisition in 1959 were key ingredients in management's learning and strategy shaping process.

Part III is about the "Growth Years," as they're called here. The beginning of this era can be precisely dated to 1955. Yet the account of this time picks up in Chapter X with a 1962 incident which removed one of the principal obstacles to the company's control of its destiny. How this single longest uninterrupted stretch of net income growth came to an end and was replaced by a new and different kind of momentum is taken up later.

CHAPTER

X

THE AMERICAN HOSPITAL SUPPLY RELATIONSHIP CRASHES: 1962–64

Tom Murdough telephoned Bill Graham on August 17, 1962. Murdough was then president of American Hospital Supply Corporation. "Bill, I'm glad I got through to you," he began. "You should know that we signed an agreement this morning to buy the AMSCO solutions business."[1]

Graham listened carefully and then asked, "Is AMSCO's solutions business going to be handled, Tom, the same way you handled the Mead Johnson solutions business when it became a part of American?"

"No, it's not," was the terse reply. "American is creating a new parenteral products division under John McConnell."

"Well, it seems clear," Graham said, "that's an intentional abrogation of our 1959 contract.[2] We better get together with our lawyers and work out the conclusion of our relationship."

Some participants have described the period that followed from 1962 to 1964 as the "war" between Baxter and American. Certainly the stakes were of that magnitude for both companies. If this was a "war," however, it did not sound like one from the remarkably calm and civil telephone conversation between Murdough and Graham. And the negotiating sessions to dissolve the thirty-year-old distribution relationship (discussions taking up most of September 1962) were of the same businesslike quality.

It appeared at first that the suddenness put Baxter at a decided disadvantage. Graham said, "We weren't quite ready to go it alone in 1962. Our product diversification efforts, while successful, needed more time. Solutions still represented more than 70 percent of our business. Baxter medical service representatives needed more experience. If I'd had the luxury of choice, I would have made the break about two years later, in 1964 or 1965."

The artificial organs business was just then reaching the break-even point. Hospital acceptance of long-term dialysis was occurring slowly. The bubble oxygenator for open heart surgery was brand new. The new international division's country-by-country strategy required both management attention and investment spending. Neither Baxter nor its Travenol products had been successful yet in making a dent in the home territory of Don Baxter, Inc. Baxter had brought medical sales representatives (MSRs) aboard in increasing numbers in the last few years, but they were still gaining experience and maturity. The split between the two companies was probably inevitable. While Baxter retained its market and technical leadership in parenteral fluids, competition from Abbott, Cutter, and now others were taking market share and putting pressure on the independent distribution system and manufacturing margins. American Hospital was committed to manufacturing more of the products it sold, and solutions were a primary candidate. The two companies had very different views of the hospital marketing and sales function, with Baxter predictably emphasizing professional hospital relationships and technical product support, and American just as predictably focusing on purchasing, distribution, and customer service.

Inevitable maybe, but the break-up could still have been less abrupt and dramatic. The following events caused the relationship to unravel quickly. Baxter's 1957 acquisition of Wallerstein had about doubled its sales and profits over a two year period, thus reducing Baxter susceptibility to American Hospital Supply pressures. Accordingly, by 1958 Foster McGaw was pursuing alternative solutions strategies.[3]

On August 17, 1959, American Hospital bought the Mead Johnson IV solutions business for $2.18 million in cash.

Mead Johnson had entered the solutions business in 1953 after approaching a number of companies already in the business, including Baxter, about acquisition. In the end, they decided to proceed with an independent start-up and hired a Cutter executive to manage it. The start-up quickly experienced market penetration difficulties. In February 1956, Mead Johnson approached American Hospital through a consultant intermediary to "shop" the solutions business for possible acquisition by American. Graham and Baxter were aware of the discussions and the acquisition. Baxter was to manufacture the Mead Johnson product line, increasing Baxter revenues and possibly reducing direct manufacturing costs.

In 1959 Baxter and American negotiated a new distribution contract to run until 1969. McGaw wrote to Dr. Ralph Falk[4] to express his satisfaction with the new agreement, which was effective on July 1 of that year. Not much later, Keith Pattengill, president of American's

Don Baxter (the Pharmaseal business), was negotiating under McGaw's direction to acquire AMSCO's solutions business.[5]

Hard on the heels of the new contract smiles and handshakes came Murdough's telephone call to Graham. It's possible that McGaw thought that a threatened Baxter would simply submit to the AMSCO move and continue its distribution relationship. Possible, but not likely. It is more likely that he believed the time had now come to put into action the words he had penciled to himself on a plan to acquire Baxter back in the early fifties: "Join or fight!" So it was finally to be a fight.

It is not that McGaw and American Hospital didn't have cause. Jim Ammon, who had become director of marketing in 1959 after serving as Graham's assistant, remembered the preliminary events and the days that followed as the most electric and significant of his whole career with Baxter. "There was already a contract clause prior to 1959 permitting us to convert certain hospital accounts to direct status because of discount and pricing pressures. It hadn't been rigorously pursued. When I moved into the marketing job, Graham told me to put teeth in that clause, and I did. I'd call John McConnell at American and tell him we were taking over another hospital account. John would grumble, but then he'd go along." Acquiring major accounts over a certain volume from commissioned sales representatives obviously plays havoc with motivation and incentives. On the other hand, in just one year preceding the break-up with American Hospital Supply, three major solutions accounts were lost to Abbott from the combined distribution system: Memorial Sloan-Kettering Center, Columbia Presbyterian, and Cornell-New York Medical. One hospital—Columbia Presbyterian—stuck with Abbott right through that company's catastrophic 1970 product recall, and wasn't reconverted by Baxter until 1990.

FIRST NEGOTIATIONS . . . THEN THE BATTLE

Graham quickly convened a war council consisting of Baxter general counsel Jack Knowlton, Ammon, Link Dowell, and others as they were needed for specific issues. After the first meeting of that council, Graham called Murdough to initiate discussions about termination of the contract.

The negotiating meetings began soon after and continued through the end of September, often on a three-day-a-week basis, and always at American Hospital's Evanston offices on Ridge Avenue.

Front row (l to r): Ralph Falk, II, Bill Graham, Dr. Falk, Ev Travis. Back row: Fred Marquart, Jack Knowlton

Participants in those discussions were Graham, Knowlton, and Ammon from Baxter and Murdough, Hough (General Counsel), and McConnell from American. By the end of September they had reached agreement. That agreement was fleshed out and signed on October 31, 1962. American was to sign no new accounts for Baxter products after November 1, 1963, and there was to be no resupply of Baxter products to and through American distribution channels beyond November 1, 1964. The negotiators may have felt, amidst their concern about the market contest to follow, a certain amount of relief that the nettlesome relationship was finally ending. Little did they know then that almost exactly twenty-three years later another group of Baxter and American negotiators would be sitting across from each other with even bigger stakes on the table.

DIFFERENT CALLS TO BATTLE . . . WITH WIDELY DIFFERENT EXPECTATIONS ABOUT THE OUTCOME

Both companies were confident they would prevail. McGaw convened a sales meeting in Atlanta, near AMSCO's manufacturing facility in Milledgeville. His plan was a simple one. American would "import" Don Baxter solutions from the west since they were better known than AMSCO (which had a marginal market share) and progressively shift their manufacture to the Milledgeville plant. The American sales force would blanket hospital accounts before Baxter's much smaller field force could get to them, and convince hospitals to stay with American, or, in other words, to switch to Don Baxter or AMSCO products. The differences in views between American and Baxter about customer switching behavior was the principal underlying factor in the two companies' battle plans. From American Hospital Supply's vantage point, a hospital that continued to use the same "order point" (American) was, by definition, *not* switching. From Baxter's point of view, on the other hand, asking a hospital to substitute another solutions product with different patient administration parameters was, of course, switching.

McGaw announced to his Atlanta audience, and subsequently through news releases and other means to the outside world, that American Hospital Supply confidently expected to keep 75 percent of the hospital accounts and 75 percent of the total solutions volume.

In Morton Grove the mood was also confident, but the pronouncements were much more restrained. Baxter held its first meeting of district managers only a few days after Murdough's August 17 call to Graham. They flew into Chicago on a Saturday, met Saturday and Sunday, then returned on Sunday night to be back in their territories by Monday morning. In this and other meetings and telephone conference calls that followed, there were no specific projections of how much business would be kept and how much lost.

In the background, of course, Ray Oddi and others ran the numbers on alternative scenarios. If Baxter managed to retain 60 to 65 percent of the existing level of hospital solutions business, the outlook was reasonably good. At a 50 percent retention level, the situation would be manageable, but tenuous. And if retention fell to 35 or 40 percent, then financial survival could be threatened.

Not long after the battle began, Dowell got a phone call from Ames Smithers of *The Wall Street Journal*. "Are you guys getting ready to go out of business out there?" Smithers asked. "Very funny, Ames. Why are you asking?" Dowell countered.

"I'm looking at an American Hospital Supply release which certainly implies that, if you read between the lines. If they take nearly all the business as they claim they will, Baxter's in trouble," Smithers probed.

"Give me twenty minutes and I'll be back to you with a comment," Dowell replied.

In fifteen minutes, after a quick conference with Graham and Knowlton, Dowell was back with a firm statement that Baxter's business was doing quite well, indeed better than expected. That was reflected in the following morning's *Wall Street Journal* story. However, no specific counterclaims were made, and none ever were made even after the tide of battle began to turn in Baxter's favor, that Baxter would take the lion's share of the business.

Baxter's strategy was to avoid public statements that could inflame an already risky situation. There was a practical concern too that a war of words could precipitate a price war, which Baxter wanted to avoid at all costs.

IN THE TRENCHES

A young American salesman, Karl Bays,[6] described his 1962-63 experience in his Oklahoma territory, "I signed up nearly every hospital account in sight. It looked like we'd comfortably beat the tough targets Foster had set. Then, things began to go the other way as doctors and anesthesiologists balked at going along with the purchasing decision."

Ed Kleid joined Baxter in 1961 in Texas and became, he thinks, the first solutions marketing representative.[7] He had been a pharmaceutical detail man and wanted to be in a medical field where he'd have broader sales and marketing responsibilities. Those he certainly got and quickly. Kleid remembered those days, "We were told by Sam Parker to concentrate on the anesthesiologists. They were the key people in use of solutions and they liked Baxter's product. We had a roller clamp which served as a hemostat. It could be operated with one hand to cut off and resume IV flow. Neither Abbott nor Cutter or American Hospital had anything to match it. Sometimes it's the little things that make a really big difference."

As the younger and newer Baxter field force gained confidence in competing with the "grizzled" American veterans, they began to use the "clamp-of-the-week" response when American Hospital periodically tried to upgrade their clamp to overcome this switching hurdle. "Oh yeah," the Baxter representative would say to hospital personnel when shown the latest American clamping device. "So that's the clamp they're trying out this week. This one looks more like the Cutter clamp, which still takes two hands to operate."

At the center of this activity were Ammon, director of marketing, and Sam Parker, general sales manager. Ammon had joined the company in 1957, with Chrysler and other big company experience. The two made a perfect team. Ammon says there were days when he did nothing but interview candidates for the expanding Baxter field force. That force grew from about 65 prior to the Baxter-American rupture to 140 by the time the dust cleared. Some of the company's successful recruiting and sales training techniques were developed and tested in the crucible of those days.

Parker was one of Baxter's first medical service representatives hired in Mississippi in the very early fifties. He became general sales manager just before this time, replacing John Peterson. Parker was the right man at the right time. He could "rough-and-tumble" with the sales representatives. He was a strong manager and motivator. And he knew how to cajole or force a buying decision. Dave Quinn, who worked for Parker during the break-up, described one of Parker's standard techniques, "In an internal meeting or with a customer, Sam would make his pitch and then just shut up. Sometimes when he did this, he'd use a cigar as a prop. I don't know how long Sam would maintain that absolute silence. There were times it seemed like five minutes must have passed. Typically, the other person would crack and Sam would get what he wanted."

The battle wasn't fought just in the sales trenches. There were many other requirements to be met for Baxter to survive. At first the most pressing was to line up, within weeks, public warehousing space to take the place of American's premier system. A second inventory had to be built because nearly all the existing finished goods inventory went with American. Then there were all the mechanics of direct customer order entry, contract administration, changed manufacturing cycles, and the like. Baxter negotiated all these hurdles. –Annual reports for 1962 to 1964 show Baxter sales and profits continuing to increase. There was one year though (1964) when the rate of increase fell sharply because of the high investment costs of building a Baxter inventory, developing a warehouse and shipping system, and fielding a sales force. Ralph Falk II, chairman, proposed Baxter take a hit for that year to reflect the costs of battling American Hospital Supply. Graham firmly refused.

AMERICAN TRIES TO STEM THE TIDE

Silence was maintained in Morton Grove about Baxter's early successes. In Evanston, midway through the battle, there was no secret about McGaw's acute dissatisfaction. Failure to achieve his declared targets couldn't be the result of non-performance by the fine organization he'd built. It wasn't. It certainly couldn't reflect superior Baxter customer and distribution service. It didn't. Therefore, McGaw apparently concluded, it must stem from technical and product manufacturing problems. And indeed, there were serious problems in manufacturing Don Baxter solutions in the AMSCO Milledgeville plant.

McGaw went after what he identified as the problem with a vengeance. Heads rolled, including that of Pattengill, who had been president of Don Baxter, Inc. Murdough was dispatched to straighten out the situation. He didn't survive the whole train of events either. Later, he was replaced as president of American Hospital Supply by Harry DeWitt. There were reports (perhaps apocryphal) that McGaw considered going out of the solutions business altogether, which was becoming somewhat less important in the total American product mix, and that that decision was averted only by a major American Hospital Supply contract win at Ohio State Medical Center.

THE DUST SETTLES

When the contest was over in 1964, Baxter had retained (or acquired, depending on the opposing views of hospital customer switching behavior) 84.9 percent of the hospital solutions business being fought for. It was not just the 55 to 60 percent necessary for Baxter's continued viability, but a commanding 84 percent. McGaw and American Hospital Supply had given it their best shot with both the Don Baxter and AMSCO product lines, and retained (or converted) only about 15 percent of the business. The winner of the contest did no crowing. The commentary in Baxter annual reports of the period is restrained. There were no "concession speeches" from American Hospital Supply, despite McGaw's extravagant 1962 market share claims. The two companies just got on with their respective businesses.

What is remarkable is that McGaw and American Hospital read their market setbacks in 1963 and 1964 as technical product problems at Don Baxter. "So," Graham recalled, "out went Pattengill, president of Don Baxter; Wendy Wall, the quality assurance director; and a number of others. It was a real purge! If Foster had thought about what was happening in Don Baxter's western states, where they kept the lion's share of the business and we couldn't gain an inch, he would have realized it wasn't a 'product' or 'technical' problem. Sure, there were start-up problems in the Milledgeville (Georgia) plant, but that's another story. . . . What was actually going on was classic customer resistance to product change and a contest of wills between the purchasing or administrative channels of the hospital and the professional users of the product. American didn't read it that way."

The outcome of the contest wasn't made widely known beyond Baxter and American until early 1965. Graham, Oddi, Ammon, and Dowell all believe that this two-year period of resisting every opportunity and temptation to put the story out about how Baxter was prevailing beyond their most optimistic expectations, while releasing just enough information to analysts and others so that they would know that the company was going to survive and continue to grow, was one of Baxter's most successful strategic undertakings ever. It took patience and restraint to bring it off.

Looking back almost 30 years in 1992, Graham still recalled Baxter's and his own restraint in refusing to crow about the company's success in its 1962-64 contest with its former distributor as one of the most successful strategic actions of which he was a part. The other two that he puts in the same high success category were the 1957 acquisition of Wallerstein and the decision to price solutions in Viaflex plastic containers in Canada at 30 percent above glass (thus persuading competitors who then knew much less than Baxter about manufacturing plastic containers that Viaflex would cost more to manufacture than glass). Asked why he selected these three events, rather than the decision, for example, to invest in Dr. Willem Johann Kolff's "orange juice can" dialysis machine, he said, "Because the dialysis investment decision was a decision made in the normal course of business. These three decisions, on the other hand, involved judgment about how competitors would react to key initiatives under certain circumstances. I always believed many business people didn't put enough emphasis on analyzing and understanding competitors."

THE TREPTOW INCIDENT

Before the Baxter-American Hospital IV solutions contest became history, there was a final flare-up. It involved one Charles W. Treptow, who was hired by Baxter on November 4, 1946, after his graduation from Monmouth College with a B.S. in chemistry. Treptow was promoted to assistant chief chemist a year later; to chief chemist on November 18, 1950; and on November 21, 1956 to director of quality control.

What caused the heated controversy and subsequent protracted litigation regarding Treptow? On June 22, 1964, he resigned his Baxter position, which then paid $21,100 per year. On August 3, he went to work as vice president of manufacturing and quality control at the Milledgeville, Georgia, plant of American Hospital Supply's McGaw Laboratories at a salary of $25,000.

This was the eastern plant acquired by American in the AMSCO purchase—the same plant where product conversion problems had so distressed McGaw that he had purged most of the top management of Don Baxter, Inc. (the western and original arm of McGaw Laboratories) when they failed to fix those problems. McGaw was convinced that the situation at Milledgeville was at the root of American Hospital's widespread loss of their solutions accounts to Baxter.

A personal memo signed by McGaw on June 26, 1964, (close to Treptow's resignation date) announced that Dr. Naurice Nesset had been on American Hospital Supply's staff as a consultant since January 1, 1963. Nesset had been with Baxter from 1936 to 1955; he was its senior scientist for much of that time, and also served as a corporate officer and member of the board. He resigned in 1955 after Graham was elected president. Nesset had hired Treptow at Baxter.

Baxter and Graham had seen enough. On July 2, 1964, Baxter filed suit in Cook County Circuit Court for an injunction to enjoin Treptow from joining McGaw Laboratories and McGaw from receiving trade secrets from him. A motion for temporary injunction was filed before Judge Cornelius J. Harrington on July 30. A further motion with additional detail was filed on August 10 and then an amended complaint on August 25.[8] The codefendants—Treptow, McGaw Laboratories, and American Hospital Supply Corporation—answered the amended complaint on September 9, in effect denying all charges. On that same date, Judge Harrington issued the requested injunction.

Here the explanations of the various parties diverge. It is clear that Treptow had talked with Nesset as early as 1963 about employment with American Hospital; and with DeWitt, then president of American, at an unknown later date; and that, at their request, he had made visits to both the Milledgeville and California plants prior to his June 22 resignation.

American Hospital, on the other hand, strenuously denied enticing Treptow into employment. Quite the contrary, it was claimed, Treptow had approached American first in 1961 because of dissatisfaction with his situation at Baxter.

The amended complaint (August 25, 1964) provides many insights into Baxter's innovation priorities and technology management approaches of the time. Treptow was a member of the seven-man "president's management committee" and of the "project control committee," which tracked all research and development projects. In those capacities, the complaint went on to allege, Treptow had access to all of Baxter's trade secrets, proprietary information, and forward plans, all of which would "inevitably" be disclosed due to the nature of his responsibilities in Milledgeville and would obviously be competitively damaging.

Some of the principal areas of research investment and proprietary information recited in the complaint were:

- Know-how for sealing plastic sheeting for solutions containers to prevent evaporation in storage. (This was 1964, about six years before the Viaflex container was commercially introduced in the United States).
- Design of the port assembly for the solutions plastic container, necessary to maintain sterility.
- Blood container designs, dies, and materials.
- Research into biocompatibility and toxicology of various thermoplastic materials including comprehensive research conducted for Baxter by Huntingdon Research Center of Huntingdon, England.
- Methods of affixing needles to plastic tubing for blood collection sets.
- Improved coatings for rubber stoppers for parenteral solutions bottles.
- Test data on hundreds of grades of medical quality plastic material.
- Knowledge of various Baxter proprietary drugs . . . Osmitrol diuretic (marketed in parenteral solution); Travase [sutilains ointment]; Chymopapain; Choloxin tablets; Streptokinase, an anticonvulsant drug . . . and also research into an artificial bone substance.

The complaint went on to say that in Milledgeville "defendant McGaw experienced high start up expenses and also encountered engineering difficulties which handicapped production. As a result, defendant American reported that its 1963 consolidated earnings were penalized by 10 cents a share, or approximately $884,000."

After the injunction in September 1964, settlement discussions, continuances, and delays protracted the matter through 1965 and 1966. It was finally settled and dismissed on September 14, 1967, "without prejudice."[9]

The defendants stipulated they did not have in their possession any Baxter plans, drawings, laboratory notebooks, new drug applications (NDA's), investigational new drug notices (IND's), product specifications, or laboratory manuals. They maintained they had observed all the terms of the temporary injunction, and agreed to submit to jurisdiction of the court in the event of any future alleged breach.

What happened to Treptow? He remained with McGaw Laboratories, and by 1967 was a vice president of both McGaw and Don Baxter, Inc. Baxter had made its point. Any "insider" technical knowledge Treptow may have had in mid-1964 when he resigned from Baxter was by 1967 certainly becoming obsolete, given the rate of continued advance in Baxter's research and technology.

For Baxter employees who have been curious over the years about the particularly strict noncompete and confidentiality provisions in employment agreements of Northern Illinois medical suppliers with managers and scientists, the origin probably dated to this mid-1960s legal battle.

For the last word on this entire 1962 to 1964 episode, an excerpt from February 4, 1965, remarks by McGaw to the Investment Analysts Society of Chicago sums it up. "Frequently, I hear American Hospital Supply referred to on the street as 'Hospital' both here and in New York. This nickname has more relevance than you might think. In 1963 we almost operated a hospital. Two members of our system had become quite ill. It took some bold doctoring and careful nursing to get them off the critical list."[10]

END NOTES

CHAPTER X

1. AMSCO was the wholly-owned solutions subsidiary of American Sterilizer company (originally begun as Hospital Liquids). American Hospital Supply purchased it for $1.7 million.

2. The current Baxter-American contract had been renegotiated in 1959 and was to run until 1969.

3. Nonetheless, on April 29, 1958, a memo by Philip R. Clarke of Lehman Brothers documents a recent discussion with Foster McGaw about the possibility of acquiring Baxter Laboratories.

4. Foster McGaw, letter to Ralph Falk, 26 June 1959.

5. Frederick D. Sturdivant, *Growth Through Service: The Story of American Hospital Supply Corporation* (Evanston, Illinois: Northwestern University Press, 1970).

6. Bays became chairman and CEO of American Hospital Supply during its most expansive growth period. He became chairman of Baxter in late 1985, then chairman and CEO of IC Industries (Whitman) in 1987. He died in 1989.

7. Kleid became president of Baxter's medical products division. He retired from the company in 1988.

8. 25 August 1964 complaint, #64-CH3919 signed by John M. Knowlton and Bell Boyd Lloyd Haddad & Burns.

9. Stipulation of September 14, 1967.

10. "Growth and Responsibility," American Hospital Supply Corporation, public relations department, 1965 reprint.

CHAPTER

XI

SIXTIES BRING MORE CHANGE IN THE HEALTH CARE AND HOSPITAL ENVIRONMENT

The sixties were a decade of images. Assassination—first, President Kennedy; later, Dr. King and Robert Kennedy. Space flight—beginning with Alan Shepard and John Glenn in 1961 and culminating with the Apollo 11 moonshot on July 16, 1969. Vietnam. Student protest. Freedom marches. The Beatles. Woodstock. Flower children. Central cities ablaze. The 1968 Democratic Convention in Chicago.

Baxter wasn't insulated from the events. The company provided medical supplies to Cuba as a part of an industry-wide $20 million contribution involved in the return of prisoners following the Bay of Pigs fiasco, working with Bobby Kennedy to carry out the Administration's request.

Kennedy was the "point man" for his brother and the Administration in trying to clean up as much as possible the embarrassment left by the Bay of Pigs failure. There was a problem with the existing limitation of two years on tax carry-forward of excess charitable contributions. When Bill Graham, representing the PMA; Lloyd Cutler, PMA's counsel, and others first met with Attorney General Kennedy to discuss the industry's provision of a $20 million "ransom" for American captives in Cuba, Graham pointed out that this limitation would make it difficult for the industry to carry out the Administration's request for donated medical supplies. In their next meeting, Graham told Kennedy's assistant, Lou Oberdorfer, later a judge, that the industry would need a five year carry-forward to make the deal workable.

Kennedy said, "That sounds reasonable to me." He picked up the phone and called Republican Senator Everett Dirksen and asked, "If the Administration proposes an extension of the carry-forward to five years, will you oppose it?"

Senator Dirksen replied that he and his Republican colleagues wouldn't stand in the way. Later, the deal was discussed with Demo-

Staff meeting at the Kennedy White House during the Bay of Pigs. Graham attended meetings under the Kennedy, Johnson, Nixon, Ford, Reagan, and Bush administrations in similar gatherings.

cratic Leader Wilbur Mills in the House of Representatives. So a byproduct of the Bay of Pigs was liberalized excess contribution provisions. The provision became law in less than sixty days—incredible speed compared with what's being called congressional gridlock today.

Baxter was, at a somewhat later point, a principal supporter of the humanitarian work of Dr. Tom Dooley in Southeast Asia. Baxter's humanitarian tradition has continued and grown in succeeding years with rapid responses to human disasters of various kinds around the world, such as the Mexico City earthquake in 1985, the Chernobyl nuclear disaster in 1986, and the Armenian earthquake in 1988.

However, the images Baxter people themselves confronted firsthand were much more positive and optimistic. They were images of Bennett Kivel going home on the twin coil artificial kidney. A young Jehovah's Witness patient undergoing lifesaving surgery thanks to Baxter's Miniprime Oxygenator, which didn't require priming with human blood (a violation of her religion). Hemophiliac twins leading more normal lives due to the Baxter-Hyland antihemophilic concentrate (Factor VIII). Open heart surgery. Dr. DeBakey calling Howard Janneck and Graham from Houston immediately after surgery to say

Dr. Tom Dooley at his medical center in Laos in 1959.

excitedly, "The heart-lung machine [oxygenator] works. It really works."

More generally, U.S. health care and hospitals began to undergo progressive and dramatic change. As the decade started, admissions to general hospitals totaled 23 million—the first drop in ten years.[1] Hospital cost per patient/day was $15.65; $31.16 for voluntary short term hospitals—a truer indicator. 126 million of the country's 179 million population were now covered by some form of health insurance.

U.S. hospitals began the decade with 1.6 million full-time employees; that number would swell as hospitals became big business.

In August 1960 the Senate rejected a Medicare Plan. The Hill-Burton Act of 1946 was continuing to fuel hospital expansion. 3,000 of the 5,000 projects proposed under Hill-Burton had been completed by this time. Hospital expansion, of course, increased the demand for disposables and other hospital supplies.

Advances in invasive surgery were spreading rapidly from one hospital center to another. Concurrently, interest in medical technology of many types grew.

On July 29, 1965, President Lyndon Johnson signed a Medicare bill, tying the new benefits to Social Security. The House had estimated the cost when the program phased in on July 1, 1966, at $6 billion; The Senate's estimate was $7.1 billion. By 1969, 48 states were participating in the Medicaid program created by the legislation.

The 1966 Baxter annual report commented on these developments:[2]

> New federal legislation which may have a significant long-range impact on the hospital field became effective in 1966. The widely-publicized Medicare legislation passed by the 89th Congress went into effect July 1, 1966. It has been called the biggest social welfare measure in our history. Title 18 . . . covers everyone over 65. Title 19 . . . provides for a greatly expanded federal/state medical assistance program for all medically indigent people, regardless of age. Many states have already established a Title 19 program, popularly called 'Medicaid.'
>
> The cumulative effect of these programs, as they become fully operative through the years, will be an increase in the need for more hospital facilities and an accelerated demand for hospital products.

Johnson's signing of Medicare/Medicaid legislation in Independence, Missouri, with Harry Truman in attendance[3] was another image of the times. It would not, however, have any major immediate business effect on Baxter. The strategic track for the company had already been shaped by the development work of the fifties, by the 1962-64 rupture with American Hospital Supply, and by the prospect of more pioneering products already in the pipeline.

It was clear from the start though that Titles 18 and 19 did result in increased access to hospital care and in a broadened sense of "entitlement" to health care. The question remained as to what effects there would be on Baxter's long term strategy of specialty market niches and working relationships with surgeons, anesthesiologists, nephrologists, and many other medical specialists.

END NOTES

CHAPTER XI

1. American Hospital Association data for 1959-60.

2. Baxter annual report, 1966, p. 10.

3. The signing was held in Independence, Missouri, to recognize President Truman's earlier efforts to win passage of such a bill.

CHAPTER

XII

RAPID SALES GROWTH REFLECTS BAXTER'S FULL CONTROL OF ITS DESTINY: 1964–72

The break-up of the thirty year Baxter-American Hospital Supply relationship left Baxter in full control of its own destiny. Furthermore, the company had been able to make the necessary investments in inventory, warehousing, transportation, and a field sales force, while continuing its growth in revenues and net income.[1] Bill Graham described looking ahead from 1964, "Our success in retaining hospital accounts gave us great confidence. Innovations in several therapeutic areas were beginning to pay off for us.[2] They also were building our reputation and recognition of the Travenol name. We believed we could look ahead to years of uninterrupted growth. Our strategy didn't change at all, but we were able to plan for a longer time period."

Through the rest of the sixties the company undertook a number of major actions to exploit its new opportunities.

DISTRIBUTION

Baxter's strategic thinking had been profoundly affected by its American Hospital Supply experience. The year after the supply provisions of the American contract wound down, Baxter terminated its exclusive distribution agreement with Ingram & Bell in Canada (1965). The Belgian distributor, A.B. Christaens, who had worked with Baxter almost as long as had American Hospital (since 1937), was phased out over time. A system which had served Baxter's earlier needs, although at a considerable cost, had been replaced. From this point forward, Baxter would use distributors only in a selective and controlled way—until the mid-eighties when, in a basic strategic shift, the company itself integrated forward to become a broad-line distributor with the largest single share of the U.S. hospital distribution market.[3]

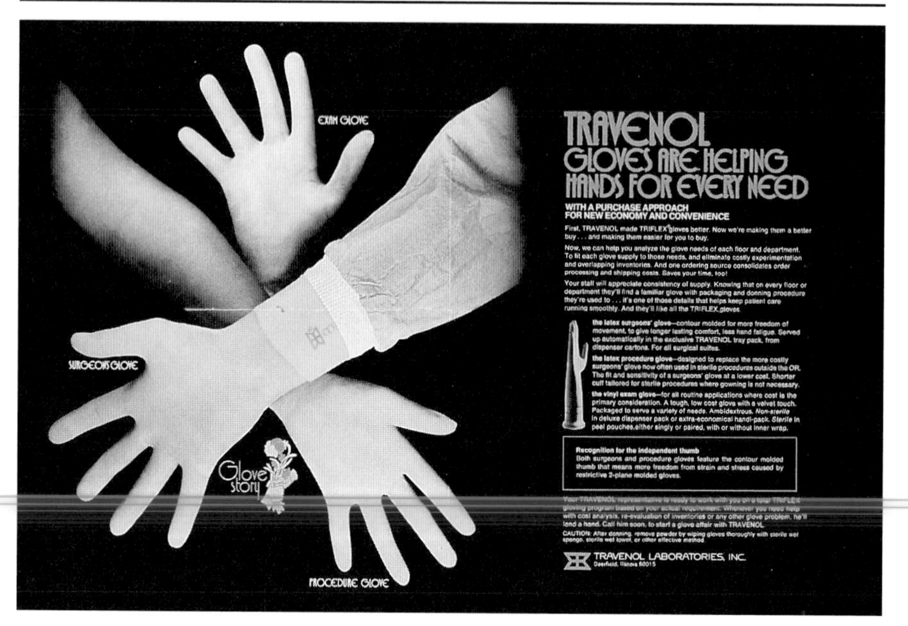

A Travenol gloves advertisement from the 1970s.

SELECTIVE ACQUISITIONS

The five acquisitions made during the sixties were generally less strategic than the additions of Wallerstein, Fenwal, and Hyland in the 1950s. There were two acquisitions in 1962: VIM, disposable needles and syringes, and Disposable Hospital Products—both reflecting Baxter's bullishness about the hospital disposables market. Dayton Flexible Products was acquired in 1967, and Baxter proceeded to become a world leader in medical "hand coverings" (vinyl and latex surgical and procedure gloves). Also in 1967, a Los Angeles maker of biochemicals for laboratories, Cyclo Chemical, was bought to complement Hyland Laboratories. And in 1969, Maryland-based American Instrument company was acquired.[4] The Dayton Flexible transaction was the first acquisition to be handled by G. Marshall Abbey, who had joined Baxter in 1965 and became general counsel four years later.

MANAGEMENT OF EXPANSION

Growth of manufacturing facilities and employment was one of the major undertakings of the decade. Hardly a year passed without a major facility expansion or new manufacturing site. In 1963, the Mountain Home, Arkansas plant was added. Expansions took place and new plants were added in Puerto Rico in 1965 and 1967. Cleveland, Mississippi, was further expanded in both 1966 and 1967; Kingstree, South Carolina, in 1963 and 1966; Alliston, Ontario, in 1963. A new plant was constructed in Thetford, England, in 1965. In 1966, 185 acres were acquired in Round Lake, Illinois, for prototype manufacturing and research. The same year, manufacturing capacity in Brussels was doubled. In 1968 another new plant was begun in Hays, Kansas. Concurrently, construction was begun on an "administrative center" in Deerfield, Illinois, and the Eaton, Ohio, plant was substantially expanded. Construction began in 1969 on a new Hyland facility in Costa Mesa, California.

What is now the Walgreen building on the east side of the Tri-State Tollway in Deerfield, Illinois, was built first for Baxter, then sold to Walgreen's for a $1 million profit. Baxter's corporate headquarters was then moved directly west of the tollway to its present location on the old Ott farm. The reason for the "intermediate" move, from Morton Grove to what is now the Walgreen corporate building and then to the current corporate headquarters, was a fierce zoning battle over the construction Baxter proposed for the 188-acre site that had been assembled from six separate tracts starting in 1966 at an average cost of about $6,000 per acre. Marsh Abbey said, "We applied to Lake County for rezoning, and both Deerfield and Riverwoods objected. We were able to meet Deerfield's concerns, but Riverwoods brought suit. It took five years to resolve the matter, which got all the way to the Illinois Supreme Court."

The land selected for Baxter's Deerfield headquarters at the northeast corner of Lake Cook and Saunders Roads is historic. In the late 1830s and 1840s, ten log houses, in what was then called LeClair, were occupied by German farming families who had come from Alsace by way of Warren, Pennsylvania. The land, which was bought from speculators, was described as abundant with gooseberries, chokecherries, wild plums, blackberries, raspberries, crabapples, and all kinds of wild nuts and grazing deer. The Ott family predominated: John Jacob Ott, Sr. and Jr., Caspar Ott, Lorenz Ott, and Samuel Ott. The chinked log hut of Caspar and Catherine Ott, built around 1836 or 1837, is preserved as a historic exhibit in Deerfield's center.

The land was settled not long after a pact with the Illinois and Pottawatomie Indians in 1833 cleared this part of the Northwest Territory. The first white trader and trapper in this immediate area was the colorful John K. "Indian" Clark. The first Deerfield settler was Michael Meath in 1835, followed by the Cadwells and Lambs, and then the Otts in 1836.[5]

Baxter expansion was proceeding smoothly because it was in accordance with the manufacturing strategy first developed in the late forties and early fifties—and implemented initially in the Cleveland, Mississippi facility. Recruiting and training new employees, however, did require extraordinary efforts. In one of these expansion years, 1967,[6] Baxter added 1,600 new employees from a base of 5,400 . . . an increase of 30 percent. Personnel managers of that time, like Roger Sekera, now a managing director in A. T. Kearney's executive search practice, still remember the Herculean recruitment drive of that expansive period.

Important as all these activities were in distribution, manufacturing facilities expansion, and selective acquisitions, it was four other continuing developments that really shaped and defined the sixties for Baxter. In general order of importance they were

- development of a Baxter "sales machine,"
- continuing progress on many fronts in technology and innovation,
- breakthroughs in international growth,
- maturing of the organization.

BAXTER SALES MACHINE

This was the business era when the "Big Blue" sales juggernaut, IBM, was creating a new industry in computing and information technology.[7] Within its chosen market niches in the hospital industry Baxter began to develop a reputation for building a "Big Blue"[8] sales machine of its own.

Baxter's sales force doubled in size during the dissolution of the American Hospital Supply relationship. Then in the next two years it doubled again to 500 representatives world-wide.[9]

The sales force was strongly influenced by the rough-and-tumble contest for customers during the American break-up. Even though Graham didn't believe Baxter was quite ready in 1962 to assert its total independence of American Hospital Supply, many of the Baxter medical service representatives were of a different mind. True, American "owned" the customers in a contractual sense, but Baxter representatives felt they had the professional relationships necessary to retain and build hospital usage of IV solutions. When the results of the contest with American swung decisively in Baxter's direction, it buoyed the Baxter sales force's confidence and confirmed that the specialized, technical approach was the right one, at least for IVs.

The sales force was shaped, too, by its early leaders. Ray Hetterick had sales management responsibility during much of the fifties build-up of medical sales representatives. After his stint as assistant to Graham, Jim Ammon became director of marketing concurrently with the final American Hospital rift. With his prior big company experience, he was able to sharpen the focus on product planning and management and to persuade Graham to step up the level of investment in marketing development activities. During the critical early sixties period he teamed with Sam Parker, who headed field sales. Later Parker became vice president of marketing.

Another key individual who influenced the sales force and Baxter's marketing direction was John T. Kimbell. Some of the other key marketing and sales people of that time were Dave Quinn, Carl Bussema, Ed Kleid, Pete Phildius (Fenwal), Jim Glavin, George Newport, Dale Smith (Fenwal), and later Sam O'Kelly, Charlie Blanchard, and C. A. "Lance" Piccolo, the latter becoming an executive vice president and member of the Baxter board of directors. Piccolo was later named as chairman and chief executive of Caremark International, Inc., a significant new health care enterprise spun out of Baxter as a separate, publicly owned corporation.

New additions to the growing sales force were recruited from other pharmaceutical and medical products companies with a smaller number of recent MBA graduates added to the mix as a part of the company's overall development strategy. Based on all these factors, the sales force began to develop its own distinctive culture, which in turn influenced Baxter's corporate culture. As one example, field sales began to identify product modifications, new product features, and product-line extensions to meet hospital customer needs and exploit market opportunities. This was an important added dimension to the motivation that already pervaded the internal Baxter organization. Of course, as the growing sales force exerted more influence, they pressed for even more specific and more difficult product modifications and extensions to meet particular customer needs. Whether such customization produces enough additional volume to offset the effects on standard manufacturing costs is always a matter of lively debate among sales, manufacturing and engineering. This healthy tension was a somewhat new experience for Baxter, and it sometimes produced the kind of response in manufacturing attributed to Henry Ford, that "the customer can have any color car he wants as long as he wants black."

As new niche opportunities emerged from this process, the pattern was to create a new specialized sales group, sometimes as few as one or two individuals, to concentrate on the specific opportunity. There were many advantages to this approach, which had been proven effective in dialysis and was similarly proving its value in blood therapy. It created a cadre of sales people with in-depth technical and application knowledge of their specific products. That in turn created effective sales and service relationships with professional customers, leading to a high success rate in market penetration and long-term retention of market leadership. Opportunities to lead and build new sales divisions were also a strong motivator for top performers.

Vern Loucks didn't begin to get intensively involved in management of U.S. marketing and sales until 1970, after his return from Europe. Later, he talked about his early observations as his corporate marketing responsibilities expanded. "We had some great sales people. I got my feet wet traveling with Brick Johnstone in Iowa. He was one of the great ones. He had been told he wouldn't be promoted. He left and joined Cobe . . . overall, though, we were kind of the 'Oakland Raiders' of medical and hospital sales. I thought a lot more discipline and training was necessary. John Kimbell was a maverick and many of us were drawn to him because of that. He was a very good sales, marketing, and customer guy. A number of us learned a lot from the way he built Fenwal's enviable ownership position and from his use of specialized sales forces. I used those lessons many times later on. The atmosphere, however, was tough on sales people. They were pushed hard and often didn't get enough support."

FORWARD MARCH OF PRODUCT INNOVATION

During the entire decade of the sixties Baxter's product innovation and contribution to health care accelerated and broadened. Despite the breadth and variety of these individual development activities, the most significant trend in science and technology within the company was that separate product and therapy areas began increasingly to support and draw upon each other, creating strength in several core disciplines. Advances in Fenwal influenced IV products. New solutions products contributed to the success of dialysis. And dialysis contributed to the development of other artificial organs and to Baxter's materials technology generally. Dialysis paved the way for machine support of open-heart surgery. So at a time when small, entrepreneurial sales divisions were being created, technology within Baxter was beginning to move in the opposing direction toward coalescence and synergy. The gradual shift did not involve any formal change in organization, just an evolution in the way priorities and opportunities were evaluated and pursued. In the early sixties,

Baxter's research priorities were listed as "Metabolism and Parenteral Nutrition, Cardiovascular Disease, Epilepsy, Biomedical Devices, Diagnostics, and Enzymes."[10]

Some of the milestone developments of this time are summarized here. Work continued on Choloxin tablets, a drug to reduce serum cholesterol levels. The development effort on Choloxin had been underway since 1953. The product was introduced first in other countries, then approved for use in the United States in 1967. Marsh Abbey remembers that, after approval, the F.D.A. objected strenuously to Baxter advertising that lowering blood cholesterol levels was a good idea.

In 1962, Fenwal introduced Plasmapheresis, which radically improved the efficiency of the blood donor process by returning blood plasma to the donor after separating and harvesting blood components for particular therapies. In 1966, the first new blood anticoagulant in twenty years, citrate phosphate dextrose, was successfully introduced. Also in 1966 a disposable blood warmer was brought to market.

DIALYSIS TECHNOLOGY

As long-term dialysis began to gain wider acceptance, product innovations came one after another. Baxter introduced Dianeal (peritoneal dialysis solution) in 1960. Dianeal solution filters wastes from the blood through the body's peritoneal membrane. It was the treatment of choice for many nephrologists, preferred over extracorporeal methods (hemodialysis). For acute dialysis, of course, there was the advantage that no machine was required. By offering a sterile solution for this part of the market, Baxter positioned itself to make later significant advances and contributions in this therapy.

In 1965 a new kidney coil, the Chron-A-Coil device, was introduced. In 1966 the RSP kidney dialyzer machine was brought to market. In 1967 the disposable Ultra-Flo kidney coil was improved and reduced in price to $20 per unit, one third of the original selling price just a couple of years before. The next year, 1968, the coil price dropped further to just over $16.00 per unit.

Basic to the management of innovation is a strategic approach to product pricing. Baxter demonstrated its approach to strategic pricing early and in particular with dialysis products. The key elements of the approach were pegging the initial price to specific characteristics of markets and customers, rather than striking for the highest immediate profit margin; using successively lower price levels to share productivity gains with customers; considering future technological advances and improvements in setting initial new product prices; and moving very aggressively down the pricing curve as market leadership was established.

In the case of the disposable kidney coil, the initial $60 price could have been set much higher. However, that would have probably retarded market acceptance and growth. It might even have indirectly and adversely affected public or political support of reimbursement for long-term kidney dialysis treatment, support that was just beginning to take root. Driving coil selling prices from $60 to $16 per unit several years after initial introduction, a final selling price improvement for professional users and patients of almost 75 percent, was certainly aggressive pricing by any standard. However, it reflected Baxter manufacturing and material economies and at the same time set a marketplace expectation that potential entrants as well as material suppliers would have to meet.

Early shipments of new kidney coils were plagued by problems. A small but significant number of coils were leaking. Dr. Robert K. Ausman recalled, "We included a card with each coil that said if you have problems in priming or run, ship this coil back to us and we'll ship you a new one. Imagine how the F.D.A. would react today, if anyone tried such a practice."

During this period of rapid development and improvement for the artificial kidney and its disposable coil, Lou Eilers of Eastman Kodak at one point approached Graham with the offer of doing some materials development to improve the properties of the Ultra-Flo coil. Graham encouraged him to do so. When the Eastman Kodak people got back in relatively short order with specific supply proposals, they had assumed a continued $60 selling price, and the Baxter price had already broken through $40 and was fast headed for $20.

FURTHER INNOVATION AND NEW PRODUCT DEVELOPMENT

There were still other significant developments going on, several of which are summarized here, and two of which are separately and individually discussed. Travase, a product derived from Wallerstein enzyme technology for the treatment of burns and chronic skin lesions, was successfully introduced in 1962-63. Hyland perfected AHF (antihemophilic factor) concentrate based on

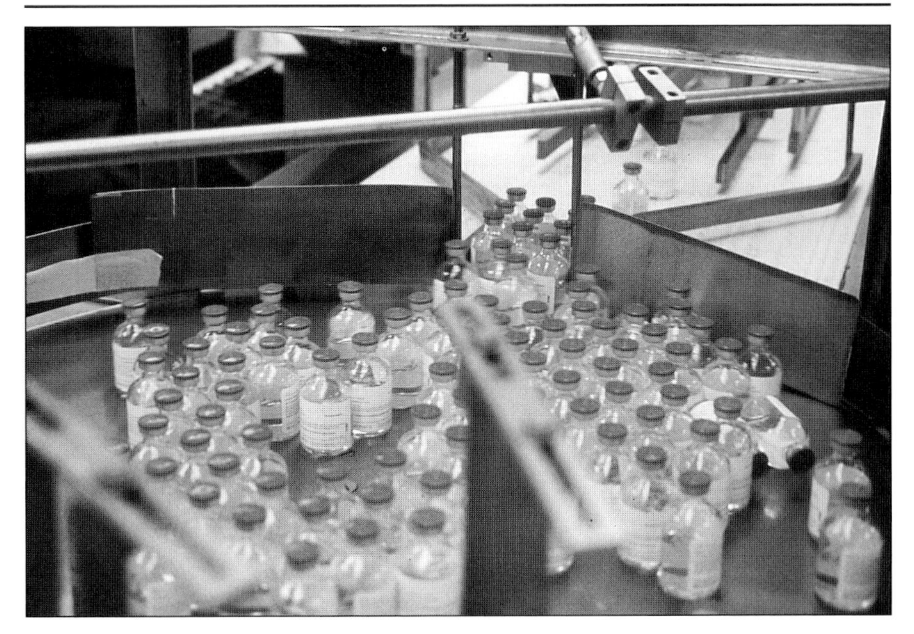

AHF production line with the new concentrate for hemophiliacs.

the cryoprecipitation work of Dr. Judith Pool at Stanford. Before concentrate became available, hemophiliacs had to take the clotting factor (Factor VIII) in a form that required them to absorb excessive liquid volumes.

During the decade, a line of Plexitray irrigation kits for various medical and surgical procedures was introduced and steadily expanded. The CS3000 cell separator, a product of AMINCO (American Instrument Company), came later, as did Uromatic solution sets and containers and related products. And, of course, throughout this whole time, development work proceeded on expanding and improving Baxter's leading intravenous solutions product line.

Of the two other developments singled out for separate discussion, one was to prove only briefly successful and then fade from the scene. The other was Baxter's fourth major medical breakthrough, following on the heels of milestone Baxter developments in intravenous therapy (1930s): the Transfuso Vac system, which made commercial blood banking possible (1940s); and long-term kidney dialysis (1950s). Actually, the fourth breakthrough, the heart-lung bypass, which is described in a later section, coincided with still another in the early sixties. The fifth breakthrough was the perfection of the Fenwal Multiple Blood-Pack Closed System, which opened the door for modern blood component therapy.

MEDICAL ELECTRONICS

The development that began with promise and then faded was medical electronics. In 1965, encouraged by its success with kidney machines, Baxter introduced System 99, a mobile cart with the 807 defibrillator and the H-L-R (heart-lung resuscitator).

These products were developed in partnership with Zenith and were targeted at one of Baxter's strategic markets. Two drawbacks soon became clear. The technology Zenith brought to the venture was not as advanced as both companies thought at the time. Baxter by this time had grown accustomed to being a technological pioneer. Equally important, the company had now evolved to a disposables focus, which is quite different from equipment or hardware orientation.

Most types of durable equipment just didn't fit the sales and manufacturing capabilities developing within Baxter. At this point, medical electronics clearly did not. Even when solutions pumps, infusers, and controllers later became important in hospital use of IV systems, the company's strategic approach to that equipment remained somewhat uncertain. Baxter chose to rely on a shifting mix of outside sourcing, small acquisitions, and selective engineering and manufacturing of equipment at its American Instrument subsidiary plant in Maryland and later at the Extracorporeal plants (purchased from Johnson & Johnson) in Tampa, Florida. The rule seems to have been to design and manufacture equipment only when necessary to protect and enhance a disposables strategic position in a therapy area of primary Baxter interest. As patient home-care and alternate-care sites outside the traditional hospital setting began to influence U.S. health care markets in the early 1980s, and then with a successful strategic adaptation beginning in 1985, the company began to take a somewhat different view of ancillary equipment. At any rate, the Baxter-Zenith venture in medical electronics was not successful.

FOURTH MEDICAL BREAKTHROUGH—THE FIRST COMMERCIAL HEART-LUNG

Development of the first commercial heart-lung machine was very different from the medical electronics experience. The most compelling image of health care progress for the new decade was open-

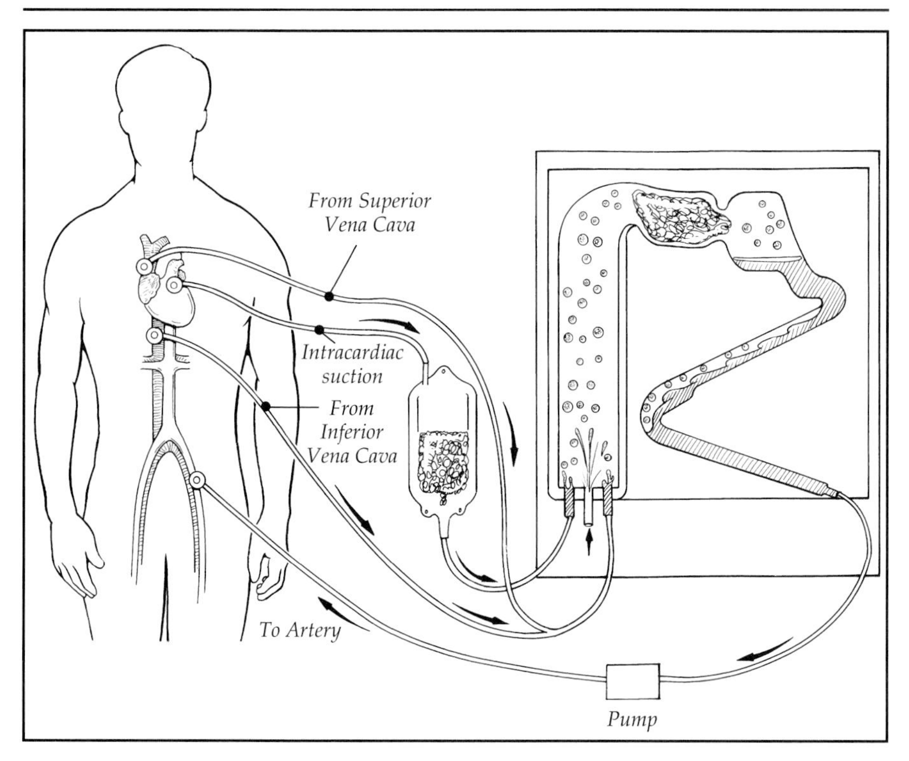

Heart-Lung Oxygenator: *This picture is a graphic illustration of the basic concept for cardio-pulmonary bypass. The important part of the system is the oxygenator, which replaces the heart and lung functions temporarily to facilitate open-heart and coronary-bypass surgery. Blood is obtained from cannulae in the superior and inferior vena cava; then it is passed through an oxygenating chamber where bubbles are formed. Subsequently, defoaming takes place, small air bubbles are released, and whole blood is returned to the femoral artery in the patient's groin. This oxygenator—designed, developed, and improved by Baxter engineers—was the first disposable device of its time.*

heart surgery. Like putting a man on the moon, it challenged the popular imagination by transcending mankind's traditional limits. And it was right "in the crosshairs" of Baxter's compelling strategic vision for its newly-formed artificial organs division.

Artificial organs are biomedical devices for taking over and performing the functions of the body's organs when they are shut down due to a disease or for a surgical procedure. Artificial organs can perform these vital functions on a continuing, long-term basis—as the Baxter artificial kidney was just then successfully demonstrating—or on a short-term basis, such as during open-heart surgery when some

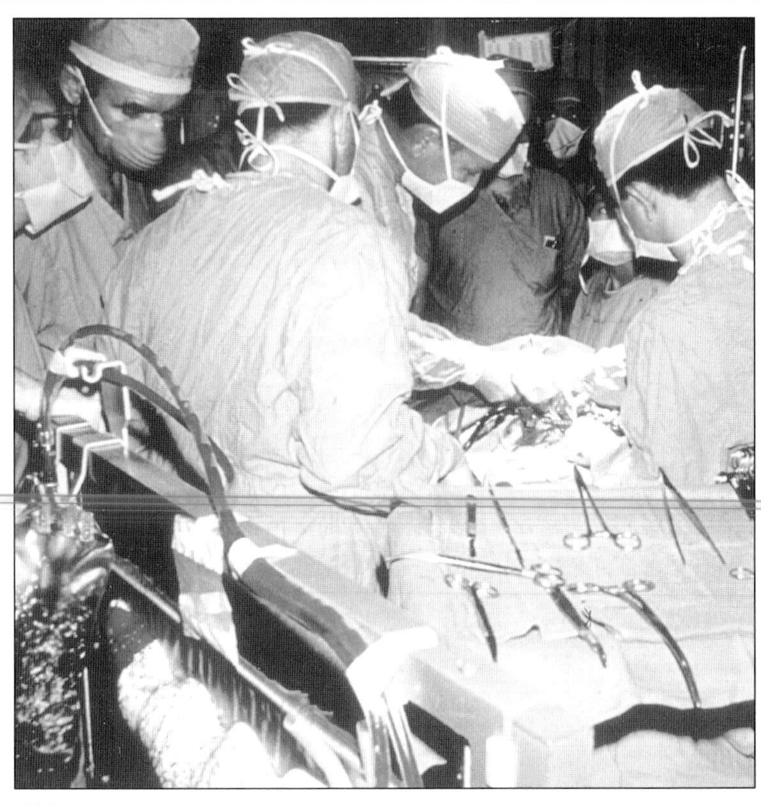

The bubble oxygenator in surgery

means other than the heart must be provided to pump and oxygenate the blood.

Dr. John Gibbons of the hospital at Philadelphia's Jefferson Medical College, from which Dr. Falk had graduated, had developed a heart-lung oxygenator in 1954. Dr. Kolff was working on a membrane oxygenator system at the Cleveland Clinic department of artificial organs, based on artificial kidney technology. Similar work was being done at other large teaching institutions. Baxter decided to affiliate with the work of Dr. Walton Lillehei at the University of Minnesota Medical School, where Bob Ausman was interning.

Ausman says that cumbersome equipment gave the operating amphitheater a "firehouse atmosphere" during early open-heart procedures. It was difficult to set up and operate. It required priming with large amounts of blood. And it presented the patient with possible air embolism and other risks. Baxter had seen this set of problems several times before in cooperating with surgeons in other procedures.

The first product of this effort was a miniature Baxter oxygenator, the Perfuso-Pac. This device was for circulating the blood from a limb when it was diverted in order for localized therapy—chemotherapy, for example—to be administered. The procedure and equipment worked well, but the therapeutic approach itself never gained wide acceptance.

1962 saw the introduction of the Baxter total bypass oxygenator, the Miniprime disposable oxygenator, notable for simplicity and reliability of use, substantial reduction of the blood priming volume, and disposability of the central elements.

These were soft-shell, or collapsible membrane, oxygenators. According to Ausman, "We used a stainless steel sponge to remove foam from the blood. If we'd had a Doppler device to detect it then, we would have seen we were putting very tiny air bubbles in the returning blood. They were too small though to have any adverse patient effect." Dr. Lillehei proved reluctant over time to finalize and "turn loose" oxygenator development. So Baxter shifted its relationship away from Minnesota to Texas, where Dr. Michael DeBakey and Dr. Denton Cooley were on their way to becoming the best known of the open-heart surgery pioneers. Baxter, Graham and Howard Janneck particularly, continued to work with them as their work became world-renowned.

Then the preference of operating room technicians swung in favor of hard-shell oxygenators. Baxter didn't react to the swing quickly enough. Its lead in this area slipped away. This is one of the two examples in its 60-year history where Baxter built a commanding technical and market lead and then gave it up. It may have been that, by now, Baxter had too many market niches to tend and nourish. Or perhaps the technical synergy initially foreseen between the artificial kidney and the oxygenator just wasn't there. Whatever the reason, the company has maintained a strong position in other cardio care products. The effects of its early contributions to open-heart surgery are still felt in the more than 150,000 such procedures now performed annually. And since the addition of Bentley products to the Baxter line, the company has reasserted its leadership in oxygenators along with a number of other important cardio-care devices.

Technical products and new product additions were becoming more important revenue generators by the mid-sixties. Most of these businesses operated as semi-autonomous sales divisions. IV solutions and systems still represented almost 70 percent of total sales (1967).

Dr. Michael E. DeBakey

INTERNATIONAL GROWTH

Investments made in other countries over a long period of time began to kick in and contribute substantially to Baxter's growth and profitability in the late sixties. Unlike most of its primary competitors of the time, who opted to focus on North America and export to other countries, Baxter set about building as many integrated country operations as it could, where economic and political conditions permitted. Thus, the company achieved effective internal integration as it grew and added products through three primary avenues: first, common manufacturing systems; second, core technology which cut across diverse product lines; third, concurrent with both of those, full integration under the direction of an international division of all operations (manufacturing, regulatory, quality assurance, etc.) in more than 10 countries outside the United States where that approach could practically be taken. This latter approach was looked at askance by others as a high-cost and high-risk strategy.

No other hospital or medical product company tried to beat Baxter at this game. For many years, the company had this set of opportunities all to itself.

There were certainly countries in which the integrated approach appeared questionable at times: Colombia; Israel, because of its continuing inflation rate; and Spain, whose growth rate lagged behind its European neighbors. The overall strategy has succeeded brilliantly, nonetheless.

The only areas of the world where this integrated strategy proved not to be feasible, understandably, were the poorer, less-developed countries where medical infrastructure didn't exist to support professional use of Baxter's advanced products. Baxter even made its approach work as an American company in Japan, although it took years of persistent and patient effort before success was achieved there.

Graham talked about the formulation of Baxter's international strategy, "It was another example of our strategic principle of trying to 'hit 'em where they ain't.' With our experience in South Africa beginning with its planning in 1947, we learned that even in a relatively small market there could be an attractive and profitable business if the operations were fully integrated.

"Pharmaceutical companies were then 'thinking export.' In our case we saw that gross margins wouldn't permit us to follow that pattern. In addition, we faced the problem of high distribution costs for bulky solutions. So once we studied the lesson of South Africa we took it on the road and sought to build an integrated operation with manufacturing, quality control, regulatory relationships, and marketing in every country we targeted.

"It was indeed a capital intensive strategy. In those days, we could introduce our product-line in no more than one or two countries at a time. Then we'd wait for those operations to become profitable before we'd make another move. The strategic advantages were worth it. We developed excellent relationships with country governments because of what we were bringing in there. Our product mix was adapted differently to the situation in each country. And once our investment was made, there might well not be room in the market for a competitor to invest."

In addition to the clear strategic vision and the investment risks undertaken, there was another important international success factor—Graham simply poured in lots of very good people. Charlie Schwartz shaped the early international division in accordance with the Graham strategy. People such as Hank Kusher and Bob Bocquet were already involved. On January 17, 1966, Loucks joined the company as assistant to the CEO; and later in 1966 Wilbur H. Gantz came aboard as assistant to Schwartz, the president of International. Both ended up soon after in Europe, after Gantz had already done a tour in Mexico. European operations really began to lift off with Loucks and Gantz working as a team in Brussels. They would continue to work together as an integral team for many years with Gantz becoming COO when Loucks became CEO and president.

In 1968 Baxter hired both Gabriel Schmergel and Victor Chaltiel, both Europeans, from that year's Harvard Business School class. They became key members of the young European management team, before moving to the United States to take on additional responsibilities. Jim Tobin, who joined the company in 1972 from Harvard Business School, and after a tour in the U.S. Navy, also was assigned to Japan in 1975, and later to Spain in 1977. Tobin became Baxter's president in March 1992 after Gantz's resignation, and resigned less than two years later to become president of Biogen. Thus, Europe in the late sixties and early seventies became the key breeding ground for an upcoming generation of independent and risk-oriented Baxter managers.

SUPPORT FOR INTERNATIONAL

Linda Olson Srodon rejoined Baxter in 1966, after taking four years off to raise her young children. She had worked in Morton Grove from 1960 to 1962. Like other employees of that era, she remembers Baxter as "a friendly company where it was always a pleasure to work." Starting as a secretary, she later was given administrative responsibility as an export assistant. During her second period of employment, her export department was shuttled out of the Morton Grove headquarters to the Cook Electric Building. From there she had an opportunity to participate in the burgeoning of International, after Loucks went to Europe in 1968. She laughs when she recalls that the other women in the Cook Electric Building would swoon when the handsome young Loucks would visit the department while in the U.S. from Brussels. She also recalls shipping fresh Illinois corn labeled as "Annual Reports" to the young American contingent in Brussels. After she left the company in 1970, she and Loucks were married on May 12, 1972 (a second marriage for both).

The company's considerable international and then global success was due to a well-conceived and consistently implemented strategy and also due to the quality and motivation of the people who were directly involved. Some of the actions and accomplishments of Loucks, Gantz, and other members of that team are described later.

Several central points already emerge regarding Baxter's international strategy. The approach chosen for market penetration and profitability serendipitously turned out to be an excellent approach from an executive development viewpoint. Also, the venturesome characteristics of the international approach contributed positively to company culture, just as did the growth of the domestic Baxter sales force in another way. And since the company's international operations were largely country-specific rather than global, it gave the company access to local health care technology in many parts of the world. The importance of and access to local technology as a strategic imperative wasn't discovered by students of management until much later. [11]

MATURING OF THE ORGANIZATION

Unlike other organizations which grew similarly through innovation, Baxter's growth did not bring greater emphasis on formal internal structure. There was neither a sudden shift to decentralization nor ascendancy of any particular business function at the expense of another.

Contrast this with the history of DuPont, for example. As that company grew beyond its black powder and smokeless powder beginnings after World War I, "boundary" problems erupted between DuPont's eastern laboratory and its experimental station. In the early 1920s R&D was decentralized to the manufacturing businesses. Then after a time the pendulum swung back in the other direction.[12]

Why did none of this strategic experimentation with organization occur within Baxter in the sixties? One reason was that while other executives began to assume greater operations responsibilities, all strategic decision-making lines continued to reach into Graham's office. He viewed corporate staff functions (law, manufacturing, engineering, R&D, finance, employee relations) not as separate entities with distinct agendas, but rather as closely-linked instruments of corporate strategy and of the CEO's own office. The informality of the organization made it possible for competent and aggressive individuals like Ed Nawoj, Dave Bellamy, Ray Oddi and then Loucks to influence corporate results in ways that reached well beyond their own organizational accountability. This is another reflection of Graham's "good man theory"; relying on talented individuals to fashion the most effective organization arrangements and relationships which contribute to overall goals of the business.

Three characteristics, then, continued to distinguish Baxter's organizational approach as the company grew:

1. Emphasis on selection and assignment of people, rather than structural design, and encouraging individual initiative to create appropriate structural arrangements;
2. Primary reliance on fluid, semiautonomous sales divisions (rather than self-contained, separate business units with their own P & L's); and
3. Unusually inventive use of legal organization forms, begun by Graham and continued by General Counsel Abbey, as means of accomplishing business, financial, or tax goals (by the 1980s the Baxter corporate structure included more than 60 different legal entities).

Since becoming CEO in 1980, Loucks has generally continued the creative, informal approach to organization in his own distinctive way.

THE ERA OF THE MBA

Organization growth and change were brought about not by adding to or formalizing structure, but by augmenting the recruiting mix. The old guard who had worked with Graham to build the company were accustomed to his making the decisions. Many of them had limits, and Graham managed knowing those limits and how far each subordinate would go before seeking his guidance. Still, they were members of a close-knit management team and of the "Morton Grove millionaires." Leavening the mix with Harvard MBAs wouldn't be easy, even after the value of the "young Turk" MBAs had been tested during the recruiting drive to build the Baxter field force in 1962-64. Baxter decided to recruit aggressively at leading American business schools.

At one point, a Stanford MBA employee raised the question with Graham why recruiting efforts focused principally on Harvard and other eastern schools. Instead of responding with reasons of geographical location, Baxter's growing visibility at Harvard, and the track record there, Graham simply turned around and gave him the assignment of leading a recruiting effort at Stanford Business School. In the next few years, some outstanding Stanford graduates were re-

BAXTER SALES AND EARNINGS
1962 - 1972

Year	$ Net Sales	$ Net Income (Before Taxes)	$ Net Income (After Taxes)
1962	42,300,000	3,900,000	2,800,000
1963	49,000,000	4,000,000	2,900,000
1964	54,000,000	4,200,000	3,000,000
1965	64,600,000	5,500,000	4,100,000
1966	77,900,000	8,800,000	6,400,000
1967	104,800,000	11,900,000	8,800,000
1968	122,100,000	14,500,000	10,600,000
1969	160,300,000	18,000,000	12,900,000
1970	187,600,000	18,100,000	14,300,000
1971	242,100,000	24,500,000	19,100,000
1972	278,800,000	27,200,000	22,200,000

Figure 8

cruited. Gradually, this new element was melded into Baxter's environment and culture, with Graham overseeing the process and personally tracking each "high-potential" manager.

The stories about this era and its effects are legion. Some of them are about individuals, some about the general Baxter atmosphere of the time. For example, there were the muttered comments to Graham by one manufacturing manager about a young MBA, "What's the guy going to do? You don't expect me to work for him, do you?" Then there was Graham's somewhat exasperated response to a small group of employees, "It's simply not true that you have to be a Harvard MBA to get ahead in this company. Look at Oddi and Abbey." And perhaps the favorite story from a slightly later period is about a Harvard MBA showing his savoir faire. At a meeting in Graham's office, Dolph Bridgewater leaned back in one the antique English chairs. There was a loud snap, the back of the chair flew off, and Bridgewater tumbled backward to the floor. Seeking to recover, he picked up the chair back as he got to his feet, studied it, and said: "Look, this has been broken and glued before." To which Loucks shot back, "Yes, in 1789."

1960S SALES AND NET INCOME GROWTH

Figure 8 shows the company's continued growth in revenue and net income from 1962 to 1972. This is just one segment—about one

BAXTER'S COMMON STOCK PRICE, 1962 - 1972

Year	$ High	$ Low	$ Close*
1962	1.074	.578	.750
1963	.977	.695	.879
1964	.961	.676	.949
1965	1.582	.844	1.504
1966	2.648	1.414	2.578
1967	5.844	2.422	5.125
1968	6.859	4.156	4.953
1969	8.063	4.906	7.406
1970	8.875	4.875	6.469
1971	9.844	6.375	8.938
1972	14.063	8.938	13.938

*Figures taken from month of December. Prices adjusted for common stock splits, which were occurring frequently during these years.

Figure 9

third—of the record-setting 29-year period described earlier. Profit levels in 1963 and 1964 reflect the cost of the breakup with American Hospital Supply.

BAXTER COMMON STOCK APPRECIATION

The stock market recognized and rewarded Baxter's consistently superior and improving performance. Of the company's seven 2:1 stock splits, four took place in the sixties—in 1961, 1966, 1967, and 1969. Figure 9 shows the trends of the company's common stock from 1962 to 1972.

TRANSITIONING INTO THE SEVENTIES

Baxter's strategy was influenced by many factors, external and internal, as the seventies began. The F.D.A. had grown in size and power during the sixties, following passage of the Kefauver-Celler Act in 1962. The Medical Device Act passed in 1976. Good Manufacturing Practices (GMP) and Good Laboratory Practices (GLP) were becoming major agenda items. Baxter's concern about rigorous compliance with GMP and GLP would involve important decisions a little later in the seventies, decisions in which Loucks played a pivotal role.

Generics were beginning to affect pharmaceutical markets. IV solutions pricing was becoming more and more competitive as the principal competitors fought for market share. In this and other hospital supply categories, the foundations were being laid for hospital group purchasing and the customer leverage it would bring to bear.

Baxter began to encounter difficult technology conversion problems in its leading dialysis position as the merits of positive pressure dialysis were tested by negative pressure dialysis, and hollow fiber and flat plate filtration came to the fore. Somewhat later (1973) Medicare Amendments would approve reimbursement for long-term kidney dialysis, giving a tremendous boost to this market segment.

Graham was keeping a lid on short-term costs, planning organization development and management succession in a preliminary way, and passing on several larger potential acquisitions which might have significantly affected Baxter's future. The latter sixties were becoming known as "the go-go years" and the prices of attractive acquisition candidates had become astronomical, soaring beyond levels that Baxter was willing to pay.

In fact, the basic reason the company did not make more and larger acquisitions during the go-go years had less to do with the vagaries of that marketplace than with Baxter's proven strategic thrust. Management believed it could better accomplish its principal goal of superior, predictable, long-term net income growth through internal reinvestment rather than acquisition. As product lines like IV solutions and renal care took off, they had first call on investment and R&D dollars. Given the steady march of innovation for many years in those products and others, there wasn't a great need to look elsewhere for opportunities. Furthermore, a strategic question Baxter management continued to ponder was what kinds of other products might fit with the unique assemblage of clinical care lines put together through the "Hit 'em where they ain't" approach. For almost 20 years now—since the late forties—the hallmark of the company's successful market leadership had been "getting a toe in the water" early in promising new therapies, using the experience to experiment and learn, and then deciding "how far and how fast to swim." That's difficult to do in many, if not most, acquisition situations.

The most significant example of holding down costs in the face of Baxter's growing success was Graham's own salary. It was increased from $45,000 in 1955 to $47,000 in 1957, then to $60,000 in 1958, $65,000 in 1959 where it held steady at that level all the way to 1965. Some saw the slow rate of growth for his own salary as a deliberate strategy to keep a lid on the company's overall executive compensation.

In a 1969 note, he wrote, "The old guard hesitates until the direction is clear. There needs to be more independent decision-making." His attention began to be drawn to managing the Baxter balance sheet and growing inventories, with the help of Oddi.

Graham moved up to chairman and CEO in 1971, succeeding Ralph Falk II as chairman. Kimbell was made president. He was followed a little later as president by Bill Jennett. Some observers at the time believed Graham wasn't yet seriously considering succession. One says that he was asked the succession question so frequently by security analysts that he simply decided to put a president in place. Also in 1971 Baxter joined the select list of Fortune 500 companies.

INTRODUCTION OF VIAFLEX CONTAINERS

No event of the sixties or early seventies had the significance or drama of the introduction of Viaflex flexible IV containers. The development had been a long time in coming. Its introduction would coincide with a major competitive recall. The new product would revolutionize the IV business in the United States and around the world, and alter its competitive structure for years to come. The story of this development, which is a unique case in competitive strategy, is told in the next chapter.

MILESTONES

1960–1971

1960	Death of founder Dr. Ralph Falk; Ralph Falk II elected chairman.
1961	Baxter stock begins to trade on New York Stock Exchange on May 15.
1961	Choloxin tablets introduced in eleven foreign countries.
1962	Baxter-American Hospital Supply contract termination. Subsequent events resulted in Baxter's retaining about 85 percent of the business.
1962	New Baxter sales districts open in San Francisco and Los Angeles.
1962	Introduction of total bypass oxygenator.
1962	Acquisitions of VIM medical appliances and Disposable Hospital Products.
1962	New Travenol "flag" symbol.
1963	Ground broken for Mountain Home plant.
1963	Additions and expansions occurring at nearly every Baxter facility around the world.
1964	First home hemodialysis patient (Dr. Bennett Kivel).
1964	Hyland introduces plasmapheresis system for blood banking.
1964	Baxter enters medical electronics in partnership with Zenith.

1965 — Flint introduces tetanus antitoxin.

1966 — V. R. Loucks and W. H. Gantz join Baxter in January and June respectively.

1966 — New artificial kidney (RSP dialyzer).

1966 — AHF concentrate (Factor VIII) introduced; new CPD blood anticoagulant; Urocare introduced.

1966 — Medicare goes into effect.

1967 — Baxter sales pass $100 million.

1967 — Choloxin tablets introduced in the U.S.

1967 — Acquisitions of Dayton Flexible Products and Cyclo Chemical.

1967 — Viaflex containers introduced in Canada.

1967 — Ground broken for Hays, Kansas, plant.

1968 — Loucks now vice president for European operations; Gantz joins him in Europe, beginning an era of teamwork between the two men which was to continue for almost 25 years.

1968 — First AHF concentrates from cryoprecipitation.

1969 — Another new artificial kidney.

1969 — Round Lake, Illinois, facility opens.

1969 — Agreement to acquire American Instrument Company

1970 — Introduction of Travase burn products.

1970 — New European headquarters in Brussels.

1970	Ground broken for North Cove, North Carolina, facility.
1970	F.D.A. approves Viaflex containers in the U.S.
1971	Major competitive solutions recall in March.
1971	Baxter sales pass $200 million.
1971	Work started on Deerfield, Illinois, facility.
1971	W. B. Graham elected chairman, CEO; John T. Kimbell elected president.
1971	Baxter joins Fortune 500.

END NOTES

CHAPTER XII

1. Rates of increase in net income did slow somewhat during 1963 and 1964.

2. It is remarkable that Baxter could carry out the market contest with American Hospital while at the same time pursuing innovation in dialysis, blood therapy, the heart-lung machine, and other areas.

3. *The New York Times*, 3 March 1991. Citing, in part, data from Sanford C. Bernstein and Company.

4. The Aminco transaction wasn't formally completed until January 1970.

5. This material abstracted from Marie Ward Reichelt, *The History of Deerfield*. (Glenview, Illinois: Glenview Press, 1928) and Paul Pitt, *The Bicentennial Plus Three: A History of Deerfield*.

6. 1967 Baxter annual report.

7. Later, information technology would become essential in all aspects of a hospital operation and Baxter would begin to provide such services to hospitals.

8. Reference to Baxter's company color was used extensively with the Travenol logo to build customer recognition.

9. 1966 Baxter annual report.

10. 1963 Baxter annual report.

11. Christopher A. Bartlett and Sumantra Ghoshal, "Matrix Management: Not a Structure, a Frame of Mind," *Harvard Business Review* (July-August 1990); "What is a Global Manager?," (September-October 1992).

12. David A. Hounshell and John Kenly Smith, Jr., *Science and Corporate Strategy: DuPont R&D, 1902-80* (Cambridge, England: Cambridge University Press, 1988).

CHAPTER

XIII

VIAFLEX: MORE INNOVATION AND STRATEGIC MANEUVER

The meeting in John Kimbell's office in what is now the Walgreen Building on an early January morning in 1971 was intense, even at some points heated. The decision pending was critical, and the three primary participants came with their minds already made up.

"Bill, it's a premium product and it should be priced here in the States above glass . . . certainly not 30 percent higher like Canada. Maybe 10 to 15 percent. We can bring the price down later when we pick up market share." Kimbell kicked off the discussion. Vern Loucks, who was visiting Morton Grove in preparation for returning that March from his successful assignment in Europe, was the other participant with Kimbell and Bill Graham.

"I talked to Ed Nawoj before coming over for this meeting," Graham broke in. "He tells me that plastic costs aren't down to glass yet, but when the North Cove [North Carolina] plant is finished he believes we can push those costs down lower than glass. We have to have the volume though."

"I talked to Ed, too. He's probably right," Kimbell went on, "but we still don't know how much volume plastic is going to take from glass. Our experience so far in Canada doesn't indicate it's going to take the market by storm. Why don't we grab the opportunity to make some extra profit?"

"Doesn't that depend, John," Loucks broke in, "on what we're trying to accomplish strategically with the plastic product? Do we expect it to be an alternative to glass or to replace glass altogether?"

"That's exactly the point," Graham said. "We've been working on this for more than ten years. It gives us a strategic advantage we don't have with glass. We should go for broke with it. We have the inventory necessary to support an all-out effort. I don't usually override you, John, but I want the product priced the same as glass—not even a couple of percentage points higher."

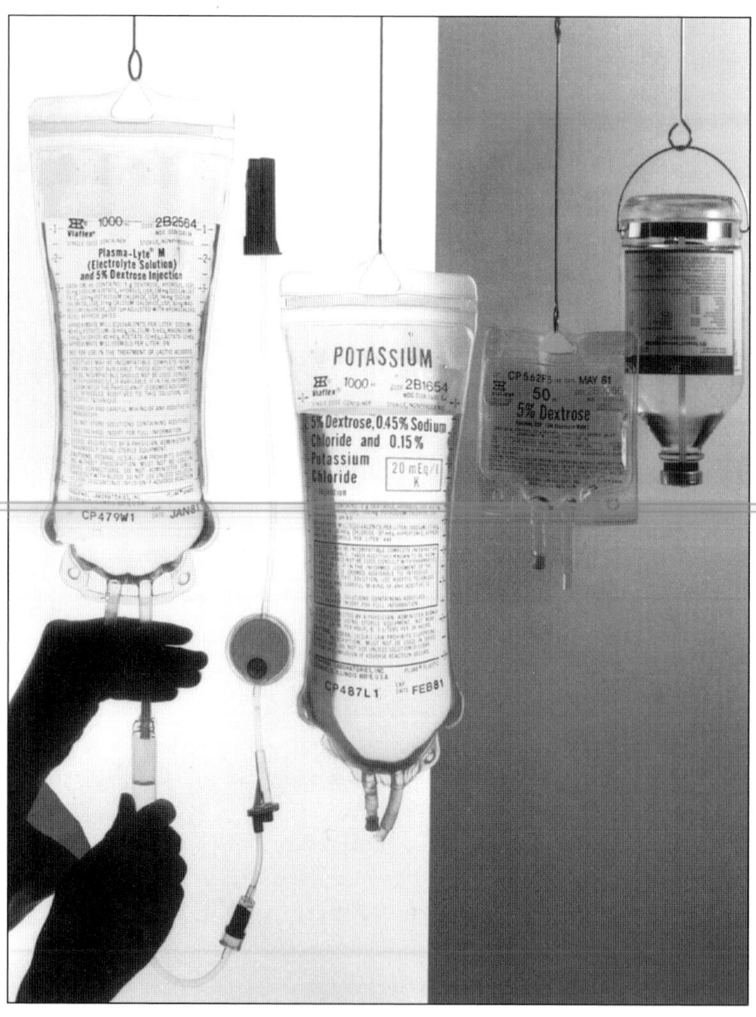

The transition from glass to sterile plastic in intravenous solution packaging.

WHAT MADE VIAFLEX CONTAINER STRATEGY SO REMARKABLE?

The product whose direction was being decided in that meeting was, of course, the Viaflex flexible IV solution container system. The name Viaflex was coined by Ralph Martison of the firm of Cummings, MacPhail & Nutrie.

Viaflex development was clearly the highlight of the sixties for Baxter, and its successful marketing around the world was a strategic triumph of the seventies. Viaflex containers revolutionized IV therapy. They turned the business and competitive structure of IV supply on its head. Ironically, after years of rivalry with Foster McGaw and Don Baxter, Inc. (now McGaw Laboratories) over who would wring the maximum market advantage from the original IV technology, that technology was obsolete almost overnight. McGaw Laboratories never fully recovered its prior product position, nor did Cutter. For the strongest IV competitor, Abbott Laboratories, it took well over five years to begin to catch up in product technology. David Bellamy claims that during this period he actually tried to benchmark how long it would take for Abbott to catch up. According to that measurement, he said, Abbott fell more than seven years behind at one point. The Travenol and Viaflex names became synonymous with IV therapy in the same way the Baxter name had been years earlier. Competitors hung in there during this period in large part because of the characteristic behavior of hospital purchasing exhibited in several situations earlier—their strong reluctance to switch from known products and practices.

Viaflex is a remarkable story because it was innovation of a magnitude that often occurs only once in a company's lifetime. It was the kind of development around which new companies are frequently formed and which then propel them for years. Yet here it was occurring in Baxter's midlife when the company was building its second and third generations of management, and hard on the heels of several other significant developments.

It didn't result from a flash of invention on the part of a single individual. Graham drove the process. Kimbell, his disagreement with Graham about strategic pricing notwithstanding, made major contributions along the way. Long before commercial development produced encouraging results, he sought and won on his own authority a small military contract with Fort Totten in New York for what would become Viaflex containers. Later, it was Kimbell who authorized a Viaflex container inventory build-up—additional to glass—that was one factor enabling Baxter to respond vigorously when the market suddenly broke open.

Nawoj, working on plastics throughout the fifties, was another key figure in Viaflex container success. In fact, the story has it that it was Nawoj who, after early attempts failed to blow-mold a solutions container, sought to make a bag from vinyl sheeting and heat-seal it. Dick Von Drasek in Canada was still another contributor, since Canada was chosen as the test-bed for Viaflex container development for strategic as well as regulatory reasons. Not only did he struggle through all the trials of having solutions bags blow up in

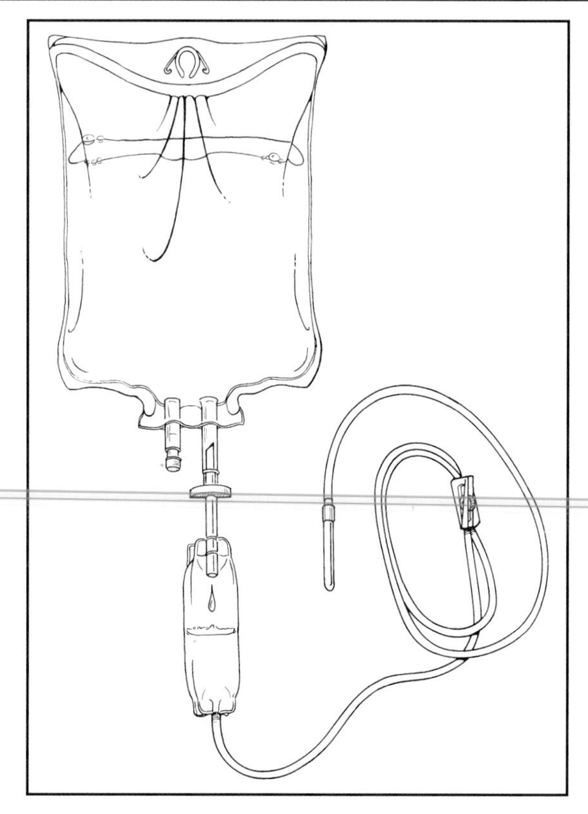

Flexible IV Containers: *Polyvinyl flexible intravenous fluid containers were made possible after Baxter engineers perfected methods for sealing access tubing into bags. Compared to glass, the shipping, handling, and administration of intravenous fluids in polyvinyl containers was a major improvement in the technology for fluid administration. An early use for flexible fluid containers occurred during the Korean Conflict when they were employed in front-line hospitals.*

the sterilizers and having to cut windows in sterilizers to see what was going on, he also cooperated closely with Kimbell in regulatory and marketing activities that led to approval of Viaflex containers by the Canadian Health Policy Board in 1967 and the first sale of the Viaflex container system to Stevenson Memorial Hospital in Alliston, Ontario, in 1968. He also somehow found time to contribute to the development of the Mini-Bag container (a related innovation, the story of which is told later) and to perfect a two-liter bag which became a significant factor in Baxter's work in peritoneal dialysis.

At the beginning of his career with Baxter as Graham's assistant from 1966 until he was assigned to Europe in late 1968, Loucks was also involved in Viaflex development. His duties were more operational than were those of some of the earlier incumbents of that job. Among his responsibilities were oversight of a troublesome IBM card system conversion and coordination of the F.D.A. IND and NDA process for the Viaflex container, working with Bellamy and Nawoj.

"In addition to those two, Kimbell, Len Ginger, Tom Garret, and Ed Pulaski were also deeply involved," Loucks recalled. "We started with six codes [products] and got it to eighteen. Fenwal still had manufacturing problems with plastics, but we knew we didn't have to centrifuge the solutions product. The process was a long one because all the parties, certainly including the F.D.A., were educating themselves about the properties of plastics for this kind of critical medical use. It was important that their understanding and ours move ahead at generally the same pace. It wasn't until four years later that the product was approved in the United States."

While this process continued, Loucks moved to Brussels in early 1969 to take up his responsibilities in Europe, returning just in time for U.S. introduction of the Viaflex container and the concurrent major recall of competitive solutions.

Bellamy was the "technical glue" in all of this, as he had been earlier in Fenwal system development. There were many contributors. This was an accomplishment of the whole organization, of people at many levels, of all the business functions and many separate product technologies pulled together and orchestrated by Graham for an overriding strategic purpose.

The Viaflex container was remarkable too because of the amount of technical risk undertaken. There were still widespread concerns in both the medical and materials communities about biocompatibility of thermoplastics. One of the leading IV competitors spoke out forcefully about the patient risks of plastic containers and lobbied behind the scenes against F.D.A. approval of the Viaflex container because of the supposed problem of DEHP[1] leaching from the plastic into the solution. There was scientific research and validation still to be done. The variety of vinyl formulations to be tried in order to find just the right one was almost infinitely variable. Attention to the smallest details proved to be critical to product success.

When the F.D.A. approved Viaflex containers for the United States in late 1970, it was a limited code approval. Shortly before F.D.A. approval, U.S. military customers for Viaflex containers intervened on Baxter's behalf with the F.D.A., which was expressing concerns about the acidity-alkalinity balance of some solutions in Viaflex containers. The Veterans Administration bought Viaflex containers early, before general approval, for use in priming dialysis coils because the Viaflex container eliminated air entrapment and thus risk of air embolism.

Then too, the company's manufacturing and distribution systems would have to be retooled to adapt to the new Viaflex container. The original distribution system had grown up with bulky, breakable glass bottles shipped to market as "miscellaneous syrups, nonmedicated,"[2] and then had adapted to both product changes and the rupture with American Hospital Supply. Manufacturing Viaflex containers required a much more vertically integrated system than for glass containers, and glass-packaged product was going to continue to be produced at the same time. Planning and authorizing the construction of the North Cove, North Carolina plant (now Baxter's largest domestic plant) for Viaflex containers at this very time was audacious. It reflected the confidence Baxter management had in its Viaflex container strategy. The initial manufacturing risk paid off over time as Viaflex container costs were driven down significantly year after year while the product itself was improved. Indeed, Viaflex container costs were still showing reductions in 1993.

The Viaflex container is a remarkable story too in the way Baxter's strategic moves were "cloaked" from the marketplace. Viaflex pricing strategy has been discussed earlier, but it's such an outstanding example of attention to strategic detail that it merits further attention at this point. Graham and Kimbell personally decided to price Viaflex 30 percent over glass in its market debut in Canada to position it as a high-end product. Baxter didn't want competitors to think it was a threat to glass, at least not yet. Then, as the reader already knows, Graham, Kimbell, and Loucks vigorously debated how to price Viaflex for U.S. introduction. Graham was determined to price it competitively with glass right off the bat, while Kimbell wanted to approach glass-plastic parity more gradually. Loucks agreed with the Graham strategy, which was to take as much U.S. market share with Viaflex as quickly as possible. Canada had been a rehearsal. Graham and Loucks didn't want to waste any time now that the main event had arrived.

Baxter may have slightly misread some early signals from hospitals using the Viaflex container. The company's early sales approach concentrated on product features like the closed system, self-sealing capability after needle insertion, and ease of admixing drugs with solutions. Indeed, these were important features. The overriding

The breakable glass bottle was far more difficult than flexible IVs to handle for both shippers and medical workers.

importance of one of them—the closed system, with no air entry, that reduced risk of product contamination—would turn out to be the major benefit for patients.

Over the long-term, the most basic and simple things about the product converted professional users in large numbers—the Viaflex container was lightweight, non-breakable, and was designed for ease of hanging and "dripping." The slight Baxter misreadings of the market didn't blunt the success of its overall strategy.

There are as many stories about Viaflex introduction as there are about the spread of MBAs within the Baxter organization. Loucks tells one of them, how the Viaflex container made it into Houston's St. Luke's Hospital.

"Don Martin was the salesman there. He had gotten Viaflex containers accepted in the Texas Heart Institute. Then one day at St. Luke's a glass solutions bottle fell and shattered at Dr. Denton Cooley's feet. He threw another bottle against the wall and said, 'I never want to see this stuff again.' The next day Viaflex was in stock at St. Luke's."

PRODUCT BEGINNING

The beginning of the concept and product development for the Viaflex container cannot be exactly dated. Nawoj recalled, "The work actually dated all the way to World War II. For most of the fifties we worked on extruding a high enough quality vinyl to be used for medical products. When we met that goal, the next hurdle was getting the cost down. Then we had to test the material for interaction with each solution type—saline, dextrose, and so on."

The project probably went formal about 1962, stimulated by Baxter's efforts with the Cube-Pak blood container and then by the successful commercialization of the Fenwal blood bag system in 1960. In a 1962 meeting, Graham spoke forcefully about the critical importance of plastic containers in order for Baxter to produce and sell its solutions products around the world. Once the project became formal, Graham drove it as only Graham in those days could drive a project.

Still, compared with earlier Baxter innovations (initial Vacoliter solutions, the Transfuso Vac and Plasma-Vac, dialysis, and both the oxygenator and the Fenwal system), Viaflex containers took longer to bring to initial marketing stages, but subsequently took much less time for full market acceptance and penetration to occur. The reason was that Baxter was dealing here not with an emerging new therapy but a relatively mature one. This was a new and different ball game.

GETTING TO PRODUCTION

The initial containers and administration sets for Kimbell's $30,000 order from Fort Totten in 1963 were far too complex and expensive. That Baxter got to full production of the Viaflex container without the benefit of a pilot plant, or what chemical and pharmaceutical manufacturers earlier called a "semi-works,"[3] for scale-up is nothing short of amazing. Alliston, Ontario, was not a pilot plant operation in a true sense.

Nawoj said Jack Homan was given the charge to design the North Cove plant for manufacturing the new product line in the U.S. before "any of us knew in detail what the Viaflex container product and product line were going to look like." Meanwhile in Canada, Von Drasek gave the order that, when glass sales fell to 20 percent of the total solutions business, customers were to be told the glass line was being shut down. TUR was a plastic-packaged product on which the F.D.A. "took a pass" because it was an irrigating solution, and the

F.D.A. didn't think approval was critical. Kimbell seized that opportunity to begin market development in the States prior to F.D.A. approval of intravenous solutions.

Then as product specifications got finalized, Kimbell ordered the build-up of a Viaflex container inventory in the U.S. plants that were producing the product before North Cove came on-stream. This was a calculated risk which paid off handsomely a little later on.

COMPETITIVE RESPONSE

Graham said, "Our competitors took a close look at our experience with Viaflex containers in Canada and concluded what we hoped they'd conclude: that it was a product which cost a lot more to produce than glass. It certainly hadn't taken the Canadian market by storm. Then there was the problem of potential toxicity to worry about. They said, let's watch this one from the sidelines. Of course, neither Abbott nor Cutter had undertaken the kind of research we had. They were reacting from a deficient knowledge base."

Competitors had sacrificed a major competitive weapon—timeliness. From that point on they were playing catch-up. Of course, no IV competitor fully shared the strategy Baxter had worked toward since the late forties—the vision of disposability for technical and professional products. Perhaps there was no reason they should, given their other product-market positions and investments outside the solutions business.

RECALL!

Soon after the meeting on Viaflex container pricing, external events took over with a vengeance. One of those occurrences which health industry executives most dread—a national product recall—was about to happen. First came a phone call from Sam O'Kelly to Sam Parker, in late November 1970. At Parker's suggestion O'Kelly called Graham. (O'Kelly had joined Baxter in Harrisburg, Pennsylvania, in 1962 after covering the same territory for Abbott.) He reported the same story to both Parker and Graham, "Some pretty reliable people around here are talking about an Abbott solutions recall. It sounds serious. In fact, I've had one hospital ask me if we'll cover them if that happens. How do you want me to deal with it?"

Only a few days after O'Kelly's report came another call to Graham from George Cain, then CEO of Abbott. "We suggest," he said, "you advise your Harrisburg sales representative to stop talking about a recall." That was followed quickly by still another call to Graham from a Richmond, Virginia, sales rep confirming O'Kelly's earlier intelligence. Clearly, a major problem was developing. Kimbell and Parker stepped up the headquarters communication with Baxter's field force. Graham recalled later that he wasn't expecting a national recall of the magnitude that soon occurred.

A CASE OF BOTTLED DEATH

This was the headline introducing *Newsweek*'s article about the Abbott solutions recall on March 29, 1971. The article said, in part:

> " . . . intravenous-feeding bottles that hang by the bedside of critically ill patients are meant to help sustain the slim thread of life . . .but . . . during the past few months they have brought death and disease instead.
>
> " . . . The U.S. P.H.S. [United States Public Health Service] Centers for Disease Control in Atlanta got wind of the trouble in early December when doctors at the University of Virginia Hospital reported that five patients in the coronary intensive-care unit had come down with blood poisoning during a single week. . . . Cultures from the patients showed they have been infected with two types of bacilli, *Erwinia* and *Enterobacter cloacae,* extremely rare causes of blood poisoning.
>
> ". . . fluids from hundreds of fresh solutions taken off the shelf proved negative . . . nor could the bacteria be found on tubing, needles, or the surfaces of IV bottles.
>
> "The search intensified in January when Detroit's Henry Ford Hospital reported 45 cases and 8 deaths from blood poisoning in the previous three months and St. Anthony's Hospital in Denver reported 24 cases and 1 death."

By March 22, 1971, 21 hospitals surveyed had reported 350 blood poisoning cases and 9 deaths.

Finally, the location of the fatal contamination was found—beneath the liner of the solutions bottle cap.

Abbott had not long before switched to a new bottle cap supplier. Somehow, none of the laboratories working around the clock to find the source of the fatal problem thought to examine the surface underneath the cap liner. It had seemed a very unlikely site from which infection would spread so virulently.

Because it commanded an almost 40 percent domestic market share, Abbott seemed sure there wouldn't be a national recall. After all, that would make resupply difficult, if not impossible. Acting, no doubt, in what they thought were the best interests of the company and of the hospitals' patients involved, Abbott reportedly took an unyielding posture towards the F.D.A.

The F.D.A., as it deliberated possible reactions to the situation, checked the inventory of other solutions suppliers: Cutter, McGaw Laboratories, and Baxter. It was not a particularly propitious time in the relationship between the F.D.A. and Baxter for discussion about Viaflex plastic container introduction. Kimbell and Marsh Abbey spent a week in Washington, D.C. at this critical juncture "negotiating" with the F.D.A. on a variety of issues.

Concurrently, Baxter was experiencing mold growth problems on the exterior label of Fenwal blood bags. It didn't help matters any. Abbey remembered being on a Chicago to Washington flight with Bobby Bonds, who was carrying some of the Fenwal bags affected by exterior mold. "You know," Bonds said artlessly to Abbey, "I don't really like to handle these things before I have my lunch."

At Baxter the F.D.A. found a double inventory of IVs—Viaflex plastic containers and glass. Made confident that the life-sustaining IV supply could be maintained, the F.D.A. ordered a total Abbott solutions recall on March 23. Abbott's North Carolina production of IV solutions was completely shut down until June, when the F.D.A. approved a new bottle closure. The number of Baxter's approved Viaflex container codes was broadened. On May 5 the F.D.A. granted dispensation for Baxter's Canadian-made Viaflex containers to be shipped into the United States.

New York's Columbia Presbyterian Hospital stuck with Abbott as a supplier throughout the recall. While Abbott was shut down to correct the problems, it substituted Cutter solutions product. Some observers wondered why Cutter would "bail out" Abbott in that fashion, although Baxter had in very different circumstances in 1947 also "bailed out" Cutter during a Cutter recall. When Abbott product came back on the market, it incorporated the Cutter cap design. And, according to some observers of the time, Abbott proceeded to clean up by taking share away from Cutter, its erstwhile supplier.

Later, there would be civil suits against the company and even criminal charges against some of its executives (the latter all resolved in Abbott's favor). This was an unfortunate, brief chapter in the history of one of America's most distinguished companies that has made many outstanding contributions in health care.

CONTRACTUAL AND SALES COMMISSION ISSUES

Not everything went smoothly for Baxter during this crisis. First, there were contract issues with hospitals being converted to Baxter. Some claimed that Baxter was playing hardball with hospital accounts to get them to sign five-year supply contracts.[4] In response, the company was able to demonstrate that solutions product was being made available to every hospital customer even though shipment priority was given to hospitals with supply contracts.

The issue of sales commissions was even more irksome. Sales people were paid one commission rate for glass and another for Viaflex plastic containers, but on Abbott account conversions to Baxter glass they got only a flat payment of $500. No doubt the scheme was devised to prevent commission windfalls and to avoid even the appearance of Baxter people profiting from the marketplace disruption. The sales force certainly didn't like it though and there was a lot of grumbling.

CHALLENGES OF GETTING VIAFLEX CONTAINERS TO MARKET

Loucks thought it was at a winter sales meeting at the Abbey in Lake Geneva, Wisconsin, that Kimbell got word of the likely F.D.A.decision to recall Abbott solutions. Before his actual return from Europe, Loucks was preparing to take over leadership of the Baxter hospital division. It was February 14, Valentine's Day, and it was 12 degrees below zero at Lake Geneva. The "Oakland Raiders of Medical Products" had trashed the Abbey. They were angry that Baxter would hold a sales meeting in this Arctic location. They asked Carl Bussema to talk to Graham about never holding another meeting at the Abbey, even though Ralph Falk II owned stock in the place. Loucks became very concerned about the ability of this group to take this new technical product to Abbott accounts and to do it as fast as it needed to be done.

Shortly after his actual return from Brussels, Loucks attended another sales meeting, this one in Hilton Head. "By this time," he recalls, "we had about 30 Viaflex specialty salesmen. There was an all day poker game going on, and no food in the place. There was absolutely no interest in training. I told them we were going to do the meeting over in six weeks and we were going to do it right. Bob Ausman, Hank Michael, and David Holder were asked to get a program together. We got into the market the right way. The old timers who didn't like my approach began to leave. And we retained 54 percent of all the business we got from Abbott."

WHEN THE DUST SETTLED

At the end of this series of pell-mell events, the IV solutions supply of the nation's hospitals had been protected. The Viaflex container was well on its way to becoming the product of choice in the U.S. market. Glass would fade quickly from the solutions scene. It's clear that would have happened anyway, but the recall accelerated the shift. The Baxter sales force had been through its second crisis in less than ten years.

By 1973 Baxter had over 50 percent of the domestic IV market; Abbott about 25 percent. Baxter more than gained back its earlier position in the marketplace, due to new technology and the Abbott recall. That sudden swing in market share reversed Baxter's position dramatically from the time when it was losing points to Abbott because of problems with the distribution contract with American Hospital Supply. It's quite likely that these swings in market share later led to aggressive pricing competition because of the two companies' competitive attitudes. Soon, hospital purchasing groups would gain leverage on the major suppliers.

Abbott gradually caught up with the new technology, but it took longer than Baxter thought it would. Baxter was in possession of a technological lead of years, not months . . . much longer than can usually be expected for this kind of product. The question was, how would the company exploit that strategic advantage? The other solutions competitors, McGaw Laboratories and Cutter, never did catch up.

One of the ways Baxter decided to exploit the strategic advantage was to use the company's growing international reach to move Viaflex containers quickly into as many countries as possible. The product was introduced in the United Kingdom in 1972, where coincidentally there was a major competitive product recall (involving the Evans company, later bought by Boots Ltd.).

A few short years later, the company was selling Viaflex containers in most of the countries where it had sales or manufacturing operations. The label and logo became widely recognized wherever surgery was performed, and the Viaflex plastic container became *the* product standard for solutions.

Another action Baxter took to build on its strategic advantage was to continue to reinvest in Viaflex technology. Thus, soon thereafter,

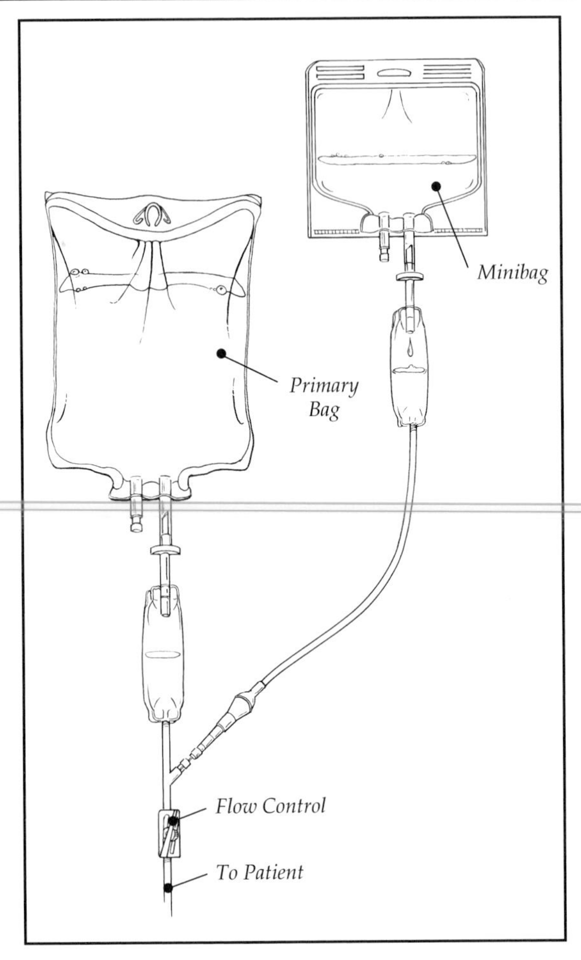

Mini-Bag and Piggyback: *These products were extensions of the basic concept for flexible polyvinyl containers. They facilitated administration of special medications including antibiotics, and helped to maintain a system free from contamination by outside air.*

(1974) the Mini-Bag container was introduced. The Mini-Bag container system was the first closed IV system for intermittent administration of drugs. Since intravenous administration of medicines has, in appropriate cases, substantial advantages over other forms of administration, the Mini-Bag container created a whole new market segment where Baxter first held 100 percent share and today still has a leading position. Other extensions of Viaflex plastic container technology followed.

The third strategic action Baxter took was to begin immediately to take advantage of its greater vertical integration and its tight manufacturing control to drive Viaflex container costs down. This has been referred to a number of times as one of Baxter's great strengths. As Loucks' authority began to increase rapidly, he placed even greater emphasis on it.

Of course, Baxter's net income and cash flow increased significantly during this hectic and stressful time. And because of Viaflex containers, the California and western U.S. markets, which first Don Baxter and then McGaw Laboratories had defended for years, finally began to open up. Prior to 1971, Latter Day Saints Hospital in Salt Lake City had been the only significant Baxter solutions incursion into Don Baxter's and McGaw's territory. 1971 was a landmark year in the company's continuing development.

END NOTES

CHAPTER XIII

1. DEHP is di(ethylhexyl)phthalate, according to the *Acronyms, Initialisms, and Abbreviations Dictionary*, 16th edition, Gale Research, 1992.

2. Rate tariffs for shipping Baxter solutions were originally the same as for pharmaceutical and medical products. This was a serious disadvantage for solutions, which were bulky and heavy. Then Ben Bannister got the idea of negotiating with common carriers for a tariff related to that for food products. Bannister was successful. Hence the tariff language, "syrups, non-medicated."

3. David A. Hounshell and John Kenly Smith, Jr., *Science and Corporate Strategy: DuPont R&D; 1902-80* (Cambridge, England: Cambridge University Press, 1988).

4. The one incident formally complained of turned out to be a transaction of Don Baxter (McGaw Laboratories).

CHAPTER

XIV

BAXTER EMERGES AS AN INTERNATIONAL HEALTH CARE LEADER

"I want to take the opportunity in International, but the responsibility should include planning and marketing. Charlie Schwartz has got to buy into that." Vern Loucks was talking to Bill Graham in Morton Grove about the position of vice president of administration for International operations, reporting to Schwartz. It was mid-1968. In his initial employment interview with Graham in 1965, Loucks had said he had a strong interest in International. Schwartz did buy in, and Loucks made an extensive reconnaissance trip through Europe.

When he returned after eight whirlwind weeks, he laid out his proposed plan for Graham. The European business was still tiny. "We can take Europe to $100 million in five years." Later Loucks recounted the reception to his proposal, "Graham gave me that cherubic smile and said, 'Why not $200 million?' I answered that it all depended on how much Baxter wanted to invest.

"But," Loucks went on, "to do that I've got to have Bill Gantz and Jack Ufheil with me in Brussels. That's the team."

Schwartz balked. Gantz was needed in his role in Mexico and Ufheil was playing an important marketing role in the Morton Grove International organization. But Loucks got his way. This young management team, none of whom had ever really run anything, was off to Brussels in early 1969. They did what Loucks said they would. They doubled the business that first year from $8 to $16 million. The second year they almost doubled it again, going to $25 million. After Loucks returned to the U.S., Gantz took it the rest of the way to and beyond the $100 million target. "We were thinking big and burning up growth capital," Loucks said. "On one of our trips back to Morton Grove we were asked by Graham to stop in New York and see the Morgan Stanley people. There, Preston and Patterson asked how much capital we'd need to feed the continued growth. Gantz and I said $75 million. When Graham heard about that, he was upset. He said it was an outrageous amount compared to the capitalization of the company."

Vern Loucks, in the seventies, after his successful management of Baxter's international business.

In the middle sixties and early seventies Baxter began to emerge as an international health care leader.[1] Just as with other successful company strategies, this didn't happen overnight, but was the result of many years of planning and investment, going all the way back to initial operations in Canada in 1936, the beginning of the long-lasting distribution relationship with A. B. Christaens in Belgium in 1937, and the formation of the 40 percent Baxter-owned South African company in 1949. What specific factors caused the company's international performance to take off dramatically at this time? Graham described the strategic approach, "It took a paradigm shift in the American export mentality. Our American pharmaceutical competitors didn't generally manufacture abroad because they didn't have to. We had to choose the country markets in which to manufacture wisely because our resources were stretched. Once we began to manufacture locally, the manufacturers there were at a severe disadvantage due to the fact that they couldn't afford our level of R&D. We could support R&D locally through the volume of our activity in the United States. It was very much like the situation local manufacturers in certain industries face today competing with the Japanese . . . the concept of 'available markets' is important. We pinpointed the ones we wanted to go after with great care. Fred Marquart's [Hyland] albumin, gamma globulin, and diagnostics were important because those were products we could export as an added part of the strategy. . . . Still it was slow. Initially, we couldn't find a market for quality in France. Germany was tough because of the strong competition there. And Italy presented receivables problems. At one point, we had sales representatives there collecting $200 [U.S.] for every $100 of product shipped (because of grossly inadequate health care budgets). Spain was slow, except for our penetration with albumin. The United Kingdom was one of the few nations which turned profitable very early."

The company's progressive successes made it possible to attract and recruit executive talent within each country of operation. Local managers and third-country nationals played an ever-increasing role in international growth. The company's tactical plans were implemented aggressively.

"Taking the ground" characterized Baxter's preferred plan for establishing a firm base in each new country—usually supplanting a distributor, establishing a manufacturing operation where feasible, seeking to create demonstrable value for that specific market and government, and adapting to the regulatory and sociopolitical environment. So using Graham's image to describe the early development of company strategy, there were now a number of Wee Willie Keelers—some American, others European, and some from other parts of the world—beginning to hit solid singles and doubles in more and more country operations. It was an outstanding business example of a cohesive overall strategy with ample room for local flexibility and initiative. In fact, that strategic and management approach is generally credited with creating in International one of the richest sources of Baxter executives: Loucks, Gantz, Jim Tobin, Victor Chaltiel, Gabriel Schmergel, Dick Egen, Lawrence H. N. Kinet, Tony White, Brian Steer, Claude Grunewald, Bob Bocquet, Jacques Fonteyne, Gerry Moufflet, Manny Baez—to name some of the many.

The best way to convey the flavor of the "European Campaign" from 1969 to 1971 and beyond is to look at events through the eyes of the participants. The brief account is assembled from the comments of Gantz, Schmergel, Marsh Abbey and, of course, Loucks himself.

Loucks and his team didn't think they could make much money in Europe in IV solutions outside Belgium and the United Kingdom. So they looked for different opportunities in each of the countries to be penetrated. Several of the early deals were in Germany. Loucks knew he would be in trouble if those first deals didn't work out. Abbey recalls traveling around Europe in those days cleaning up the details of lots of handshake deals. He also remembers evening cocktails at the Hotel Macdonald in Brussels with Loucks shouting over the lobby telephone at Schwartz back in the U.S. Schwartz was experiencing heartburn with this young European management team.

Loucks sped through Europe with Ufheil while Gantz held the fort in Brussels. They "bootlegged" the new Kieffel-Korting manufacturing equipment (which later profoundly influenced U.S. manufacturing technology) with $50,000 they took from somewhere else in the budget. They began to work with negative pressure dialysis, fast becoming the dominant renal technology in Europe, despite the fact that Howard Janneck and others back at corporate were vehemently opposed to it.

Marketing drove everything else. Loucks believed they were educating Europe. He concentrated on growing the blood transfusion business in the U.K., making contracts for gamma paste in Spain at $2500 a kilo, and seeking the advice of Arthur Andersen and General Motors as to how Baxter could start doing business in Italy.

There were periodic conflicts with Baxter management in the United States. Diagnostics were an important part of the European thrust. The Brussels team didn't believe Hyland Diagnostics management in California had the vision to see the importance of immunology. The ultimate decision to replace Hyland management (called the "Costa Mesa Saturday Night Massacre" by Baxter veterans), sending a team, called the "Chicago Seven" headed by Sam Parker, to Costa Mesa to take over and then to move Hyland Diagnostics to Round Lake, Illinois, came too late, in Loucks' opinion.

And the disagreements about dialysis didn't go away. Janneck continued to oppose negative pressure dialysis and sent Marty Peskin to Belgium to dampen the commitment to the alternative technology at Travenol International Services, the European subsidiary of Baxter, incorporated in 1971.

In the midst of this, the word came down from Jim Ammon and Janneck to discontinue manufacture of kidney coils in the U.K. and

Belgium. "We can save more than $100,000 shipping from Puerto Rico," Ammon said.

"That's peanuts," Loucks answered. The order then came from Graham himself to shut the lines down and to do it within 24 hours. Coil shipments from Puerto Rico were 25 percent "leakers." Within six months, Baxter's hemodialysis business in Europe had lost major market share.

A number of participants in this period still remember the triumphs and the frustrations of developing Europe as the high point of their careers. And the future Baxter management philosophy about risk-taking, listening to the customer and thinking big and imaginatively, were being shaped by these events.

Today the question raised by this part of the history might well be: was the overall approach taken by Baxter international? multinational? or global? As with a number of other Baxter strategic elements, it is difficult to fit Baxter International concepts into the usual management frameworks. The answer to the question is that it was none of the above precisely, and it was, at the same time, all of them during different stages of development and for different product lines. For example, Dale Smith, who started with Fenwal as a California sales representative in 1962 and became group vice president for Blood Therapy Products, early on began to guide that part of the business towards a global mode of operation. Dialysis progressively took on global characteristics. Intravenous solutions, on the other hand, remained more of a local business for several reasons, including product bulk and weight. So the world-wide marketing approach to solutions had to be different than for blood therapeutics or dialysis.

Integration was the strategic concept that shaped Baxter's international development. That meant, first, integration of business operations (manufacturing, engineering, quality control, and regulatory affairs with marketing and distribution) within each country where that was feasible, and then integration of those country entities into the total corporate system. Initially, technical innovation and product development were not part of that concept, which led, of course, to the product battles Loucks and Gantz fought from Brussels with their U.S. colleagues in diagnostics and dialysis. Overall strategic design made it possible, though, to add them later.

EARLY YEARS, 1936 TO 1949

Baxter began activities outside the United States early. Canadian operations were launched in 1936. Two key distributors were appointed early: A. B. Christaens in Belgium and Ingram & Bell in Canada. During World War II, of course, Baxter products were shipped to military theaters around the world.

However, there wasn't any plan. Harry Falk traveled to countries where Baxter had exclusive rights under its original 1931 contract with Don Baxter (rights confirmed by the landmark trademark litigation about the Baxter name) and executed distribution agreements somewhat randomly. Much of what Harry Falk did during these years later had to be undone.

Then in the late 1940s, Graham began to look at international opportunities as another kind of market niche where Baxter could "hit away from the competition." In 1949 the Keagrams South African joint venture provided early evidence of the advantages of an integrated operation, in a relatively small market.

Figure 10 shows how long it took from 1950—when Baxter's total net sales were only $10 million—for the international business to grow to substantial proportions.

FORMATIVE YEARS, 1949 TO 1966

Several events in the 1950s stand out in terms of their contribution to Baxter's international growth. The first, while not itself internationally related, was the intensive planning for the first manufacturing operation in the Commonwealth of Puerto Rico. That first plant in Hato Rey didn't open until 1958, but the preparation went all the way back to 1950 when the Cleveland, Mississippi plant was coming on-stream. By the time Puerto Rican operations were launched, the company had built a depth of knowledge about meeting manufacturing requirements in a new and different environment.

The second event was the opening of Baxter's first European manufacturing operation. This occurred in 1954, in space leased from the Belgian distributor, A. B. Christaens. Don Madsen, already proven as the Baxter "point man" in start-ups at Cleveland, Mississippi; Greenville, Tennessee; and South Africa, moved to Brussels to spearhead that project. Because of early and continuing investment in Belgium, first in manufacturing and distribution and later in research and development, Baxter and Travenol names would, in Kinet's words, "become as well known there for hospital products as Kleenex tissues for consumer goods."

Because industrial and food enzymes were international in their sale and use, Baxter's 1957 Wallerstein acquisition provided additional impetus, in addition to its specific purpose as a takeover

BAXTER INTERNATIONAL SALES DEVELOPMENT

Year	Total Sales (Millions)	International Sales (Millions)	% of Total Corporate Sales Increase
1950	10	N/A	
1966	78	19	25%
1970	188	N/A	
1971	242	58	24%
1972	279	80	29%
1973	356	117	33%
1974	466	149	32%
1975	564	183	33%
1976	681	219	32%
1977	844	263	31%
1978	1,004	335	33%
1979	1,191	436	37%
1980	1,374	520	38%
1981	1,503	528	35%
1982	1,671	557	33%
1983	1,834	558	30%
1984	1,796	579	32%
1985	2,446	614	25%
1986	5,700	1,117	20%
1987	6,223	1,330	21%

Figure 10

defense to counter pressures from American Hospital Supply. Soon after, Baxter acquired Societé Rapidase of Seclin, France, just south of the Belgian border. That business, which made enzymes for the textile industry, provided an additional base of sales volume during the years when Loucks and Gantz were "pouring the coals" to European expansion.

Wallerstein, Schwartz recalled, also influenced Baxter's entry into and penetration of hospital and medical markets in the United Kingdom. He said, "With Wallerstein came a small office near the Tower of London which had its inception years before as an export-import business.

"The office was vintage Charles Dickens, run by two elderly gentlemen, Mr. Wheeler and Mr. Potton, with their clerk, Mr. Purchase. They handled imports of Collupulin[2] for Wallerstein and provided fine chalk to toothpaste manufacturers. It gave us a place to begin.

We hired a British national to make a study of the potentials for us in England, Scotland, and Ireland.

"Intravenous solutions were being made in each hospital under the control of the British Ministry of Health, and there was profound resistance to change, particularly to an imported product. There were, however, a couple of factors working in our favor. Baxter's development of the artificial kidney was of considerable interest to the British medical profession as it was to doctors around the world. More specifically, hospitals were witnessing patient reactions to cleaned, re-used administration sets, and hospital personnel didn't like to do that kind of work anyway. So we had an opportunity to sell disposable sets manufactured in Belgium with the understanding that, as soon as possible, units would be manufactured in the United Kingdom.

"Initial assembly of products with parts imported from Belgium began in rented space in High Wycome. Then in 1964 we built our own manufacturing plant in Thetford, Norfolk, England. It produced solutions, disposable administration sets, kidney coils, and had enough examination glove capacity to serve the United Kingdom and all of Western Europe at that time. Baxter Laboratories, Ltd., soon became the market leader there in intravenous solutions and administration sets. We also emerged as the dominant factor in the disposable blood container business under the Fenwal name, working through the Red Cross communities in England and Ireland just as we did in other European countries."

This was the general pattern from country to country as the company raced to establish positions in as many of them as market potentials and management and capital resources permitted. International sales were still small even though they were growing at an annual rate of 40 percent in some of those years. It would take time for these small beach heads to take hold and for support and transporting links to be forged among them.

INTERNATIONAL SALES TAKE OFF 1966 TO 1978

We have already seen how the right people at the right time caused Baxter Europe to take off. When Loucks returned to the U.S., he was succeeded first by Gantz, who remained close to international strategy and operations for his entire 26 year career with Baxter; then by Schmergel in 1975; Steer in 1979; and Egen in 1983. After Egen returned to the U.S. in 1985, the TIS (Travenol International

A Baxter Travenol truck readies for shipping product in Thetford, England

Services) organization changed, as did Baxter's whole global business structure.

Loucks recalled this period of rapid European growth, "It was a great experience for me. I concentrated on a few high pay-off initiatives. We established a European headquarters in Brussels in 1970. That improved our visibility and identification in Europe and provided a base for broad marketing programs. More importantly, as more decision-making began to migrate to Europe from the U.S., we developed a cadre of energetic and self-reliant managers there.

"Travenol International Services was formed in 1971. Our first Euro-financing followed soon after, and, of course, our marketing success in major European countries helped that financing. We began to learn to be astute currency exchange managers. That became even more important toward the end of the seventies.

"When I arrived in Europe, we already had manufacturing facilities in Belgium, France, and the U.K. However, some of these were precariously small. We were able to solidify and expand these positions and prepare for manufacturing start-ups in other countries. The Castlebar, Ireland plant was begun in 1973. Ground was broken for a plant in Norway in 1975."

After Loucks' return to Morton Grove headquarters to assume other responsibilities, Gantz—while still in Europe and subsequently—initiated several other key actions which have left a lasting imprint on the company's international business. In 1978, he formed a task group which led to the formation of Baxter's first R&D facility outside the United States in Nivelles, Belgium. That center, identified for many years with Bocquet, was to concentrate on the company's leading products throughout Europe: blood therapy (Fenwal), Artificial Organs, and IV solutions. It was also to serve as the company's technical eyes and ears in the Common Market. This began a gradual but profound change in orientation, which will be discussed later. Related to that step, Gantz also initiated a system of area directors, each of whom also had a product-line responsibility for all Europe, as follows:

Steer: United Kingdom and Scandinavia; IV solutions products.
Chaltiel: France; artificial organs, dialysis.
Fonteyne: Belgium, Spain, and Germany; blood therapy.

These three area directors were responsible to Schmergel in Europe, who in turn reported to Gantz at headquarters. Thus, a "matrix management" system was begun. It has recurred in different forms over the subsequent years of Baxter's international growth, and is discussed again later.

INTERNATIONAL GROWTH OUTSIDE EUROPE

Before this time, there had been manufacturing operations in other countries outside the United States and Europe; specifically, in Canada, Colombia, Brazil, South Africa, and Mexico (where Gantz had been assigned before his move to Europe).

Puerto Rico, of course, continued to grow in importance as a Baxter manufacturing center of a different kind.

The non-European countries made up a second international division known as AMPAC (Americas and the Pacific). Development in this sector began to speed up at the same time as it did in Europe. The Ashdod, Israel plant (part of AMPAC) was begun in 1971. A replacement plant in Australia was completed in 1973. Baxter had entered the Japanese market early through a Sumitomo distributorship in 1968, followed by a joint venture with Sumitomo in 1972. There were early difficulties and frustrations there. Loucks explained, "Sumitomo didn't seem to think that we were nearly as important as we thought we were."

As in other countries, Baxter persisted. First, it pushed its ownership interest to 51 percent. Manufacturing of Baxter products in Japan was begun in 1974 in a Sumitomo-owned facility in Ibaraki, and in 1979 the 49 percent Sumitomo interest was purchased by Baxter, taking advantage of a change in Japanese law. The Japanese operation, headed in recent years by a Japanese executive, Katzutoyo Komatsu, went on to become one of Baxter's larger and more important businesses in a country that is both a major consumer of health care goods and services, and increasingly, a key source of advanced medical technology.

REMARKABLE SUCCESS IN JAPAN

Because it is such an important part of Baxter's story and because of wide interest in doing business with and in Japan, the specific milestones of Baxter's steady expansion in Japan are recounted here. In order to do so, we move somewhat beyond the time frame covered in this chapter, as has been done elsewhere. The story is told in two parts, before and then after 1983. The cast of characters grows somewhat larger at this point. The continuing contributions of Graham, Loucks, Gantz, Tobin, Schwartz, and Kinet have already been mentioned. In 1983 Katzutoyo Komatsu joined Japan Travenol Laboratories as its president,[3] a watershed event in the growth and orientation of Baxter in Japan. Also a number of world leaders and other luminaries became involved in developments from 1983 on. They included President Reagan, Prime Minister Nakasone, Health and Welfare Minister Hayashi and his successor, Minister Masuoka, Secretaries Schultz and Baldrige, Trade Representative Hills, Senator Percy (Illinois), Assistant Commerce Secretary Prestowitz, Foreign Affairs Ministry Director Kunihiro and his aide, Mr. Moriga. This was a busy and hectic time in Japan-U.S. trade relations. A summit meeting occurred between the two heads of state ("Ron-San and Yasu", as *Time* then reported it) in Los Angeles in January 1985, followed shortly after by the MOSS talks. Due in part to a key visit (requested by Mr. Reagan) by Senator Percy to Prime Minister Nakasone in December 1984, but also because of quietly effective efforts by Mr. Komatsu and senior Baxter executives in the U.S., sharp focus was maintained on medical devices and supplies amidst all the many other difficult issues to be addressed.

All of these individuals became involved, in one way or another, in the issue of the Japanese government's tediously slow approval of CAPD. Japan was for more than two years the only major country which had not made CAPD available for its end stage renal disease patients. Clyde Prestowitz, Department of Commerce point man for international trade in the Reagan administration, recalls how impressed he was with Baxter's aggressiveness in both blood fractions and CAPD in the face of these continuing obstacles. "The fact that Baxter was so persistent," he says, "made it an appropriate issue for Secretary Baldrige and me to single out for special emphasis with MITI and the Health Ministry."

Remember, in accordance with the recurring theme of managing on multiple levels, the company had other international businesses to tend at the same time that windows of medical opportunity began to open in Japan. At the beginning of the period covered in this chapter, Baxter's international sales were less than $20 million. They reached $335 million in 1978 and $520 million in 1980. By 1980 the company had sales and marketing organizations in 20 other countries and manufacturing in 17 (this, of course, does not include Puerto Rico).

EVENTS BEFORE 1983

Given the dimensions of Baxter's success in Japan, there's a lot of credit to go around. Lawrence Kinet says the lion's share of it in the late seventies and formative period of the eighties should go to Bill Gantz. Kinet recalled, "The AMPAC Division, including Japan, wasn't formed until mid-1981 and I came from London to head it. Long before that, after he came back to Deerfield from Europe, Gantz successfully carried out the protracted negotiations with our Japanese joint venture partner, Sumitomo. The outcome was two companies in Japan: the Osaka joint venture with Sumitomo and the wholly-owned subsidiary we started in Tokyo. Then he pressed insistently for approval of a number of blood products such as Factor VIII and PPF, which was achieved, I think, by 1981.

"Meanwhile, along came the long slow climb with CAPD [continuous ambulatory peritoneal dialysis]. The clinical concept was little known in Japan and the Japanese trial and registration are rigorous with key decisions made behind closed doors. With Gantz' leadership our Japan business was producing about $100 million in revenues by 1981-82, mostly in hemodialysis kidney coils, blood products, and diagnostics. Then hemodialysis technology changed the market in Japan, as it had elsewhere. A number of Japanese competitors came in, and our margins and market share both fell. CAPD became all-important."

It was at this point that Baxter's integrated, patient, and long-term approach asserted itself strongly, and began to turn the tide. Graham was clearly unhappy about the delays in making CAPD available for the benefit of Japanese renal patients. He and Kinet met with the Japanese Minister of Health to express their concern. The next day, the minister saw Ed Harper of the Reagan White House staff, who exerted more pressure. And so it went from there. Baxter approved extensive modifications of the Gifu plant for CAPD manufacture before completion of the long approval process, another strong signal to the Japanese government of its commitment. Even when CAPD was approved, it was restricted to hospital use, negating its greatest patient life-style benefits, and the reimbursement schedule was far from satisfactory.

Gantz's recollections provide additional perspective on JTL. "Baxter's approach to Japan has been somewhat unique, reflecting the Graham philosophy. We started in the late sixties in a joint venture with Sumitomo. Frank Wandell (who joined Baxter from Fenwal) recommended Sumitomo because of Upjohn's experience with them. We began to sell the artificial kidney, gained a major market share, and the Japanese established a manufacturing plant in Osaka.

"We decided, when foreign ownership laws changed in Japan, to discuss with Sumitomo's chairman Hasegawa establishment of a separate Baxter company in Tokyo. Sumitomo would handle blood and renal products and Baxter would handle everything else. During those early years, Charlie Schwartz and Des O'Connell played key roles, along with Graham. Jim Tobin also performed a critical function, moving to Japan in 1975 and keeping the business moving ahead at a time when there were two separate organizations."

Gantz found Japan's growing markets for Baxter products underserved because of the two organizations.

"We were trying to get Sumitomo to register a new product, Factor VIII. They did a market survey that said there was no potential. Of course there was. Hemophilia was just being undertreated in Japan. Graham, Loucks, and I decided to ask Sumitomo to dissolve the joint venture. It was unheard of at the time. In fact, Upjohn just recently [1992] ended its joint venture with Sumitomo. Vern and I went to Japan. We were surprised when Sumitomo said yes. Then began the arduous process of spelling out the agreement. In 1977, I made 10 trips to Japan. Sumitomo was interested in continuing to sell albumin so we agreed to them being a distributor. That relationship went on for many years.

"Now Baxter had to build a manufacturing plant in Gifu and combine the Osaka and Tokyo organizations. It was blazing new trails for an American company in Japan and was about to break all the conventions there. This is where Tobin's experience and insights were particularly useful. The tough decision was made to consolidate and move the Osaka operation to Tokyo. That was traumatic for Japanese employees. It proved, however, to be one of the lift-off points for Baxter in Japan. While tailored to the unique aspects of Japan, the strategy was similar in many respects to what Baxter had done earlier in Canada, Belgium, the United Kingdom, and France."

"Then," said Gantz, "we began a full court press on regulatory approvals. From 1976 to 1986, we took one product after another through the difficult clinical trial process: Factor VIII and IX, IV gamma globulin, Proflex, and CAPD, among others. It was the most complex and difficult management task we had going on at the time."

1983 AND BEYOND:—JAPANESE COMPANY BECOMES BAXTER'S LARGEST, MOST PROFITABLE INTERNATIONAL BUSINESS

"I'm convinced this is the right man to do the job for us," Lawrence Kinet said enthusiastically. It was late at night in Tokyo, but Kinet was eager to get approval by telephone to extend an offer. "Sounds like an outstanding executive," Gantz replied, "but what chance do we have of attracting him?" They were, of course, discussing Mr. Komatsu, who had spent his entire successful career with Japanese companies Sony and Kenwood.

Komatsu was persuaded to join JTL as president in 1983, and is now its chairman. If combining the Osaka and Tokyo organizations was one lift-off point for Baxter in Japan, as Bill Gantz said, surely this was another, even more significant one.

Another striking example of the Graham good man theory, Komatsu was able to bridge cultural differences and catalyze effective action. Where Americans saw Japanese review and approval processes as obstructionist, he understood the need for careful, sensitive education of government officials and doctors about CAPD benefits.

As these two points of view came together, and as earlier pressures began to yield results CAPD approval finally began to move ahead, as shown in this chronology:

CAPD Events	
July 1979	Started stability tests (2 years real time plus safety factor)
January 1980	Clinical trials started on Japanese patients
September 1980	File submitted to MHW
September 1981	First investigation sub-committee review
May 1982	Final sub-committee review
July 1982	Special committee review
August 1982	Permanent committee review
September 1982	MHW approval
February 1983	Materials reimbursement (Yakka) approved (but only for CAPD practiced in the hospital)
1982–	The company spends $4 million from 1982-end through early 1983 to convert Gifu plant for manufacture of CAPD products in Japan
December 1982	Registration file amended to include local (Gifu) manufactured product in addition to U.S. imports
June 1983	Gifu plant licensed by MHW and Gifu prefecture to produce CAPD products
July 1983	Home care aspect of CAPD approved (via direction sheet amendment)
March 1984	Doctor's fee reimbursement (Shinroyhoshu) for CAPD approved although not at levels recommended by Japan Medical Association Committee Gigikai Shakuinkei

BAXTER'S INTERNATIONAL BUSINESS MATURES

As the company's international business began to mature in 1980 at one half billion U.S. dollars, there were a number of complex management issues to be faced and resolved. Among them was the most forward-looking coordination or matrix management system to complement Baxter's predominant individual country focus. This is extraordinarily difficult since health care practices, regulation, and economics are essentially local in nature, while many health care technologies and therapies are global in their application.

Other issues were the need for greater R&D presence outside the United States, which was begun with the Nivelles Center in 1978, and which had already been underlined in importance by the threat from European dialysis technology during the seventies; the challenges of taking certain businesses global; learning to rely less in International on expatriate American executives; developing means of meeting health care needs in less developed countries which lack advanced health care infrastructures; and, of course, meeting the cost and other challenges to health care that have arisen since the early

1980s in every developed country around the globe. It is, no doubt, economic forces that will drive and shape the future direction of health care across national boundaries, as much as medical technology or patient needs.

Baxter has done an effective job of adapting to the changing global health care environment. However, since the company's response was determined by critical decisions and events in 1985, that part of the story is told at a later point.

REASONS FOR BAXTER'S INTERNATIONAL SUCCESS

Beginning in the late 1960s, then, Baxter's international businesses became a key source of leverage for continuing sales and earnings growth. What were the contributing factors? First, Baxter took a long-term view of international opportunities just as it had of technological and product innovation. The company adopted a pioneering strategy, which was to build integrated country operations including manufacturing. It was the first within its industry group to do so. No matter that this probably wasn't an appropriate international strategy for pharmaceutical companies then. The fact is, Baxter chose a strategy that worked well for its specific goals and competitive position, stuck with it, and executed it extremely well. In particular countries, Baxter's first-in approach blocked direct competitors from making a later market entry.

Then too, the company effectively adapted its domestic market niche approach to the international arena. Thus, solutions and administration sets became the lead element in the United Kingdom; Blood-Pack systems in Ireland; dialysis in France; solutions in Belgium; and diagnostic products in Germany. Whatever the lead product in each country market, the company skillfully used global interest in its high-tech products—principally dialysis, but also blood separation and processing systems—to build recognition and prestige.

Interconnections and close control of manufacturing systems across national boundaries made it possible to move new products and technological innovations quickly throughout the company's world markets. Thus, Viaflex containers—the most recent and most significant Baxter innovation at the time when international growth began to take off—rapidly achieved market leadership in many countries around the world. Manufacturing and manufacturing equipment advances in other countries—most notably in Germany, with Kieffel-Korting forming and sealing lines perhaps the most significant example—were incorporated in Baxter's processes. And very early, dating from establishment of the first off-shore R&D Laboratory in Nivelles, Baxter began to scan and apply product advances from other countries.

Most importantly—on a par in importance with the effects of a consistent, long-term strategy—the company poured in the management talent. That paid a double dividend. Not only did it produce superior business results, the international businesses also became a major breeding ground for the company's next generation of executives.

BAXTER'S INTERNATIONAL ENTREPRENEURIALISM CREATES ITS OWN MANAGEMENT LORE

Senior Baxter executives and international alumni still recount stories from the period of rapid international growth to make a point or to illustrate their own management philosophy.

Early on the company attracted more than its share of management characters. One of those characters was Nick Castlejohn, an "internationalist" who had a source somewhere in the world for the best of everything: "bespoke" suits, handmade shoes, Havana cigars, and performance automobiles.

When telephone squawk boxes made their appearance on the executive scene, the only one in Baxter's Morton Grove headquarters was Graham's. As usual, despite its growing success and profitability, Baxter was controlling every dollar of expenditures. Castlejohn told Ken Furlong, the headquarters office manager since the 1940s, that he had to have a squawk box. Furlong turned him down, then consulted with Link Dowell. "I don't think he's going to take no for an answer," Furlong said. "What do I do next?" Together Dowell and Furlong cooked up a strategy.

Furlong was to go back to Castlejohn and tell him that Graham had decided there was to be only one squawk box in Baxter headquarters, but if anyone really needed the squawk box more than Graham, he could have Graham's. Furlong smiled broadly as he thought about this airtight strategy. When he told Castlejohn of the management decision, Castlejohn replied, "Fine, send it over." So, for a time, Castlejohn had the only telephone speaker in Morton Grove.

Later when Lawrence Kinet was in a staff position in Deerfield during 1973-74, Steve Lazarus asked if Kinet would go to Israel for two months to help improve the Ashdod plant's warehouse system. He quickly agreed. The two months turned into four years.

Kinet recalled, "The plant was run by a distinguished Israeli soldier, Uriel Eylatt, who after the 1967 war became general secretary of the Ashdod Development Corporation. After the Baxter plant started up, he brought in an old army crony, Moshe Goldwasser, to help run the operation. By early 1975, they had become bitter adversaries. I reported to Eylatt and was in between the two, a very uncomfortable position. Inflation had roared out of control and our prices didn't budge an inch. Eylatt kept product costs locked in his own desk and wasn't motivated to make us profitable.

"Victor Chaltiel was then area vice president with responsibility for Israel. He would call me and in his Gallic accent say, 'How are things going? I don't have time to come to these small countries.'

"Goldwasser was moved to a staff job as director of technical operations, in an attempt to solve the Ashdod problems. Then Chaltiel did fly in. 'Well,' he said to Goldwasser, 'how is life?' 'Thanks for asking,' Goldwasser replied.

"Victor went on, 'And how is the new job?' 'It's a little early to answer that question,' Goldwasser answered.

"'I think you ought to resign right away,' Chaltiel said. And Goldwasser replied, 'I believe this changes my plans.'

"Two months later, just before Chaltiel's plane was to touch down in Israel again, Eylatt resigned anticipating a similar conversation was about to occur with him. After that the Ashdod business grew from $6 million with 300 people to $9 million with 225 people. We were able to get 45 percent price relief from the government."

END NOTES

CHAPTER XIV

1. In addition to company records, interviews, and the personal recollections of Senior Chairman Graham, this chapter draws particularly on two other sources. One is a memorandum prepared by Charlie Schwartz on the formative years of Baxter's International Division. The other is an unpublished five-part case prepared for the University of Chicago Graduate School of Business by Lawrence H. N. Kinet. The latter is a remarkable and insightful piece of work, and we want to fully credit and gratefully acknowledge its contribution to this chapter.

2. Collupulin was an enzyme used in the brewing industry.

3. Mr. Komatsu, now chairman of Baxter in Japan (with Bob Hurley as president), provided written records and other materials regarding this period.

CHAPTER

XV

THE SEVENTIES: BAXTER'S MOMENTUM CONTINUES, WHILE MAJOR DOMESTIC HEALTH CARE MARKETS BEGIN CHANGING

The decade of the seventies ushered in a very different kind of business era for most American corporations, including Baxter. The first of the oil shocks hit early in the decade (1973). Ray Oddi and other executives scrambled to develop programs to keep domestic plants ahead of energy problems and risks. Inflation began its long, dizzying, upward climb early in the decade. It was to continue unchecked throughout the seventies.

The investment climate also changed drastically. Because of high interest rates, price earnings ratios (PEs) for the most attractive stocks fell from the fifties into the twenties. Late in the decade, currency fluctuations became more extreme. Then, exchange rates turned against Baxter, which had been bringing back cash from Germany, Ireland, and the United Kingdom, where taxes were high. Some of the European subsidiaries had been incorporated as subdivisions of Baxter Ireland in order to facilitate international cash management.

In the United States, Medicare and Medicaid were continuing to outstrip government budget estimates. Early federal attempts to control those costs began in the Nixon administration, and continued throughout the decade. The trend away from professional, scientific purchasing in hospitals, which favored Baxter's niche approach, toward a more corporate form of purchasing was accelerating. Supply contracts with hospitals were lengthening from one to two or three years, making it more difficult to pass along inflation-fueled cost increases. One observer recalled that Abbott's bid during this time on solutions to the Veterans Administration Hospitals (which were, in effect, an open-ended purchasing group) was a "memorable disaster" because of low pricing levels. Of course, it has to be remembered that Abbott's displacement by Baxter after the Abbott recall still rankled, making for a bare knuckles competitive situation.

Despite these issues, the seventies were another decade of outstanding performance for Baxter in both sales and earnings growth. And the sparkling performance wasn't due just to the success of Viaflex containers and international growth. The company was "hitting on all eight cylinders." In 1975 sales exceeded $ .5 billion. Then in 1978 they passed $1 billion. Net earnings more than kept pace. This was the first decade free of all the constraints Baxter had had to overcome since the company's founding in 1931. Those constraints had been: the burden of paying royalties to Don Baxter, Inc. on an unpatented product; restriction of its United States territory to the eastern states; Harry Falk's exclusive distribution contracts in the United States, Canada, and other countries; the initial high cost manufacturing location in northern Illinois; and some confusion about the Baxter name because of its multiple use. In fact, looking back, Bill Graham said, "The strategic work during earlier years seemed to be as much clearing away obstacles as it was creating opportunities."

Although all the shackles had come off Baxter's strategy as the seventies began, at the same time the company—growing during the first part of the decade at annual rates of almost 30 percent—was becoming larger and more complex. So transitions in management style and management responsibilities were taking place. Oddi remembers Graham talking with him on a number of occasions during this time about the inescapable conclusion that they weren't much longer going to be able to run the company the way they had—in the face of all the many and growing signs of company success. By mid-decade, Graham had been president for more than 20 years and CEO for 15.

A 1974 investment analyst's report nettled Graham when it suggested that Baxter needed to improve its asset management. He had Oddi plunge into that challenge personally. Oddi was assisted in looking at every aspect of Baxter asset management around the world by a new company addition, Dave Castaldi, who later went on to become president of Hyland Laboratories. The asset management ratios improved quickly and dramatically. And this crash program paved the way for later, successful value improvement programs.

With growth in size, of course, came more interaction with the health care and hospital environment. The most profound and far-reaching shifts were occurring in that environment since the dawn of modern health care in the United States. Baxter's own long-term

RISING HOSPITAL USE
1960-87

	No. of Admissions	Average Length of Stay	No. of Outpatient Visits (Millions)	Total Expenses ($ Millions)
1960	22,970	7.6	N/A	5,617
1970	29,252	8.2	134	19,560
1980	36,198	7.6	207	76,970
1981	36,494	7.6	207	90,739
1982	36,429	7.6	251	105,094
1983	36,201	7.6	214	116,632
1984	35,202	7.3	216	123,550
1985	33,501	7.1	223	130,700
1986	32,410	7.1	234	140,907
1987	31,633	7.2	248	152,909

SOURCE: American Hospital Association, *Hospital Statistics*, 1988 ed., table 1.

Figure 11: *Average length of stay is indicated in days; other numbers are year totals.*

strategy had taken shape in the early 1950s concurrently with the emergence of modern health care and hospitals. There was a question how these landscape transformations would affect Baxter's strategy. On the surface, the trends seemed favorable. Health care expenditures in the United States were growing rapidly. At a deeper level though, changes were contradictory and somewhat ominous. Later, some would question whether the foundations of the U.S. health care system would survive the rush of change in their present form. It consisted then of one billion physician visits and thirty-four million hospital admissions per year. Physician visits rose on a tide of medical specialization as shown in figure 12, causing some to raise the question of whether the general practitioner's traditional role of gatekeeper for the health care system was going by the boards.

Would the system destabilize,[1] transforming U.S. health care supply markets? Baxter senior management had to ponder these broad questions, which were (and in most respects still are) puzzling the health care pundits, while managing its exploding growth at home and internationally.

Those are the twin themes of the Baxter story in the seventies, cross-currents in the domestic health care environment and internal management growth and adaptation.

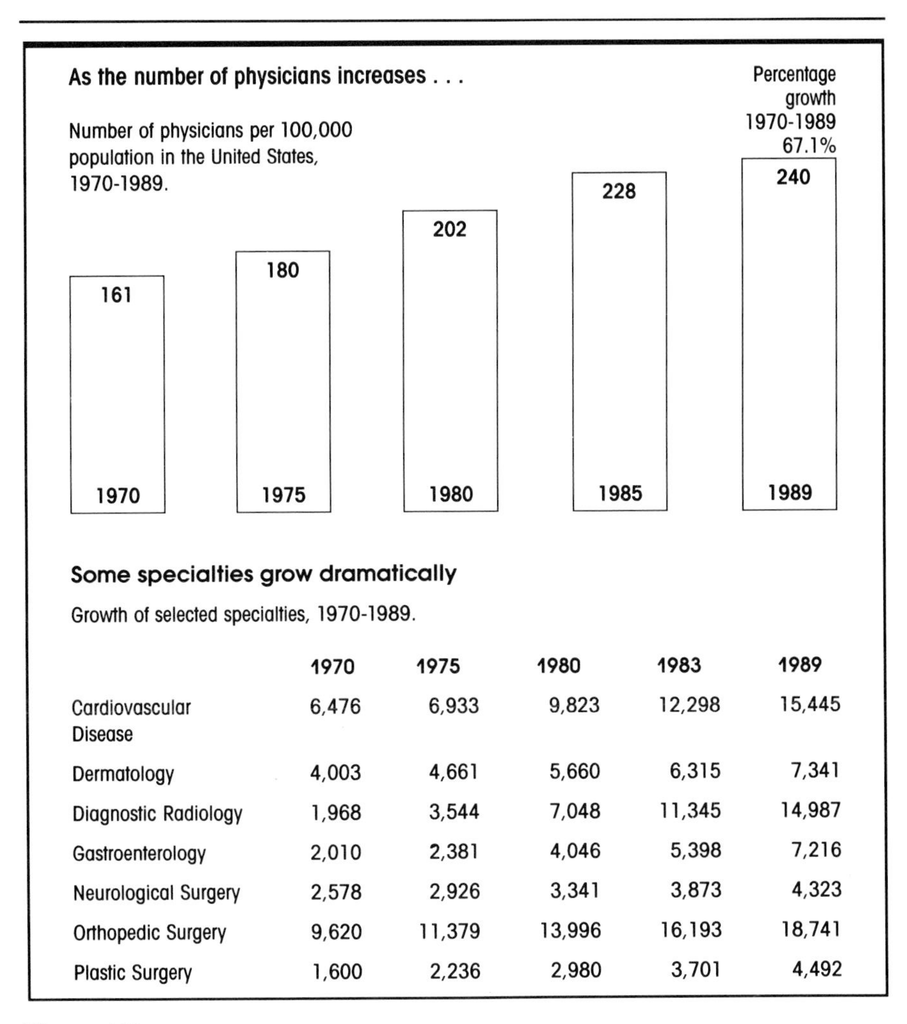

Some specialties grow dramatically

Growth of selected specialties, 1970-1989.

	1970	1975	1980	1983	1989
Cardiovascular Disease	6,476	6,933	9,823	12,298	15,445
Dermatology	4,003	4,661	5,660	6,315	7,341
Diagnostic Radiology	1,968	3,544	7,048	11,345	14,987
Gastroenterology	2,010	2,381	4,046	5,398	7,216
Neurological Surgery	2,578	2,926	3,341	3,873	4,323
Orthopedic Surgery	9,620	11,379	13,996	16,193	18,741
Plastic Surgery	1,600	2,236	2,980	3,701	4,492

Figure 12[2]

THE SEVENTIES HEALTH CARE ENVIRONMENT

Changes in Baxter's operating environment weren't limited to health care developments alone. As noted, by 1973-74 the stage was set for a long, steady rise into double digit inflation in the U.S., and the economy experienced its first energy shock.

More specifically within the U.S. health care system, roles of various players in the system shifted perceptibly. In 1965, of health care expenditures (HCE) totaling $41.9 billion, 26 percent were represented by government, another 22 percent by for-profit organizations, and the remaining 52 percent by non-profits or community-based organizations. Then, starting from a base of about $5 billion in federal government expenditures (1.8 percent of the total federal budget), federal spending ballooned to $100 billion (11.5 percent of the budget) by 1984. During approximately the same period the states' share of cost for 22 million Medicaid recipients swelled to $15 billion.[3] Summarizing these trends most graphically, Medicare spending doubled from 1970 to 1975, and then doubled again from 1975 to 1980.[4]

The government was now in the medical marketplace with both feet. What had been a finely-balanced system was now skewed heavily to government. Not-for-profit and for-profit hospitals, insurers, employers, health care suppliers, the legal community, and consumers were affected by this shift. Revenues of U.S. medical schools rose from $2.2 billion in 1972-73 to $8.2 billion in 1983.[5] "First-dollar" health insurance coverage became more prevalent. The total assets of short-term hospitals grew from $16.4 billion (1965) to $47.3 billion (1975).[6] As hospitals tapped the capital and debt markets, the influence of hospital trustees waned.[7] For-profit hospital chains grew and their common stock attracted investment attention.

The inflationary impact of the federal government's looming health care presence was quickly apparent.[8] While length of patient stay was already declining in the seventies (for myocardial infarction from 19.7 days to 10.6 days and for breast cancer from 10.5 to 3.3 days during the period of 1964 to 1981), the average cost per patient day rose sharply, even after adjusting for base inflation.[9]

The rhetoric of the time was about "market-based" and "competition-based" health care models. But how could there be effective markets and real competition when the consumer wasn't really "in the system"? By 1980, 92 percent of health care payments were being made by third parties.[10] The reality of competition was redundancy and overlap among different players in the system.[11]

ENVIRONMENTAL EFFECTS ON BAXTER

Short-term, the effects of these developments on Baxter's domestic business were positive. Certainly growth in U.S. government health care spending contributed to some extent to the company's continued volume growth (although statistically the effects were not as great as those resulting from market success around the world of the company's Viaflex container innovation).

Long-term, however, market issues for Baxter were clearly being created. For example, these same trends led to changes in hospital

SHORT-STAY HOSPITAL PATIENTS
1965, 1985, and 1987

	1965	1985	1987
Total number of patients discharged	28.8 million	35.1 million	33.4 million
Male	38.8%	40.4%	40.6%
Female	61.1%	59.6%	59.4%
Under 15 years of age	14.8%	8.5%	8.1%
65 years and older	16.0%	30.0%	31.3%
Average length of stay (all patients)	7.8 days	6.5 days	6.4 days
65 years and older	13.1 days	8.7 days	8.6 days

SOURCE: National Center for Health Statistics. "Inpatient Utilization of Short-stay Hospitals by Diagnosis—U.S. 1965," series 13, no. 6, 1970, selected tables; *Advancedata,* no. 127 (September 25, 1986) and no. 159 (rev.) (September 28, 1988).

Figure 13

purchasing behavior, as described. Emergence of hospital buying groups began in the late seventies to exert downward pressure on prices of critical hospital supplies like IV solutions. Health care manufacturers, in general, were still concentrating on technology and innovation to a greater extent than on costs.

More importantly, government spending, together with the wider availability of debt capital to hospitals and changing hospital depreciation policies, put emphasis on "big technology" requiring large capital investments. Baxter's long-running success in medical innovation had, on the other hand, been in "small technologies" centered on supplies and disposables. The big versus small distinction is not necessarily a measure of relative effect on patient care. It reflects an attitude among some hospitals and other health care decision-makers that emphasis on major capital investment may be the best way to provide improvement in the quality and accessibility of patient care.

There can be little question that long-term kidney dialysis has been one of the most significant therapy developments of the twentieth century in its impact on quality of life and life expectancy for patients with end stage renal disease. If this development had occurred not in the fifties, but in the seventies, with increasing institutional emphasis on investment and profit considerations, gaining clinical acceptance for long-term dialysis probably would have been even more difficult than it was. And it was tough enough beginning in the fifties; it took more than five years from start-up to introduce the commercial dialyzer, and then more than another ten years until 1973 for broad reimbursement for treatment to be approved through amendment to the 1965 Act.

CULMINATION OF STRATEGIC INITIATIVES IN THE SEVENTIES AND SIGNALS OF CHANGE TO COME

The seventies were proving to be the best decade yet for Baxter, but it was concurrently a time of transition. Some questions about transition remained in the air until 1983.

Besides the worldwide success of Viaflex containers and later the resounding success of CAPD, there were two other defining events in this decade. They were: opening up the other half of the solutions market, which illustrates how to keep moving ahead from one strategic market opportunity (traditional solutions market) to the next (administration of drugs); and the company's reaction to the F.D.A.'s tighter and tighter regulations, which illustrates an appropriately proactive response to government requirements.

NEW MARKET FOR VIAFLEX

"What would you think about an $8 IV?" Vern Loucks asked as he walked into Graham's office one day in 1972 while Viaflex was still taking over the surgical solutions business in the U.S. and other countries.

Graham looked up from his desk and laughed, "You were the guy who was arguing against Kimbell not long ago for a plastics price as low as glass." Then he looked at the product Loucks was proposing. The idea was simple, and became the Continu-Flo and Add-a-Line sets and then the piggyback Mini-Bag. Bill Sahlin, Cliff Latiolet of Ohio State, and Harold Godwin at the University of Kansas worked to develop and perfect these ideas from 1972 through 1974. The device allowed medication to be premixed in the Mini-Bag and then added safely, effectively, and efficiently via the IV administration line. The required preferential flow couldn't be accomplished with glass bottles. The Viaflex container made it possible.

The market was receptive. Baxter held seminars all over the country showing hospital pharmacists how to be "heroes" using these sterile fills. "I was only the advocate," Loucks said, "but it was very satisfying. We were helping hospitals to set up and run central IV admixture factories on the night shift. Interest was spreading everywhere. That led to our own admixtures as Dave Bellamy directed necessary stability studies, then to frozen drugs. Jim Tobin got the idea of setting a target of covering 70 percent of appropriate drugs within three years through our admixture program. We almost made it too. We had the market pretty much to ourselves. And then later Abbott introduced their own version, Advantage, and our folks proved perhaps to be too locked in to the original design ideas."

Though this particular new market has become more competitive, it was at that time a dramatic example of redefining a market and application to obtain significant competitive advantage. The drug admixture business provided a significant "kicker" for Baxter's growth during the seventies and into the early eighties. It also led to further innovation in patient drug delivery systems.

THE F.D.A. GETS TOUGHER

The F.D.A. was, through the early seventies, tightening regulation through Good Manufacturing Practices (GMP) and Good Laboratory Practices (GLP). Actions taken included the Abbott recall in 1971, the recall of Cutter in 1973, and the McGaw recall in 1975. During this entire period, Baxter was not shut down. But the F.D.A. did pose a challenge for Baxter.

An inspection by Dick Shepherd of the F.D.A. at the Baxter small volume parenterals (vial) line in Hays, Kansas, led to a notice of violations (a "483"). Some recall that Kimbell wanted to play hardball with the F.D.A., and that this disturbed Graham. It was the critical factor in the later decision to move Kimbell out of the president's job.

Graham said he wanted a positive and energetic reaction to the situation. He, Marsh Abbey, Kimbell, Ed Nawoj, and Dr. Leonard Ginger flew to Washington, D.C. and drove to Rockville, Maryland, to negotiate with the F.D.A. The Baxter contingent floated some trial balloons. F.D.A. officials didn't react. Discussions went nowhere. The Baxter team returned to National Airport. As they headed up the ramp to board their plane, Graham was paged. It was the F.D.A. general counsel. Back again went Graham and Abbey to the F.D.A., where the general counsel handed them a proposed document which Abbey described as "onerous in language and onerous in effect." The Baxter executives checked into the Madison Hotel and called Lloyd Cutler to seek his legal advice. Cutler was at dinner so Abbey went to the restaurant and left the F.D.A. document with the maître d'.

"The next morning discussions finally reached the point of an F.D.A.-Baxter agreement in principle," Abbey said. "I was working on the substantive details of the agreement when I looked up and saw Graham wasn't there. I asked and was told he had taken a limo to the airport to catch a flight to Chicago. He'd concluded, after talking to Cutler, that that was the best deal we were going to get."

What Graham decided to do next was brilliant and "gutsy" according to Loucks. He built up inventory and ordered raw material stocks until the normal summer vacation closing. Then he shut down not just Hays, but Cleveland, North Cove, North Carolina, and Puerto Rico. He shut down the entire solutions manufacturing system so that full compliance could be examined and assured. This gave Baxter the initiative and, since the company had decided to close down voluntarily, flexibility to decide when to bring parts of the system back up.

"We knew what we had to do and how fast we had to do it," said Loucks, "but we didn't have the people to get it done." Loucks went to NASA and talked to experts in program management and statistical control. Then an Emerson Electric Company director, General Bernie Shriever, suggested he get acquainted with a retiring Air Force Surgeon General, Dr. Robert H. "Patt" Patterson. Shortly thereafter, Patterson was with Baxter, first as a consultant, then as a full-time employee. Patterson in turn recruited other U.S. Air Force officers, such as Bob Gallivan. These additions helped avert what might have been a crisis, but was never allowed to develop into one.

However, that was only part of the answer. The important actions had to occur at the individual plant level within the corporate systems. Loucks assembled a team of three young managers: Dekle Rountree, Steve Shaubert, and Bob Carpenter. He made assignments and said to them, "You're the process managers. Each of you will buy a block of airline tickets and get out in the plants. We'll meet here every Saturday morning to review results." Loucks' response built Graham's confidence in him further. The program affected and shaped Baxter manufacturing for years.

BAXTER OPERATING TRENDS CONTINUE STRONGLY UPWARD

The effects of basic shifts in health care institutional roles described earlier were not immediate. Baxter's sales increased 29 percent in 1971 over the prior year; 15.0 percent in 1972; then 27.7 percent and 31 percent respectively in 1973 and 1974. Indicating resounding success in Viaflex containers and pioneering in the drug admixture or drug delivery business, production of solutions products doubled in 1971, and production of administration sets tripled. The proportion of total corporate sales represented by solutions and blood containers rose from 31 percent in 1969 to 38 percent in

1971. In 1972, Baxter introduced Viaflex plastic-container-packaged solutions in Puerto Rico, Costa Rica, the United Kingdom, Norway, and South Africa—having already, before that time, opened Viaflex container markets outside the mainland United States and Canada in Australia, Israel, and Colombia. The company's record-setting earnings growth, which began in 1954-55, continued throughout the seventies.

In summarizing Baxter's actions and accomplishments during the seventies, several themes predominate. They are:

- Management growth and transition;
- Growth and reinvestment choices;
- More innovation . . . including CAPD (continuous ambulatory peritoneal dialysis);
- Corporate acquisitions playing a lesser role than in the fifties and sixties;
- Competitive attempts to contest Baxter's lead in kidney dialysis;
- Foundations laid for patient Alternate Site care (non-hospital sites) and home care;
- Financial results continued glittering . . . but the investment climate changes and PE multiples of the "nifty fifty" companies tumble.

MANAGEMENT GROWTH AND TRANSITION

Following a dominant leader is a challenge for most corporations, and Graham had dominated Baxter since 1945, particularly since 1953 when he was elected president.

Oddi said that Graham became even tougher and more demanding as he began to work through the transition and succession issues. When Graham became chairman in March 1971, replacing Ralph Falk II, Kimbell became president and chief operating officer. Bill Jennett was senior vice president for finance and Loucks was vice president for marketing. By 1973, Kimbell had become vice chairman. Jennett was president, and Loucks executive vice president.

On February 2, 1976, Loucks was elected president and Jennett became vice chairman. As described, Loucks had swiftly and effectively cleared up a potentially serious problem with the F.D.A. in the Hays, Kansas plant—a problem Kimbell had said would take care of itself. Some believe that coming on top of Loucks' many earlier accomplishments, his Hays success accelerated the decision to name him president. Kimbell had by this time left the company. The same annual report that announced Loucks' election as president (the 1975 report) also noted two executive additions from outside the company: Dolph Bridgewater of McKinsey as executive vice president; and Dr. Patterson as senior vice president for scientific affairs. Bridgewater resigned from the company in 1979 and became CEO of the Brown Group. However, he remained on the Baxter board until 1986. Patterson retired from the company in 1986, having led successful efforts in the seventies and early eighties to further improve the company's compliance with F.D.A. Good Manufacturing Practices (GMP) and Good Laboratory Practices (GLP); assure compliance with the Medical Device Amendments of 1975; and initiate a pervasive quality leadership program throughout every company business unit and staff function.

Other people, some of them mentioned earlier, began to take on greater responsibility. Oddi was elected vice president for administration in 1977 and senior vice president in 1978. Wilbur Gantz was also elected a corporate officer in 1977 and became executive vice president in 1979.

Don Johnson, a three-star U. S. Air Force general who had among his other responsibilities commanded the Defense Nuclear Agency, joined Baxter in 1977 as vice president for personnel. In 1978 two other corporate officers were elected: Dale Smith and Steve Lazarus, who joined the company in 1974 after successful careers in the Navy and then in civilian federal government. Don Madsen, a veteran of the company's manufacturing expansion since the forties, and Victor Chaltiel were elected officers in 1979.

There were several notable patterns and trends during this era of broadening the management team. The "old guard-new guard" relationships and attitudes had to be managed with skill, and they were. Serving the company well during the beginning of transition were its informal and flexible organization and even more particularly its emphasis on strong, self-reliant individuals. Some, including Jim Tobin, recall the late seventies as a time when there was a certain amount of overlap between Loucks' and Bridgewater's responsibilities. When Loucks became CEO in 1980, according to Tobin, management teamwork became a higher priority. That increased emphasis combined with earlier elements of Baxter's management approach to form a distinctive culture. That period of the very early eighties, despite its market challenges, is still remembered by members of the team as a kind of "Camelot."

The move into the Deerfield headquarters in 1975, after the protracted zoning dispute, was a milestone of sorts because it reminded

Vern Loucks at an annual stockholders' meeting.

employees of how far they'd come from Morton Grove, and from Glenview. The initial impressions people most often recall, however, are of Graham attending meetings in sunglasses because window blinds had not been installed, and of seeing cowboys (yes, cowboys) riding over the bridge by the Baxter pond one day trying to round up some horses that had strayed.

Later in the seventies, Graham's wife of many years, Edna Kanaley Graham, became seriously ill with cancer. She died in 1981. Those closest to Graham felt that her illness and care had an understandably strong influence on the direction and increased speed of the management transition from that point forward.

REINVESTMENT CHOICES

While Baxter's sales, net profits, and cash flow flourished through the seventies, it remained very much a niche company in both market and technology leadership.

Accordingly, the company's reinvestment choices, with growth, became strategically more complex. What was the long-term future in the fast-changing U.S. health care market for the largest niche producer? What would be the continuing opportunities for technological innovation of the kind at which Baxter excelled? The company could continue to explore and occupy new niches through internal efforts and judicious acquisition; concentrate on defending existing leadership positions, such as in dialysis, against new competition and new technology; seek to broaden certain niches into wider markets with different characteristics; or build organization and manufacturing capacity around the world to keep pace with major demand growth for Viaflex container products. What was the right combination of priorities?

By 1979 the number of solutions products had been doubled from 50 to 98. Manufacturing facilities continued to expand. In 1973 Baxter entered the solutions business in Spain through acquisition of part ownership of Laboratorios Hesperia S.A. Other expansions were new facilities in 1974 at Round Lake to produce 400 reagent products because of changes in Hyland Diagnostics strategy; construction of the Mountain Home, Arkansas, plant in 1975; and breaking ground for the plant in Gifu, Japan, in 1978. Corporate employment swelled from 13,600 in 1972 to 33,100 in 1979, before tailing off slightly to 32,200 in 1980. 1979 proved to be the high water mark for Baxter employment until 1985, when events changed the scale of the company.

Actually, company management elected to pursue *all* of these options or priorities during the 1970s. While perhaps not explicitly recognized at the time, the fact was that double-digit inflation was siphoning off a large part of the 20 percent annual net earnings growth to which Baxter and its shareholders had grown accustomed. Graham said of the latter part of the decade, "We had to run harder just to stay ahead. As the market leader in a number of different therapies by then, I felt we had to be charging ahead on all fronts."

Principal emphasis was on reinvestment in existing market leadership positions, particularly Viaflex containers and kidney dialysis products. While pervasive in their effects on patient therapy, Baxter's innovations had not been of the blockbuster variety—like a Xerox machine, where a single concept yields a product with a long and definable life cycle. Baxter's contributions tended to combine product, service, and application elements in a manner that required more than the typical amount of continuing investment as clinical practice and knowledge continued to advance rapidly.

MORE INNOVATION

Baxter's strong commitment to health care innovation continued, but it was becoming more focused. The decade's major breakthroughs in technology were Viaflex containers, the Mini-Bag and drug admixtures, and a major new advance in kidney dialysis, described in the next chapter. These undertakings alone would have been enough of a stretch for many innovation-minded companies. Work continued on Viaflex container products throughout the decade.

The new Mini-Bag container system was introduced in 1974. Drug admixtures in Mini-Bag containers followed, for improved and more labor-efficient administration of drugs through the basic IV system. Frozen drugs in Mini-Bag containers came later (1981-1983). By 1979 work had begun on a new generation of thermoplastic materials (polyolefins) for solutions and blood products.

The 1973 law providing reimbursement for long-term dialysis and the growing number of patients on dialysis attracted competitors into the market Baxter had created. So for much of the seventies Baxter's Artificial Organ management and technical team were anticipating and reacting to new materials and new technology in that therapy area. As the leader in hemodialysis[12] Baxter was strongly committed to pushing ahead on all the technological and material fronts that were emerging: hollow fibers, flat plate dialysis, and other techniques for negative pressure (versus positive pressure) dialysis.

In spite of that necessary emphasis, there were innovations on several other fronts. A new heart-lung oxygenator, the Modulung, was introduced in 1971. The 1974 annual report described progress with chymopapain (an enzymatic material trade-named Discase), which dissolved certain spinal disc materials usually removed through surgery. The initial new drug application (NDA) for Discase lyophilized solution was withdrawn by Baxter in 1975, but research and testing continued. Ultimately, while continuing to show promise and producing successful results for a number of individuals, Discase solution failed to achieve wide acceptance because of the risk of potentially serious side effects and the need for extreme skill in administration.[13]

The company did extensive work during this time on a specially-designed "transporter" for live human organs for transplantation. It was abandoned because of technical difficulties. By 1978 the early foundation for a home care (or Alternate Site) business had been established with the introduction of the Travacare Division to provide total parenteral nutrition (TPN program). Kent Kirkhoff and then John Arlotta were early champions in getting initial Alternate Site services launched. By 1980 less than 30 patients were being served. Respiratory therapy programs were also growing at this time, that area having been researched by Teri Louden for Dick Egen, then heading the medical products business.[14] Louden, who has now run her own company for 10 years, says she was put to work on the respiratory therapy project because Egen was asked about that market by Graham in a management review meeting. "Dick didn't know anything about the market," she recalls. "He told me to start a market analysis immediately. My undergraduate degree is in industrial engineering so I went out and spent six months following respiratory therapists around to observe what they do. That's what an IE does, right? Among other things, I found out that the greatest product use in RT was water for infection control. We quickly launched two closed respiratory fluid delivery products—one sterile water, the other saline solution; both were great successes."

The 1975 annual report cited the company's research work in human heart valves and Foley catheters.[15] In 1979 Baxter introduced the CS-3000 blood cell separator, another in a long line of blood processing advances.

RELATIVE QUIET ON THE ACQUISITION FRONT

Acquisitions played a relatively minor role in 1970s growth and innovation. In 1973 Baxter acquired Vicra, a small manufacturer of catheters, for 67,369 shares of common stock. Clinical Assays, a producer of radioactive immunoassays, with sales of $5.8 million, was acquired in 1976. That form of clinical testing was later overtaken by other technologies, and the acquisition, therefore, had relatively little long-term impact on Baxter's market position.

COMPETITORS BEGIN TO CHALLENGE BAXTER'S DIALYSIS LEAD

Medical advances in dialyzing techniques continued in the United States as well as Europe. There were strong proponents among nephrologists for all the various approaches. In the 1970s the Holtzenbein single-pass batch dialysis system was introduced and, at about the same time, the Kiil parallel plate device. The latter didn't require a blood pump and presented fewer blood leakage problems. Then came the Steward hollow fiber design, very similar to the Abel-Rowntree-Turner device of many years before.[16] Competitors began to pursue these alternatives to the Kolff-type kidney coil as a way to attack Baxter's market.

When Cordis-Dow in the United States and Gambro in Europe introduced attractively-priced products based on new technology, Baxter was in a defensive position because of its commanding market position and existing patient base.

The market signals were different from country to country depending on practices and preferences of nephrologists. Because of their substantial experience there, both Loucks and Gantz initially gave substantial weight to the signals from Europe, which tended to favor the flat-plate dialyzer. Howard Janneck, an architect along with Graham of early artificial organs market successes, was replaced by Pete Phildius, indicating top management's dissatisfaction with dialysis strategic direction.

The new dialysis products introduced in nearly every year covered all the technical bases. In 1971 the Ultra-Flo II Kidney Coil was released. The RSP Clear Canister Kidney Dialyzer came out in 1972; then in 1974 the Para-Flo Plate Dialyzer. These were followed in 1975 by the CF 1500 Capillary Flow Dialyzer and in 1976 by the Holtzenbein Capillary Plate Dialyzer.

Holtzenbein technology never became widely accepted in the United States, and by 1979 discussions were underway to license it to a joint venture in Yugoslavia. Baxter's investment in alternative dialysis technologies was also recouped by using some of these designs to good advantage in the Japanese market. Another substantial benefit of this activity was that it provided Baxter management with important experience in managing a complex technology, which was advancing in many developed countries, on an integrated global basis. Baxter would continue to refine its management skills in that process.

Management change in Artificial Organs continued. In 1975, Phildius was succeeded as the head of that business by Lazarus, who was in turn followed by Chaltiel in 1978. From 1975 to 1978, developments in peritoneal dialysis, beginning at first outside Baxter and with early applications in Canada, changed the competitive situation again. These developments bolstered Baxter's market and technical lead, provided a new focus, and made the company the broadest-line supplier in kidney dialysis, which it still is today. This business, like IV solutions earlier in the decade, was expanding its boundaries and becoming somewhat less of a specialty niche. How this affected Baxter's successful long-term strategy would be one of the first issues tackled by Loucks as the new CEO in the early eighties.

STRATEGY OF HOME AND ALTERNATE SITE HEALTH CARE

The company's early entry into Alternate Site health care was, in one sense, a by-product of the technologies in which it had built a leadership position; principally in dialysis, but also, to some extent, parenteral nutrition. After all, dialysis for long-term care had, from its very beginnings, been performed in non-hospital as well as hospital settings. The timing for this new emphasis was consistent with changes in the U.S. hospital scene. And it allowed Baxter to build a commanding lead in the business and then to maintain it against smaller and more specialized competition. There were many strategic issues inherent in this burgeoning new business—for example, pricing and reimbursement for Alternate Site care; economics of scale; appropriate quality control techniques; and managing the effects of Alternate Site ventures on principal hospital customer relationships. Not all these issues could be sorted out as the Alternate Site business began to grow in importance.

Baxter people have different recollections of when Alternate Site first began to be looked at as a major strategic opportunity and a separate business with distinctive success characteristics. Was it originally another of many niches or niche extenders? It also took some time, understandably, for the company to transfer its proven skills in medical product innovation into the newer and even more challenging area of *services* innovation.

BAXTER COMMON STOCK PRICE PAUSES

In the mid-seventies, Baxter's common stock price had already begun to plateau. It was in substantial part a reflection of general stock market conditions. In addition, analysts and investors had perhaps grown too accustomed to the company's superior earnings growth and were now discounting it. There was some developing concern about trends in the U.S. health care marketplace and about the Carter administration's "jawboning" on health care cost escalation. And in the last three years of the decade, the company's annual

BAXTER SALES AND EARNINGS
1970 to 1980

Year	$ Net Sales	% Increase Over Prior Year	$ Net Income	% Increase Over Prior Year
1970	187,606,000	—	14,343,000	—
1971	242,146,000	29.1	19,116,000	33.3
1972	278,841,000	15.0	22,183,000	16.0
1973	355,974,000	27.7	27,889,000	25.7
1974	466,284,000	31.1	36,288,000	30.1
1975	564,085,000	21.0	44,472,000	22.6
1976	681,364,000	20.8	60,395,000	35.8
1977	844,446,000	23.9	75,120,000	24.4
1978	1,004,196,000	18.9	91,683,000	22.0
1979	1,191,200,000	18.6	111,900,000	22.1
1980	1,374,400,000	15.0	128,400,000	15.0

NOTE: Percentage increase of revenues over prior year averages 20.9%. The average increase of net income is 24.7%.

Figure 14

rate of sales increases declined slightly from the low twenties to the high teens. Net income increases, however, continued above 20 percent. The financial data for this period, we remind the reader, represents another third of Baxter's remarkable, record-setting 29 years of superior returns to its shareholders.

A DECADE OF ACHIEVEMENT

The seventies were a decade of remarkable accomplishment for Baxter. Its record-setting financial performance continued. The number of patients served by its many product innovations grew substantially. Baxter's leadership in the markets it had largely created and then built was still strong. Its contributions in parenteral nutrition, dialysis, and blood therapy—among other areas—were widely recognized around the world. It was beginning to explore a major new opportunity in services (as distinguished from products and supplies). And management transition to prepare for a new health care era was well underway.

END NOTES

CHAPTER XV

1. Eli Ginzberg, *The Medical Triangle: Physicians, Politicians, and the Public* (Cambridge: Harvard University Press, 1990).

2. *The New York Times*, 7 July 1991, charts based on data from the American Medical Association.

3. Ginzberg, *The Medical Triangle* p. 13.

4. Rosemary Stevens, *In Sickness and In Wealth: American Hospitals in the Twentieth Century* (New York: Basic Books, 1989), 284.

5. ibid., 318.

6. ibid., 287.

7. Ginzberg, *The Medical Triangle*, p. 5.

8. Stevens, *In Sickness and In Wealth*, 286.

9. ibid., 287-88.

10. ibid., 305.

11. ibid., 333-34.

12. Hemodialysis is the procedure of diverting blood flow outside the body through a filtering device to remove waste products before returning the cleansed blood to the body.

13. Discase lyophilized solution achieved more acceptance in Canada and Europe than in the U.S.

14. Respiratory therapy services for the home were later discontinued because of their low tech nature.

15. The Foley catheter is an indwelling catheter or hollow tube for draining the bladder.

16. For more detail, see Patrick McBride, *The Genesis of the Artificial Kidney* (1987).

CHAPTER

XVI

A LIGHTNING-FAST PRODUCT DEVELOPMENT IN 1977

On January 12, 1977, Dr. Grady Harris telephoned Baxter's Deerfield Headquarters from Bethesda, Maryland. He was a senior Baxter scientist who had joined the company in 1972 and was soon to be promoted to senior vice president for R&D. His first call was to Steve Lazarus, then head of the Artificial Organs business, insisting that Lazarus' meeting be interrupted. "Steve," he began excitedly, "I've broken out of a session I'm attending with Rich Greff here at the National Institutes of Health meeting to talk with you. The reason is I've just seen the future of kidney dialysis. We've got to move on this and fast! The work we've been doing on the Coil CD Dialyzer, Compact Plate Dialyzer, and Hollow Fiber CF Dialyzer is important to protect our base. But I'd assign all of those a lower priority in order to jump into this technology with both feet. We have a real opportunity to help a lot of patients and at the same time leapfrog the market."[1]

"Slow down," Lazarus interrupted. "You haven't told me what the technology is and why you're so excited about it. We've got our hands full now in Artificial Organs with development projects. In fact, that's exactly what we were talking about when you called."

Harris knew Lazarus too well to try to sell him in a few minutes on the telephone. He pressed for a meeting. "I'd like to brief you first thing in the morning. I'll be at your office at 7:00 or 7:30 or whenever you plan to arrive. I think Loucks ought to be at the meeting. It's that important. The technology is the new approach to peritoneal dialysis that's being worked on in Austin. You and I have both seen references to it in the literature. It's got a jaw-breaking name, Continuous Ambulatory Peritoneal Dialysis (CAPD). Jack Moncrief and Bob Popovich, who've done the work, just reported on it. I'm excited about it because while they've only done eight patients, clearly it works. It's elegantly simple. Baxter has the knowledge and experience to commercialize it rapidly and with minimum investment. While we need to know more, it looks like a very cost-effective procedure. It's going to open things up with those nephrologists who never did like hemodialysis. And most important, for patients who fit the procedure criteria, the benefits in independence and lifestyle will be enormous. Not a bad list of benefits, huh?" Lazarus agreed to change his schedule for the early morning meeting the next day and encouraged Harris to touch base by telephone with Vern Loucks and Bill Graham.

Harris reached both before rejoining the NIH sessions. Loucks was immediately intrigued. "Do you think we can reach a reasonable agreement with Dr. Moncrief and Robert Popovich?" Loucks asked. "I like everything I hear about this situation. I'll make it a point to be at your meeting tomorrow."

"I haven't gone beyond the point of expressing the possibility of a strong Baxter interest," Harris said. "If you're going to be at the meeting tomorrow, let's hammer out an approach, and Steve and I and Rich Greff will get on a plane and meet with them in Texas."

With Graham, Harris was somewhat briefer. "I want you to know, Mr. Graham," he began, "that we're looking at a development in peritoneal dialysis that may be as much of a breakthrough in its own way as the original Baxter commercial disposable kidney work of the fifties. If it continues to look good, we'll need top management commitment to move very, very, quickly."

Graham reacted as positively as had Loucks. "Vern's already been in here to tell me about it. I won't join you in your meeting tomorrow, but I do want to be kept informed. This sounds like our kind of product."

By the time Harris headed back to the somewhat slower pace of NIH technical papers, he had done a day's work of selling. Lazarus was already disposed to proceed. And as a sign of Baxter's growing management maturity, CAPD was the first major dialysis development which Graham didn't personally initiate or become deeply involved in.

THE JANUARY 13 MEETING

On the plane back to O'Hare on the night of the 12th, Harris prepared carefully for the morning meeting. He took his morning run in Lake Forest earlier than usual so he could be in Deerfield before 7:00 a.m.

He briefed Lazarus and Loucks in somewhat more detail than he had been able to by telephone, "Here are the papers on the CAPD concept. Jack Moncrief was trained at Georgetown University Hospital and now runs a clinic in Austin. Bob Popovich, the engineer doing the fluid mechanics work, worked with Scribner at the University of Washington, and is with the University of Texas. In their contract with NIH to develop this procedure a third man, Dr. Carl Nolph from the University of Missouri, became involved as NIH's interest grew. They did their early experimental work with an infant patient where blood access was not possible. Then in 1975 a patient named Peter Pilcher was referred to Moncrief and Popovich in Austin. Pilcher was in his mid-forties and couldn't go on hemodialysis because of fistula clotting problems. His situation was dire and he was advised to go to them. Based on the work they'd done, Moncrief and Popovich were able to figure out the kinetics and put him on a program of five peritoneal exchanges a day, every four hours. It has worked marvelously. They've since been able to reduce the number of exchanges to four a day.[2] They've gone on to show good results with six or seven other patients."

"Peritoneal dialysis has been around a long time," Loucks broke in. "We all know its advantages and disadvantages. Are we looking at a development that is going to significantly broaden its use? Are many patients going to be able to administer this treatment themselves safely? How will it compare in cost with hemodialysis in a center or a hospital?"

Harris started to respond and then Lazarus broke in, "Apparently they're using dialysate solution in bottles now. With Fenwal and Viaflex container technology we already have, we can come up with a completely closed system that should significantly reduce the risks of peritoneal infection. We're going to have to look carefully at the issues of long-term access to the peritoneal cavity."

The discussion turned to the kind of agreement to be sought with CAPD's inventors. Loucks said, "The patent they're seeking will have to be enforced on doctors. That's tough. Probably the best we can do is get them tightly and publicly aligned with Baxter through a royalty agreement. Is that workable?"

Lazarus answered, "I understand from Grady that Popovich really believes they should stay actively involved with the company that produces the system."

ACTION RACES AHEAD

Not long after the meeting, Harris visited Austin to begin to explore an agreement. They visited Dr. Moncrief's clinic and had the opportunity to observe CAPD treatment of a Mexican-American woman who spoke little English. The limited amount of patient com-

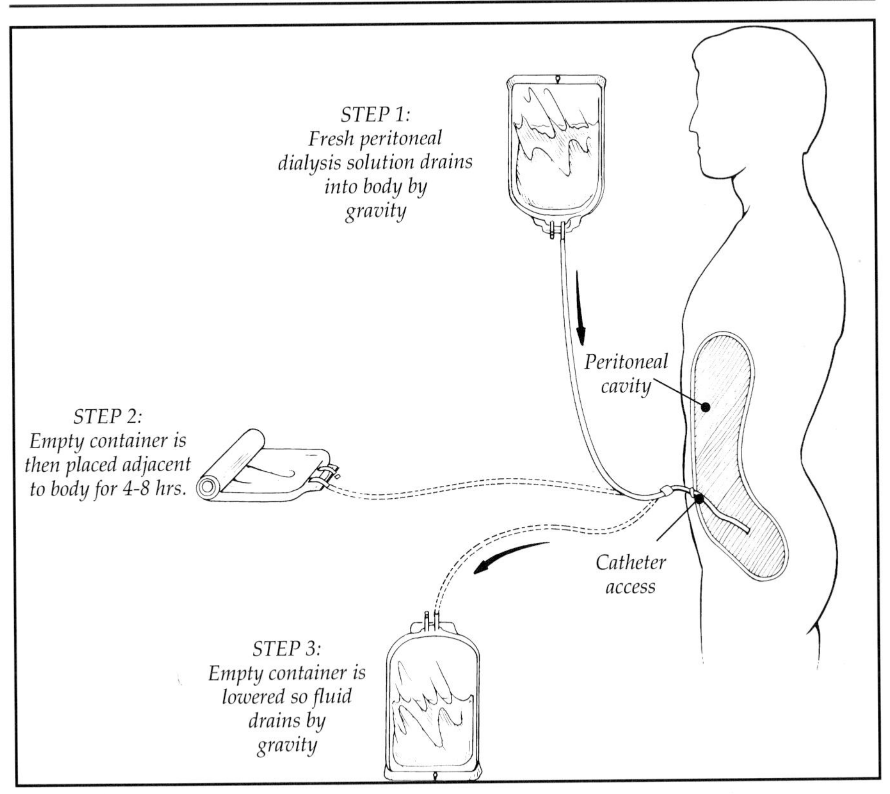

CAPD: *Continuous Ambulatory Peritoneal Dialysis (CAPD) has created a new opportunity for a nearly normal lifestyle for patients with chronic end-stage renal disease. Patients manage the infusion and subsequent recovery of fluid into the peritoneal cavity independent of supervision by medical personnel. The patients are relieved of trips to dialysis centers, do not suffer from chronic blood loss anemia, and have a more even and steady chemical balance than patients who are treated with hemodialysis. The Renal Division of Baxter devised techniques for providing all necessary services and support to patients who adopt this dialysis treatment.*

munication and instruction necessary for successful treatment was another advantage they hadn't thought of. Of course, the Austin Clinic was still using bottles. The first use of flexible containers in a closed system would occur in Canada.

It was the summer of 1977 before an agreement was finalized and signed, giving Baxter worldwide rights, but with royalty payments only in the United States.[3] In the meantime, Rich Greff, who became the project manager for Baxter's development, also began visiting Austin in order to plan and scope out his work.

Greff was a young development engineer. He worked almost alone, sometimes traveling to Puerto Rico to consult with a Baxter engineer colleague there. The project resources and support were modest. In one of the most successful development projects in the company's history, commercialization was complete in months.

The hurdle of F.D.A. approval still lay ahead. Greff tackled that one too with the help of Tom Schmitz. In three months F.D.A. approval was obtained—unheard of response time, even then. The F.D.A. had never approved a two-liter bag (the volume needed for CAPD) in the United States, and had to be regularly reminded that this was for dialysis, not an intravenous solution. Schmitz and Greff managed the process through regular, disciplined contact and follow-up with the F.D.A. Of course, they had lots of interested help from nephrologists, the Kidney Foundation, and others eager for as many patients as possible to benefit from this remarkable new procedure.

The management team obviously functioned effectively because after the opportunity was identified at the beginning of 1977, a preliminary agreement with its developers was quickly reached. The commercial CAPD product was rolled out in 1978, federal reimbursement was approved in 1979, and by 1980 2,500 patients were benefiting from the new treatment. It was a casebook study of successful new product development and launch.

There were only a couple of snags along the development path. First, there were more than a few people in Baxter's organization, even in Artificial Organs itself, who had a ho-hum reaction to the new technology. They said, "What's the big deal? We're already manufacturing Dianeal [peritoneal dialysis solution]." The reaction points out the need to include the medical professional, and in this case the patient, in that systems view, just as the developers of Fenwal blood containers and IV drug infusion as total systems had had to learn earlier.

Later, as CAPD volume began to grow, Loucks had to referee another boundary war between the parenterals sales force and Artificial Organs about who would reap the dividends. The parenterals people argued, "This is just another large volume of sterile solutions in containers with tubing sets. We ought to handle it." They took the traditional product view rather than thinking in systems or process terms. Loucks didn't take much time to make this decision. The CAPD business stayed in Artificial Organs.

A mother administers CAPD to her young son in 1981 after the successful promotion of the new dialysis treatment.

Reimbursement approval came quickly, compared to the long wait from 1956 to 1973 for long-term hemodialysis under Medicare/Medicaid amendments. When a combined end-stage renal disease reimbursement rate was being considered in 1983, to apply to both hemodialysis and peritoneal dialysis, there was another lesser issue. One of the major hemodialysis center operators, who had seized the initial business opportunity Baxter innovation had created and used Baxter equipment, testified against CAPD as "medically dangerous." That proved to be more an annoyance than a problem.

HELP FROM CANADA

Just as it had in the breakthrough with Viaflex containers, Baxter's Canadian operation played a pivotal role in commercialization of CAPD. Years before, Dick Von Drasek had directed development of a two-liter container there. Now that development from the sixties was going to save critical time.

In the summer of 1977, Dr. Dimitrios Oreopoulos of Toronto Western Hospital read an abstract by Moncrief about continuous ambulatory peritoneal dialysis.

He found the abstract unconvincing. Nonetheless one of his patients needed unconventional dialysis treatment due to injuries suffered in a stairway fall. Without an alternative, Dr. Oreopoulos and his nurse, Sharon Izatt, experimented with CAPD. Two-liter bags were in stock at Toronto Western Hospital thanks to Von Drasek and Baxter. The advantages of the flexible closed system in preventing infection became quite apparent. One of the problems Dr. Oreopoulos and Izatt experienced in treating this patient was the tubing hookups. Ron Hamadi, the local Travenol hospital representative, suggested an in-stock Baxter tubing which became (with minor adaptations) the standard peritoneal tubing used in 1979, 1980, and 1981, as CAPD treatment spread. Experience with two liter lavage in Canada was also helpful, if not decisive, in obtaining F.D.A. approval for CAPD in the United States.

There were a number of other remarkable twists and turns in the CAPD story as it continued. First, in addition to its many other advantages and patient benefits (for example, holding BUN [blood urea nitrogen] levels steadier than hemodialysis did) the reduction of peritoneal infection for patients using Baxter's closed container system, instead of the glass bottles used initially, promised to be truly dramatic. Yet in the early days, only Canada and Dr. Oreopoulos had the Baxter containers. They hadn't yet been approved in the United States. There was muttered talk by one of the originators in Texas of "driving a truck to Canada and smuggling in containers."

Minimizing patient infection (peritonitis) was an overriding objective from the start of Baxter's work on CAPD. Average frequency of patient infection with the new dialysis method started out at a little more than three months and has now been stretched to more than two-and-a-half years due to continued work by Baxter.

Much later, as the dialysis containers became the object of wider interest, all kinds of stories circulated about the marvelous convenience of the system. There was a Texas sales representative who warmed his dialysis containers on the car engine headliner, then hung the container on the car coat hook. In response to a question from an interested health care worker about whether CAPD patients suffered "discomfort," another story had the reply being given, "A pilot who flew upside down while dialysate was being drained did have some discomfort."

Another interesting aspect of successful CAPD introduction was the almost unprecedented surge of doctor and patient interest and demand. Don Joseph said, "Home dialysis didn't work real well until then. If you did something wrong, somebody died. So you had people out there talking about this development. The medical community was beating on the F.D.A.'s door to press for approval . . . there were telephone calls from both physicians and patients. The product was in *Time* magazine and on the Merv Griffin Show. . . . Once approval came, we did an impeccable job of delivery. We retained 40 major medical consultants around the world, including Oreopoulos (who incidentally assigned all his income from this work to Toronto Western Hospital). This was insurance against patent infringement, which we thought might come . . . and also allowed us to do a truly outstanding job of education. . . . While all this was going on, I had one physician say to me 'Will you guys please turn all this publicity off'."

Baxter's agreement with the developers and their patent application are significant parts of the CAPD story. Tom Schuman, a patent attorney who joined Baxter in 1972, tells that part of the story. "I was involved in the first negotiating meeting when the inventors came in, together with David Bellamy and Rich Greff. . . . At first, I said to myself, this is not a big deal. Then after that first meeting, I talked to Bellamy. He said to me, we absolutely have to get the rights to this. . . . He saw the solutions business—two liters five times a day for every patient.

"I didn't think their patent application would be granted either. What happened was that an ASAIO abstract had been published and if they didn't file an application within a year after publication, they might lose their rights to file. Carl Nolph at the University of Missouri learned about this. He talked to a small-town patent attorney, Ray Snyder from Mount Prospect, Illinois, who used to 'walk the halls' at the University Medical School to see if they needed any patent help. So Snyder ended up handling the initial patent application. Later, there were some concerns about whether the original application was effective in controlling patient use. They finally ended up hiring the firm of Arnold White & Durkee in Texas to finish the work. But for his efforts, Snyder got 10 percent of the royalties per his initial agreement.

"The final agreement was complex, dividing royalties among the University of Texas, Austin Diagnostic Clinic (Moncrief's organization), the University of Missouri, and Moncrief, Popovich, and Carl Nolph personally. We were able to cap the annual total royalty payments at $1.2 million. The formal document wasn't signed until December 16, 1980."

All these events paved the way—echoes of Bennett Kivel going home—for the first Baxter CAPD patient. He was William Kronish, 57 years old and a patient of Dr. Robert Longnecker and Dr. Bert Alpert at Baumritter Hospital in the Bronx, New York. He had a bad heart, and would go into shock in his first hour on hemodialysis. He and his doctors heard about this marvelous new procedure. Kronish consulted with the Veterans Administration in New York. The VA, which had done pioneering evaluation of hemodialysis in the sixties, was helpful. He was referred to the Truman VA Hospital in Missouri, where he received peritoneal solutions from Canada in Baxter containers, and was trained in CAPD administration by Nolph and his nurse, Barbara Prowett. Beginning in November 1978, the Veterans Administration assisted him for two years.

Not long ago, Bill Graham was reflecting on the immense success of CAPD, "One of the critical elements of that strategy was the enlistment of many medical consultants. Some people don't realize the impact of having the leaders in a medical specialty support your device. When the leaders are committed to your product, it's hard for competitors to follow. We had many elements of leverage—the existing two-liter bag, dianeal, the best means of preventing infection, and the best administration set. Under Vern Loucks' skillful direction, the management team used those advantages extremely well."

CAPD TODAY

Looking back through the lens of time, CAPD still represents one of Baxter's finest achievements both in terms of patient benefits and development success. CAPD sales by Baxter around the world today are not far short of a billion dollars.

The story of CAPD is one of opportunity, serendipity, commitment to patient benefits, the exercise of leadership in a specific area of therapy, and perhaps most of all, decisive, effective action by a small team of hard-working individuals. Changes in leadership of the Artificial Organs division—with Lazarus succeeded by Victor Chaltiel, and then Chaltiel succeeded again by Dekle Rountree—did not alter the successful equation. Graham and Loucks had created and maintained the kind of corporate environment in which inventiveness and responsiveness could occur.

The picture to keep in mind in reflecting on this remarkable sequence of innovations stretching from CAPD all the way back to Viaflex containers, Fenwal blood packs, and the Mini-Bag container, is of one starkly simple product—a flexible, closed, patient- and doctor-friendly packaging system—and, at the same time, an ingenious complexity and variety of systems, clinical applications, and manufacturing techniques.

Leadership attracted competition. In 1984, Baxter filed suit against Abbott for direct infringement of Baxter's CAPD rights. That suit was finally settled in 1988.

The benefits of CAPD to end-stage renal disease patients and their families have been enormous. The number of those patients gaining independence and quality of life from CAPD grew from 2,500 in 1981 to 80,000 in 1992.

Perhaps the most graphic way to capture the full impact of CAPD is to quote Harris again, reminiscing in 1991 about Baxter and these events.

"Until Moncrief and Popovich and then Nolph got involved, peritoneal dialysis was a heroic procedure. It required a couple of doctors and nursing support. The patient was in pain during the procedure and after it . . . and by the time he or she was about recovered, it was time to do it again. Nobody wanted to be sloshing around in all this liquid. So peritoneal was a life-saving procedure, not a life-sustaining and quality-enhancing procedure.

"I still remember Popovich's words at that meeting in January 1977. He said, 'How would you react if I told you we had an artificial kidney which requires no power, requires no access to the blood, doesn't need Heparin administration, and operates seven days a week, twenty-four hours a day?'"

Harris paused, then continued, "It certainly didn't take much analysis to figure the potential out. And here was Baxter, the only organization in the world with the experience and technology, built under the leadership of Graham since the mid-fifties, necessary to turn this vision that Popovich painted so dramatically that day into a commercial reality.

"Not only did it result in a substantial business and affect dialysis practices in every developed country around the world, most important of all, it gave dignity and quality of life to thousands of kidney patients."

He thought for a moment before concluding, "You know, not only was the combination of Moncrief's, Popovich's, and Nolph's creativity and Baxter's dialysis technology able to do all the things Popovich described that day 14 years ago. We reduced the cost of dialysis through this procedure. And the Baxter closed system also cut in half the number of patient connect and disconnects, thus reducing by at least that amount the risk of patient infection. Minimizing patient infection [peritonitis] was an overriding Baxter objective from the start of its work on CAPD. Few people have the good fortune to be a part of a development of this magnitude that does so much good."

Thus, as the seventies wound down in the midst of turbulence and change in the U.S. health care system, it certainly seemed that Baxter still had its spark of inventiveness. The niche marketing strategy, which kept the company and its people very close to real patient need, was continuing to work well.

MILESTONES

1972–1979

1972	Introduction of Ultra-Flo II artificial kidney coil.
1972	Robert K. Ausman, M.D., elected vice president clinical research.
1973	Part ownership in Hesperia S.A. acquired.
1973	Plant expansions completed in Belgium and the United Kingdom.
1974	Twenty years of consistent earnings growth at compound rate of 20 percent.
1974	Vicra Sterile acquired.
1974	Manufacturing begun in Japan.
1975	Capillary Flow Dialyzer introduced.
1975	Deerfield headquarters construction completed.
1975	Vernon R. Loucks, Jr., elected president.
1976	Viaflex Mini-Bag plastic container introduced.
1976	Clinical Assays acquired.
1976	Company adopts new name: Baxter Travenol Laboratories, Inc.
1977	New plant opens in Halden, Norway.
1978	Wilbur H. Gantz II elected vice president.
1978	Sales top $1 billion.

1978	Peritoneal dialysis solutions in plastic bags introduced.
1978	Raymond D. Oddi elected senior vice president.
1979	Continuous Ambulatory Peritoneal Dialysis (CAPD) introduced.
1979	Production begun at new plants in Japan, France, Spain.

END NOTES

CHAPTER XVI

1. What Harris and Greff had seen was a totally new concept for peritoneal dialysis called CAPD. It is described as this chapter proceeds.

2. Peter Pilcher subsequently received a kidney transplant.

3. Laws in many other developed countries did not permit patents to be issued for patient therapy systems such as CAPD.

CHAPTER

XVII

BACK TO THE BEGINNING POINT

The story of Baxter's growth and accomplishments has now covered almost fifty years. We've returned to the point in May 1980 when Bill Graham turned over the reins to Vern Loucks. Graham was then sixty-eight, Loucks twenty-two years his junior. The company had come a long way since 1931,[1] most of the distance having been traveled since 1945 when Graham joined the small company struggling to adapt to the post-World War II economy.

The half-century that had passed had been filled with turning points for Baxter, many of them dramatic. This account of the company's history is constructed around those turning points, some of the most significant of which were:

- Repurchasing Dr. Donald Baxter's interest in the fledgling company in 1935 to achieve independence;
- Solving, throughout the balance of the thirties, the various technical problems of IV products inherited with the Don Baxter royalty agreement (flocculation, discoloration, storage and temperature instability, the rubber bottle stopper, etc.);
- Development of the Transfuso Vac system in 1939, establishing early that the company would be more than a single niche, single product company;
- Dr. Falk's recruiting of Graham in 1945;
- Planning of the Cleveland, Mississippi plant in 1949, which shaped not only manufacturing strategy, but also contributed to labor, financial, product, and cost strategy for years to come;
- Graham's election as Baxter president in 1953;
- The commercial artificial kidney in 1956;
- In 1957, acquiring Wallerstein to help avert the possibility of a takeover attempt by American Hospital Supply;
- In 1959, the Fenwal acquisition, leading to some remarkable technical synergies;
- The break with American Hospital Supply in 1962 after an affiliation of thirty years; and winning 85 percent of the hospital solutions accounts in a battle for its continued survival;

- Introduction of the first commercial heart-lung machine (oxygenator) in 1962;
- Concentrated Factor VIII for hemophiliacs; developed principally within Hyland by Murray Thelin, himself a hemophiliac;
- Introduction of Viaflex containers in the U.S. in 1970. This revolutionary system—and it was indeed a system rather than a product—transformed intravenous solutions administration throughout the developed world; changed the way many drugs were best given in certain circumstances; and profoundly altered many kinds of sterile medical packaging. It was just as significant an innovation as tableting, the ampule, or the original Baxter Vacoliter container;
- In 1974, Viaflex Mini-Bag containers;
- CAPD, as just described, in 1978;
- . . . And Loucks' succession in May 1980 to the CEO's position, which is where we began this history.

So this turning point in 1980, as important as it was, was another in a long series. It would be followed in turn by several others between then and 1994 when this history concludes. There appear to be several reasons why Baxter's history has more critical junctures than other leading corporations. First, its strategy was extraordinarily well attuned to changing needs of patients, doctors, nurses, and other health care professionals for a long period of time when modern clinical care was being created. During the many formative years when Baxter's bread-and-butter IV solution products were exclusively sold and distributed in the United States by American Hospital Supply, this spirit of close identification with the patient and health care professional was not isolated in a sales or marketing department. It necessarily permeated every part of the organization: a strong product-service function, manufacturing, quality and regulatory affairs, purchasing and distribution, law and finance, as well as R&D, product development, and engineering.

Then too, Baxter didn't have a single "heavyweight" product, like a Xerox machine or an IBM card tabulator, adequate to sustain and build a broad, solid financial and market foundation. It's back again to the Wee Willie Keeler motto of "hit 'em where they ain't." As each new product line was invented or added, the company was in the process of further inventing and defining itself. The cycles of change for the company within its core market of hospital care and clinical medicine reflect these characteristics.

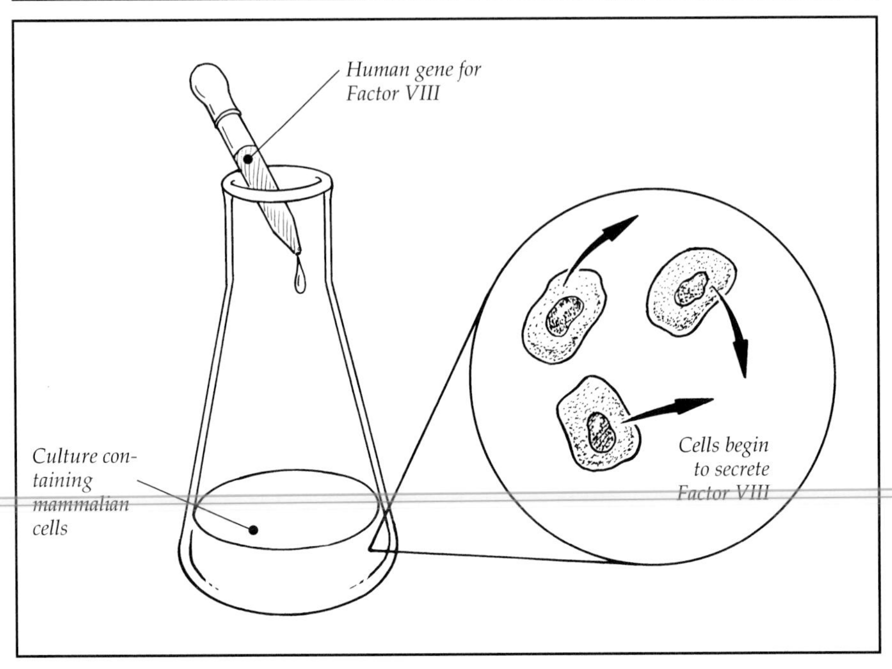

Factor VIII: *Factor VIII produced by recombinant DNA technology excludes the possibility of blood borne infection transmission from unsuspected donor-provided plasma. This product will be used by hemophiliac patients who will not be exposed to HIV infections when using the genetically engineered preparation.*

Another factor influencing the number and frequency of turning points for Baxter was its approach to overall financial management, which kept the company in position to take aggressive risks as individual opportunities warranted. For example, in the events most recently described, the company entered into a know-how royalty agreement and consulting contracts for the revolutionary new CAPD treatment at a time long before a U.S. patent was issued; when many—including both Tom Schuman, the Baxter attorney directly involved, and Graham himself—believed that a patent probably would never issue; well before F.D.A. approval of Baxter plastic containers for this purpose; and even while some uncertainties existed about the risks of peritoneal infection and consequent liability issues.

Granted, that decision didn't itself require an up-front cash outlay. Other such decisions did. For example, as described earlier Loucks aggressively pushed ahead with the decision to equip a CAPD manufacturing plant in Gifu, Japan, while the Japanese Ministry of Health was still "foot-dragging" on approval for this treatment. As noted, for a period of time, Japan was the only developed country in the world without general access to CAPD for end-stage renal disease patients. Then ironically, when the Ministry finally approved CAPD, it was designated as a hospital treatment despite the fact that its greatest benefits were clearly in home care. CAPD was finally approved for patient home use in Japan in 1985. The liberation of renal patients in Japan from the tyranny of the machine had taken six years since the treatment was made available to patients in the United States—the same number of years after Baxter first applied to the Japanese Ministry for approval, and seven years after Baxter broke ground for its Gifu (Japan) plant to produce CAPD materials there. Japanese marketers themselves, at their most patient extremes, cannot eclipse this Baxter record of persistence. It was this confidence not only with CAPD, but earlier with plasma albumin, and with other products that ultimately made Baxter one of the most successful American companies in Japan with sales in 1992 approaching $500 million.

WOULD ANOTHER TURNING POINT IN THE EIGHTIES BE A SHIFT IN BAXTER'S LONG-SUCCESSFUL STRATEGY?

A key question, as the eighties began, was whether there was more of a transition going on than the passing of the baton from Graham to Loucks. The company had grown to considerable size in relation to its original specialized market niche strategy. The more important of those market niches (solutions, blood therapy, and dialysis) included hundreds of products, which attracted specialized competition sharpshooting at particular subsegments of the market. Would Baxter as a billion dollar plus organization remain nimble enough to react to these challenges?

While it's certainly over-simplifying, Baxter's success in the late forties and fifties had been as a technology and manufacturing innovator led by Graham, "chemist and patent attorney." The company's burst of growth in the sixties had come from technology and *marketing* as Graham's strategic leadership was augmented by the marketing talents of individuals like John Kimbell, Jim Ammon, Sam Parker, and Vern Loucks; and the seventies turned into the decade of marketing and finance as executives such as Loucks and Ray Oddi put more of their imprint on the company. What would be the hallmark of the Baxter of the eighties?

Some, inside the company and outside as well, believed Baxter should and would continue its emphasis on innovative technology in order to create new product niches. Others felt the company should break out into broader product lines. And still others took the position that what Baxter needed to do in the eighties was to concentrate on driving down operating costs. Loucks was moving on all these fronts. At the same time, he was thinking particularly about *services* . . . services like Alternate Site and home patient care (which CAPD and parenteral nutrition had already contributed to launching); like distribution; and hospital information and consulting services. Did services of this kind provide an opportunity to both broaden Baxter's line and build new niche markets?

The broad implications and requirements of the transition in 1980 were read differently by various Baxter executives, depending, in part, on how they interpreted the external environment. Jim Tobin, who returned to the United States in September 1980 after a series of international assignments, reflected on the years leading up to this juncture, "In the early to mid-seventies we were growing 20 percent a year like clockwork. International was moving even faster. Then later on in the seventies we had to dig a little deeper every year. When we'd miss on one or two cylinders, we'd simply push harder on the other six . . . I remember years when we'd be asking ourselves 'Is we is or is we ain't going to make 20 percent?' By 1980 and 1981, we were emphasizing value improvement. The asset management program of 1974 became the cost improvement and the value improvement program . . . named by Bill Gantz in the North Cove cafeteria. We really went to work on Viaflex container products. One of the key marketing executives said, 'I don't care what you do; just don't touch the product.' We made seven changes in the Viaflex container nobody ever noticed. . . . The stiffener bar, the hanger hole, more air in the bag, tighter brown tip, dating, thinner container sheeting, the over pouch, and the change in the V-shape column. . . . Our margins went from 30 to 44 percent. Even with the success of the improvement work and the promise of the early drug admixture development led by Jennifer Graham and Bill Younkes, it seemed our strategies might be getting tired."

Gantz' description of the period is the same in some respects, different in others. "The seventies were a time of explosive growth. There wasn't a country or a product where we weren't making major inroads. Inflation effects lulled us somewhat, and we probably didn't pay enough attention to how full the new product pipeline was. We had built a culture of growth and there was going to be less growth

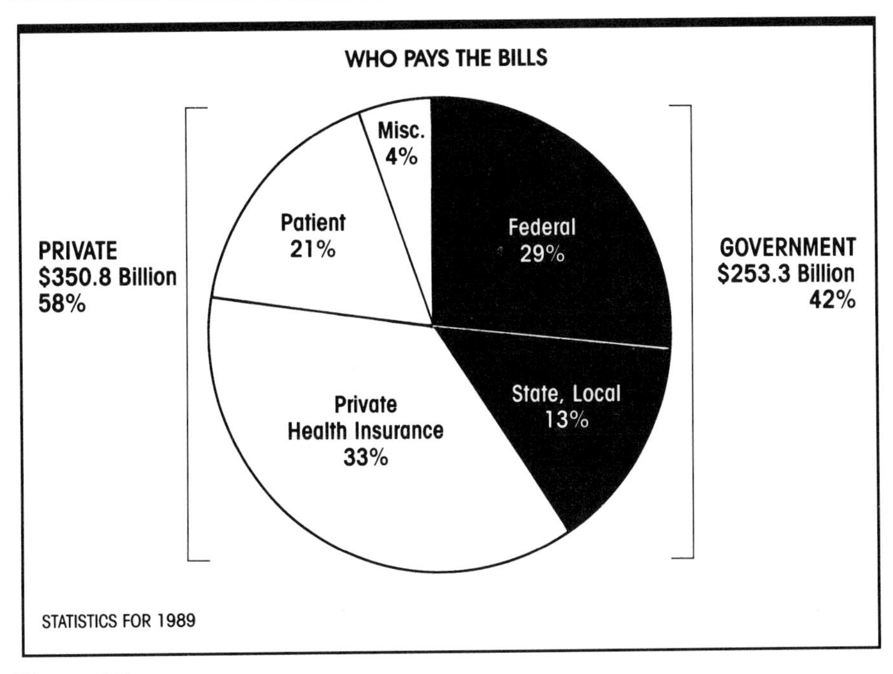

Figure 15[2]

in many of our narrow product lines. We had to get R&D, which was very centralized, closer to the businesses. . . . First, in 1980-81 we went strategic with the Alternate Site business in a classic Bill Graham strategy. Then we niched the hospital information systems business.

"We also niched premix drugs with frozen drug technology, built the necessary infrastructure, and got to market very fast, building a $250 million business . . . Still the basic strategy was to get more out of what we already had through value improvement."

THE CHANGING MARKET ENVIRONMENT AFFECTS BAXTER STRATEGY

As already described, federal government money flooded into the U.S. health care system during the 1970s. Not only did it drive up the rate of health care cost inflation, which has consistently exceeded the rate of inflation in the consumer price index (CPI) in recent years, it also affected the structure and accountabilities of the system. For-profit hospital chains began to loom larger. So did academic health centers (AHCs). In response to these developments, closed- and open-end hospital group purchasing continued to grow stronger. Control of supply contracting in the patient care niches Baxter had so carefully nurtured subtly shifted. Discounting became more prevalent. Hospitals were becoming big business. As they slugged it out for market share, hospital operating statistics began to soften before 1980.

Loucks knew even then that these trends would accelerate. The "Reagan Revolution" would bring even more change to U.S. health care, most notably in 1983 with cost caps for hospital care reimbursement (DRG's). After the 1981-82 recession, the climate improved for American business, but not necessarily for health care.

The new Reagan administration moved on many fronts to deregulate, but not so in health care. Before the decade was over, even some corporate employers stung by employee health care cost increases that seemed virtually out of control were railing against the system. Health care became headline and sound byte material in the popular media during this era; the most frequent topics were "Health Care Is the Largest Single Cost Component in Producing an American Automobile!" and "37 Million Americans Go Bare of Health Insurance!" Politicians, the media, and the public itself by this time were demanding that cost, access, and quality problems be "fixed."

The following charts show what was going on:

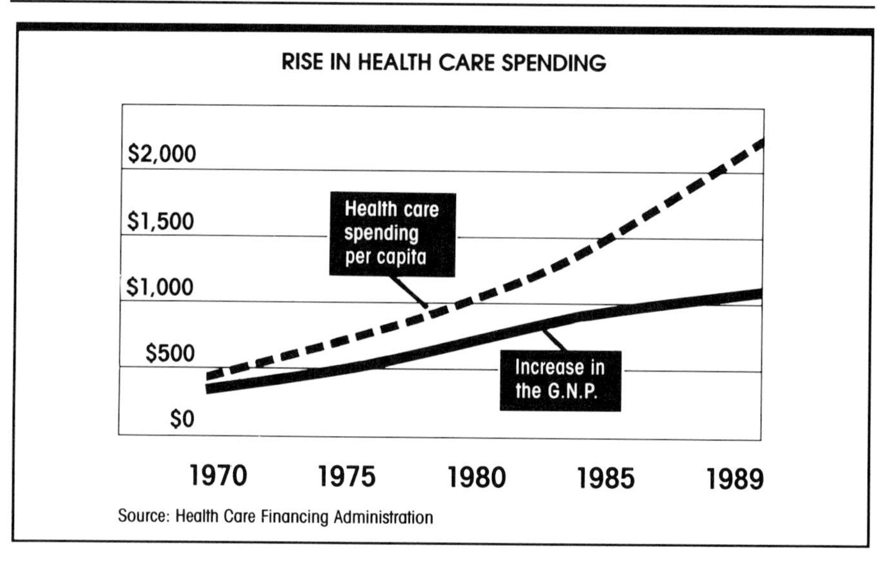

Figure 16[3]

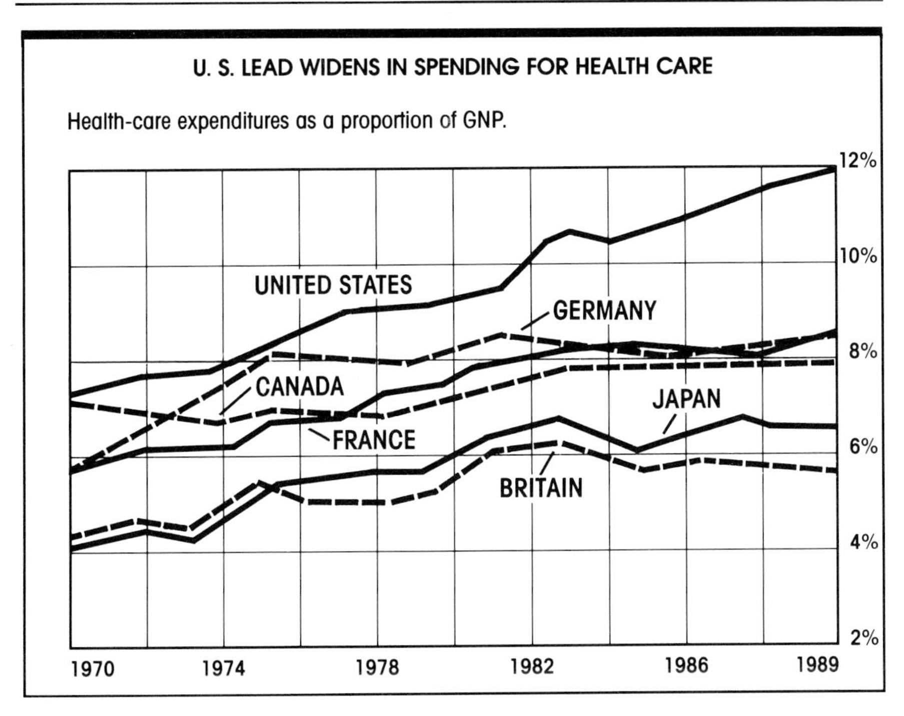

Figure 17[4]

BAXTER STRATEGIC RESPONSES TO THESE TRENDS TAKE SOME TIME TO DEVELOP

Contrast these charts just presented with the pattern of Baxter health care contributions over the years, which, even more than its unparalleled financial performance, had driven and motivated the company and its people.

It would have been difficult in any circumstances to extend this record of life-saving, life-enhancing innovation. The destabilization of the U.S. health care environment made it even more difficult. Beyond health care itself, the upcoming decade would be remembered for persistent, towering U.S. government deficits; for an increasingly short-term business point of view in the United States; for financial excesses that accompanied that view; and for what appeared to many to be a startling decline in the United States' relative economic position in the world community.

The following section, taking Baxter's history through 1993, describes how the company continued to grow and change.

END NOTES

CHAPTER XVI

1. Baxter celebrated its fiftieth anniversary in October 1981.
2. U.S. Health Care Financing Administration (HCFA).
3. ibid.
4. *The New York Times*, 19 May 1991, and George J. Schieber and Jean-Pierre Poullier, *Health Affairs* Spring 1991.

PART FOUR

A MAJOR TURNING POINT IN BAXTER'S HISTORY

The Growth Years, as they've been called here—the 29 years of record-setting net income growth—were going to continue for a few more years. Why interrupt the flow of events at this point?

Despite the smooth effectiveness of the transition to Vern Loucks from Bill Graham, events were beginning to take a radically different turn. Could it be there was a reckoning on the horizon of the kind described by David Halberstam in his book about Ford and the global automobile industry?[1]

Some of the signs were there. Admission and length-of-stay statistics for Baxter's principal customers—U.S. hospitals—began to remind people of trends and statistics from the 1930s. Furthermore, some observers thought the company's R&D cupboard was beginning to get bare.

So, in one way, history began to repeat itself. When Graham joined the struggling company that had less than $2 million in commercial sales and many problems crowding in, he took the time to study, analyze, experiment, and plan. It would be a number of years before a strategic platform for lift-off was built. Now, because of unprecedented turmoil in the domestic hospital environment, and also because Graham had predictably tapped a successor who was also a consummate strategist, Loucks began to go through the same process.

One huge difference between the two eras stands out. When Graham began, the company wasn't yet public, and he had time to devise a course of action that would produce results in a steady upward slope. Loucks faced a very different set of problems and constraints in the opening years of the eighties. For a public company of over $1 billion in revenues and with investment attention already focused on the quarterly sprint rather than the marathon distance, how much time would he really have?

1. David Halberstam, *The Reckoning* (New York: William Morrow and Company, Inc., 1986).

CHAPTER

XVIII

A NEW ERA IN U.S. MEDICAL AND HOSPITAL CARE: 1980-84

The years 1980 to 1984 were watershed years for the U.S. health care system and for Baxter Travenol.[1] The 50-year old company had now seen four successive, very different eras in its market environment:

- 1931-42, The pre-clinical medicine era
- 1942-60, Emergence of the modern health care system
- 1960-79, The medical-industrial system increasingly fueled by third-party payments
- 1980-, The emerging era which is still today being shaped and characterized

At the same time, other trends were at work in different countries around the globe where Baxter had major stakes.

The new era in the United States affected hospitals and hospital suppliers (representing about 39 percent of total domestic health care expenditures) most heavily. Total payments for doctors' services continued to grow, contrary to expectations.[2] Pharmaceutical manufacturers were also less affected because pricing and purchasing behavior for drugs were not directly influenced; also because some of the major drug companies were experiencing a highly productive period of new discovery. The pharmaceutical industry may have escaped greater cost control strictures because it was a relatively smaller slice of the health care expenditure pie. Americans paid $50 billion for prescription drugs in drug stores and hospitals, while the rest of the world shelled out another $120 billion. Drugs and related supplies as a percentage of medical spending (HCE) have declined markedly from 16 percent in the 1960s to about 7 percent today,[3] despite annual price increases of 12 to 14 percent a year throughout the eighties. See figure 18, charting the overall growth in health care spending for the leading nations.[4]

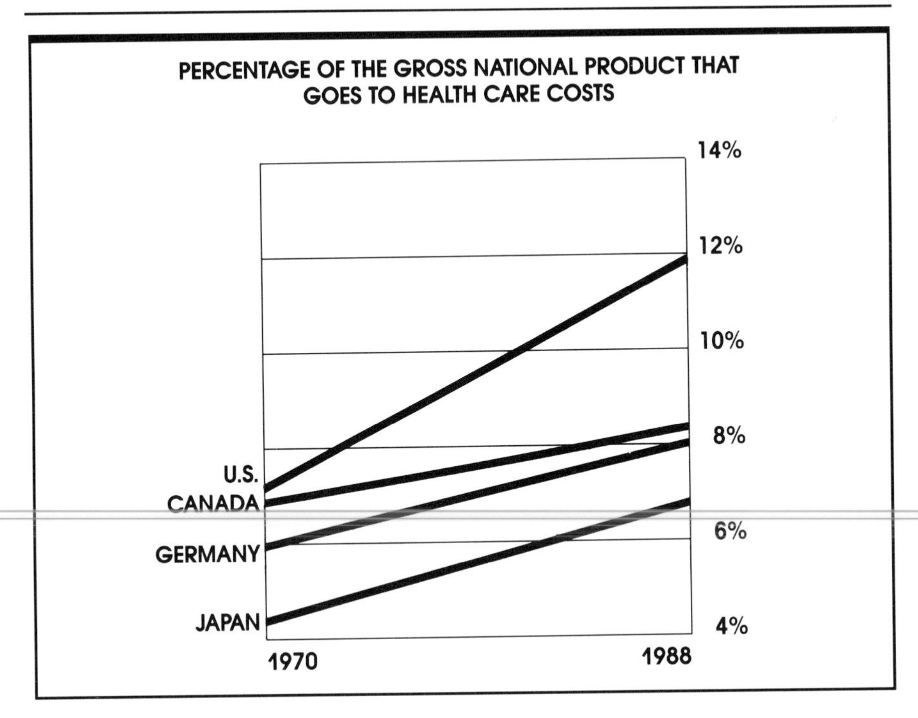

Figure 18

Their exemption from the perils and constraints of the new era would not last, however. By the time this history was being completed, new government regulations for drug pricing were being discussed, and unfavorable comparisons were being made with drug costs in other countries. Senator Pryor, Arkansas Democrat, was beginning to sound like Senator Kefauver in the old days, with his drumbeat criticism of the pharmaceutical companies.

Pricing pressures on Baxter's hospital-oriented product line (particularly parenteral solutions) became immediately more intense. Trends toward group hospital purchasing and the leverage of competitive bidding, which have already been described, became even more of a market factor. Vern Loucks pointed out, "By 1982 or 1983 Cutter was out of the solutions business. People going after Cutter's leavings couldn't seem to stop there. From 1977 to 1989, we got no price relief in solutions, and then in 1989 we got only 3 percent."

Erstwhile U.S. distributor and now competitor American Hospital Supply Corporation was bundling product bids through its corporate marketing program (which was unsuccessfully challenged in the courts by regional hospital distributors) and using ASAP (an automated order system) to its competitive advantage.

Loucks got a Baxter corporate marketing program started. Strong people like Harold Callicoat were assigned to it. The effort was moderately successful. "Still," Loucks commented later, "when I talked with top hospital people about our corporate program I'd see their eyes roll over. They were tuning me out. It was obvious we weren't going to be able to keep ahead of changes in hospital purchasing and usage behavior without doing something a lot more radical."

Nor were these signs the only indicators of change. Baxter's 1983 annual report made reference to the AIDS virus, which would have profound effects on the safety of and public perception about the nation's blood supply. Data from a variety of sources (the World Health Organization, U.S. Department of Health and Human Services, and the Harvard School of Public Health) show 6.5 million HIV-infected people around the world as of 1992—one million of them in the United States. New AIDS diagnoses in the U.S. have risen to over 36,000 per year (with many cases, of course, unreported).

Years of working life lost due to AIDS in the U.S. have now passed years lost due to cancer and to heart disease, and are approaching losses due to accidents. This sobering statistic reflects the younger age groups typically stricken by AIDS. From 1982 to 1993, U.S. federal government spending for AIDS (entitlements and discretionary spending) rose from nothing to about $5 billion per year. Non-federal AIDS expenses are estimated to total another $8 billion annually. Quite understandably, those being devastated by the disease clamor for more spending.

In 1983, Baxter was engaged through its Cambridge, Massachusetts Clinical Assays Division in the National Institutes of Health competition to develop an AIDS test. It later withdrew from that race. The fact that Baxter won neither the hepatitis nor the AIDS test race underlined its lagging position in diagnostics vis-à-vis its long-term rival, Abbott.

The 1982 annual report announced the acquisition of a minority interest in Genetics Institute of Cambridge, Massachusetts, a leading biotechnology company headed by Gabriel Schmergel, one of a number of Baxter alumni playing leadership roles in that emerging health care sector. In 1983, Baxter formed a joint venture with another biotechnology company, Genentech, for the purpose of developing diagnostic applications, and the Cambridge, Massachusetts Clinical Assays Division was folded into that joint venture. So a significant new health care technology, very different from those where Baxter had traditionally exercised leadership, was coming to the forefront. Biotechnology could be regarded as either a threat or another opportunity for Baxter.

ADAPTATION OF CORPORATE STRATEGY

The company's annual rate of revenue growth declined somewhat (to an average of slightly under 12 percent) while its earnings continued to grow at a strong 19 percent until 1984 when events took a dramatically different turn.

BAXTER FINANCIAL RESULTS
1980 - 1984

Year	$ Net Sales in thousands	% Increase Over Prior Year	$ Net Income in thousands	% Increase Over Prior Year
1980	1,374,000	+ 15	127,300	+ 15
1981	1,504,000	+ 9	150,600	+ 18
1982	1,671,000	+ 11	186,900	+ 24
1983	1,843,000	+ 10	218,100	+ 17
1984	1,800,000	− 2	29,100	− 87

Figure 19: *1984 net income shown after a special charge of $116,100 net of related tax benefits.*

Product mix had settled into a pattern. Parenteral solution sales in 1982 were $700 million (45 percent of corporate revenues); blood products $362 million (23 percent); renal products $238 million (15 percent); and other products $265 million (17 percent). It did not appear that any of the three established market niches could provide the necessary growth kicker.

Loucks undertook a slight, but intricate, shift in long-term strategy. It would take some time to achieve the level of financial return from this shift that had come to be expected of Baxter, but earlier strategies had also taken years to become fully effective. Bill Graham's strategic marketing objectives were established as early as 1949 when the Travenol brand was created and were reinforced in the early 1950s with successful product diversification efforts, but it was not until 1962 that independence from the American Hospital Supply distribution system was achieved.

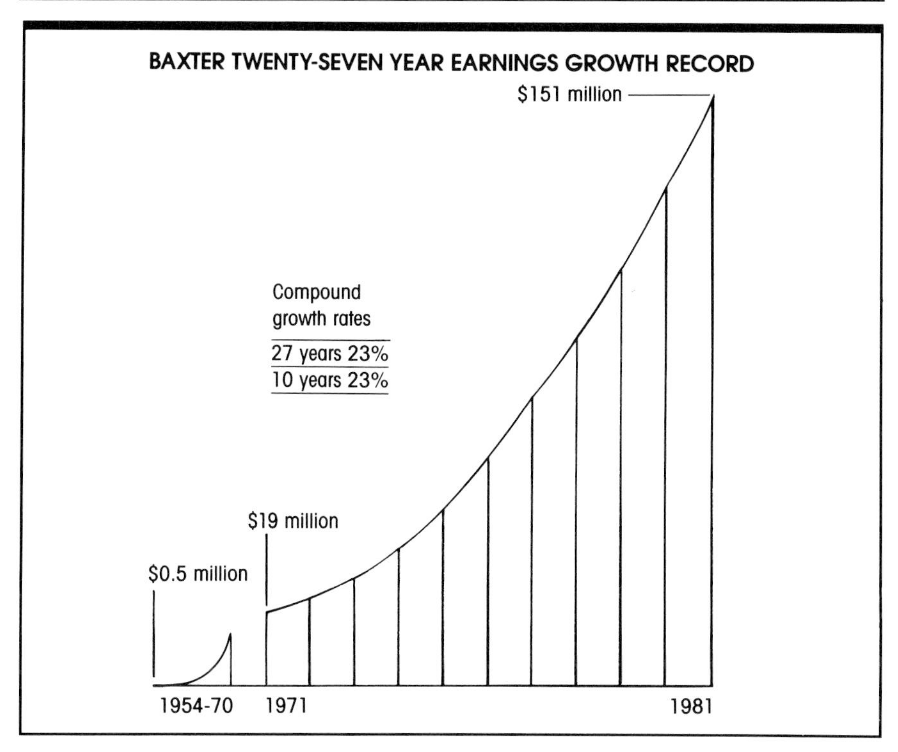

Figure 20

Loucks' imprint on Baxter strategy in the early eighties focused on the following principal elements:

- Rigorous cost management—already a Baxter tradition, but now using more advanced management techniques. Consultants from Bain and Company, Inc., came to Deerfield in 1981 to assist with value management, which was the beginning of a long-term consulting relationship. In 1982, gross margins were improved to 45.7 percent from 42.7 percent in 1981.
- Seeking appropriate mechanisms to share competitive cost advantage with hospital customers through "value partnerships."
- What the company then called "appropriate site therapy";[5] that is, following the patient to alternative care settings outside the hospital, offering the potential of a greater Baxter share of total health care expenditures.
- Other service niches, such as hospital information systems and hospital consulting. In 1983, Travenol Management Systems

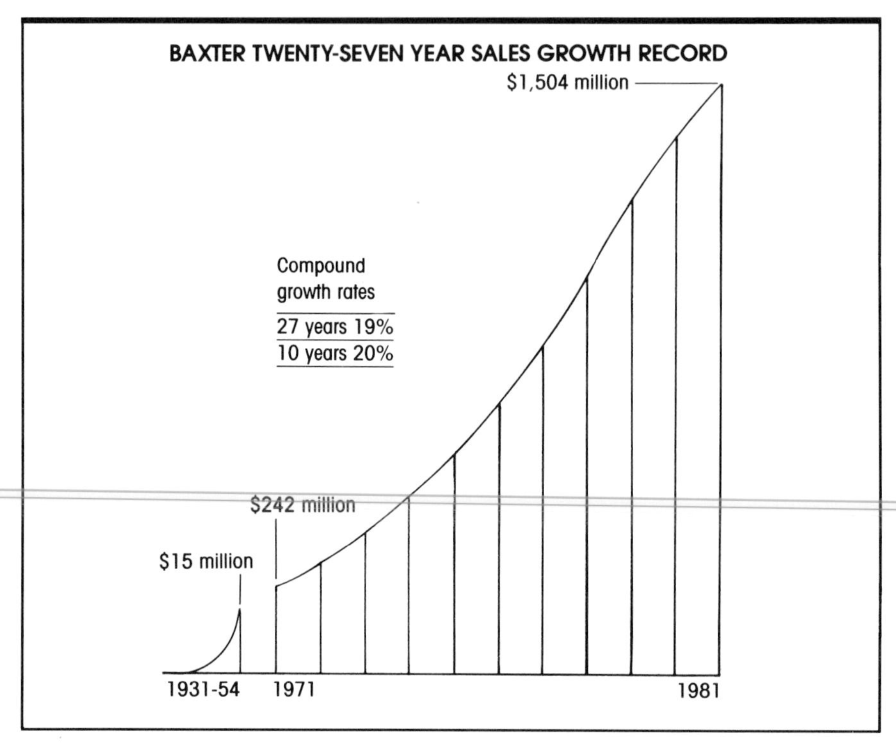

Figure 21

(TMS), was formed with Ellen Rudnick as president, to assist hospitals in developing best demonstrated practices. Also in 1983, Dynamic Control Corporation was acquired to build a market position in IBM-compatible information systems.

- Priming the new product development pump.
- . . . And seeking in various other ways to change the company's basic relationships with hospitals.

COST AND PRODUCTIVITY MANAGEMENT

Value improvement programs implemented by Loucks and Bill Gantz, who became chief operating officer in 1982 and was elected to the Baxter board in 1984, produced remarkable results. Don Madsen, elected a senior vice president in 1983, drove the implementation of this initiative. Over a relatively short term, Baxter manufacturing employment was reduced by 7,000 people, generally by hiring controls and attrition. What had been within the overall Baxter system a customized, small clean-room approach to manufacturing evolved into a semi-automated manufacturing process which produced impressive gains in both product quality and control. One of the important contributors to manufacturing efficiencies was the same Kieffel Korting forming and sealing line that a younger Loucks had bootlegged into Belgium in the late sixties, and that Bob Bocquet and Andre Husson then developed for Baxter Travenol applications.

Then in 1984, a broader value improvement program was introduced, aimed at both indirect and direct product costs. This program also helped to arrest the growth of selling, general, and administration (SG&A) expenses. Not only did these efforts protect Baxter's existing market share positions, they may also have headed off potential domestic market entry by health care companies from outside the United States because the cost competition was getting so much tougher.

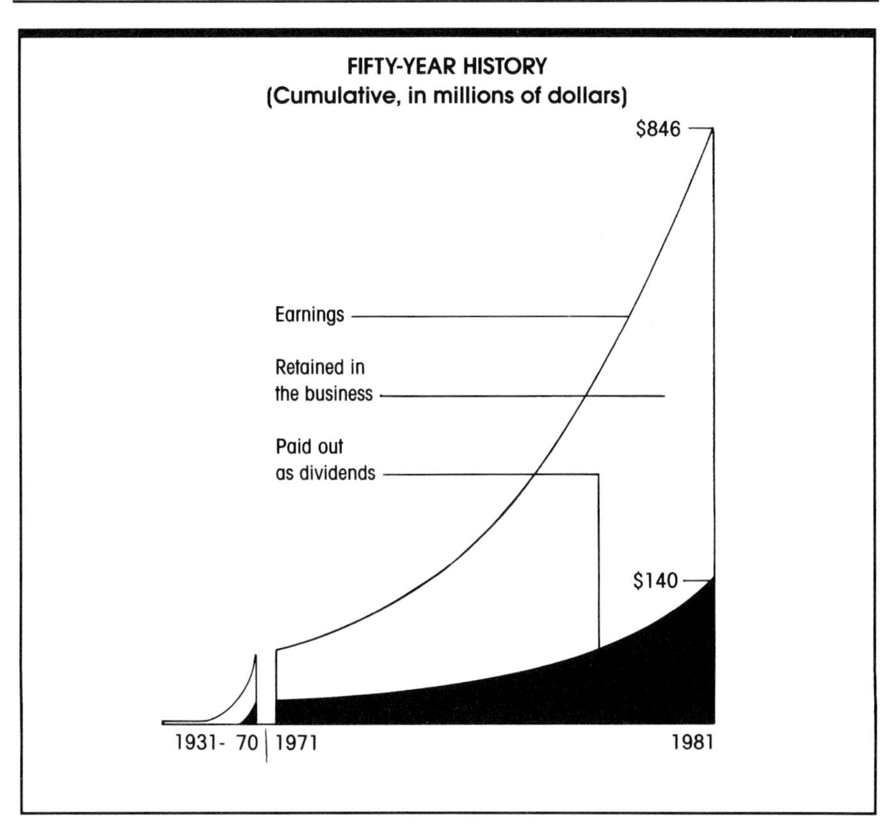

Figure 22: *Baxter chose to reinvest the major portion of the company's earnings in the business, while following a policy of consistently increasing dividends. From 1931 through 1981, it retained and reinvested over $700 million of earnings.*

TWO PIVOT POINTS FOR NEW STRATEGY

Loucks boiled down the turbulent health care environment and his assessment of the company's competitive position to two fundamental strategic tenets. Like the strategic principles which had guided Graham in the forties and early fifties, they were simple, somewhat contrarian, and not all that easy to implement.

The first was that Baxter would go where the patient was. Since both cost pressures and technology were clearly going to move more treatments out of hospitals, and since the company already had substantial home care and Alternate Site experience through dialysis (CAPD) and parenteral nutrition, making the Alternate Site business a major strategic initiative was a natural. Loucks was then using a management council, called the Homestead Group because of its annual meeting site, for strategy formulation. The decision to "go strategic" in Alternate Site was discussed, confirmed, and announced at the spring 1981 Homestead Group meeting. The risks of this decision were, on the one hand, the low-tech, mom-and-pop nature of parts of the Alternate Site business, and on the other hand, the possibility that Baxter's success in this sector could affect its relationships with hospitals.

That led to the second strategic principle. Baxter would broaden its relationships and services to hospitals. That was contrarian because industry analysts were saying that hospitals were in trouble and therefore their suppliers were in trouble too. Loucks said at the time, "Nonsense. Patients are going to have to be treated somehow. It's not going to be done with mirrors." He believed hospital relationships would progressively shift from "product to process" and that distribution would be the key in that shift. This would appear to be a significant departure from the "Hit 'em where they ain't" approach. Was it actually a departure? Readers should reach their own conclusion after following how the strategic direction continued to develop from this point forward. So broadening relationships with hospitals and breaking out of Wee Willie Keeler-type niches was the principal agenda item for the spring 1984 Homestead Group meeting. It wasn't until 1985, almost exactly a year later, that a way was found to implement those ideas.

THE ALTERNATE SITE BUSINESS

One of the more successful strategic initiatives of the early eighties was the Alternate Site business. The way had been prepared through

CAPD, which continued its rapid and profitable growth. From a few hundred patients in the late seventies, CAPD burgeoned to 9,000 patients in 1981 and to 18,000 in 1983—the 1983 number representing 9 percent of all dialysis patients around the world. While the renal business (formerly Artificial Organs) and CAPD specifically contributed to Baxter's Alternate Site penetration and success, it continued to be a separate business based on strategic decisions made in the late seventies.

Loucks rapidly built on that beginning to establish the necessary Alternate Site infrastructure: distribution, reimbursement systems, and various kinds of direct patient support. The effect was preemptive because once the national system was in place, it was difficult and expensive for major competitors to duplicate it. Quickly, Baxter emerged as the U.S., and probably world, leader in Alternate Site services.

At this time, Alternate Site services such as respiratory therapy, for which there is a relatively broad market, were being emphasized and showing double-digit growth rates. Later, Baxter decided to concentrate on high-tech services, and segments like respiratory therapy were managed down or disposed of.

Another strategic issue to be sorted out was the internal and external positioning of Alternate Site in relation to Baxter's hospital business. Alternate Site could be viewed either as a competitive threat to functions performed within the hospital's four walls or as an adjunct to those services. In either case, hospital staff was one of the sources of patient referral to Alternate Site care providers.

After having been started up within the hospital business, Alternate Site became a strong, separate business group. The business was under the direction of Lance Piccolo from soon after its initial formation. A proven marketing and sales executive, Piccolo had risen through field ranks since 1968. He was elected a corporate vice president in 1981 and became group vice president in 1982. In 1987 he was elected executive vice president and a member of the Baxter board of directors. Piccolo's sales drive and creativity were exactly what was needed to make Alternate Site a major new source of Baxter revenue and profit growth. In a dramatic shift, Piccolo would become chairman and CEO of a new health care company on November 30, 1992. More about this later.

The Alternate Site initiative did far more, however, than increase Baxter's internal rate of growth. It caused Loucks and the Baxter management team to think strategically about how to apply the company's exceptional product innovation skills to the development of service market niches. It brought the company into closer contact with the patient (the end-customer) through provision of direct care. One only has to observe and listen to customer service representatives in the renal division talking with end-stage renal disease patients in their homes about needs and problems, and to talk with patients directly about this life-line to comprehend how this influenced Baxter philosophy and strategy. Dr. Ralph Falk, after all, had formed the company in large part because of his abiding interest in patient care. Now larger numbers of Baxter people were in touch with a broad universe of patients with human as well as medical needs. Baxter, a leader in traditional quality control and compliance with FDA and other regulation, moved quickly into the nontraditional areas of customer service quality and quality leadership.

Major strategic initiatives, of course, reflect individual executive leadership at a particular time. We've noted several times that over all these years since 1931, there had been only three Baxter CEOs (Dr. Falk, Bill Graham, and now Vern Loucks) and this continuity had been an important contributor to the company's success. Each of these three CEOs, however, saw the company's basic commitment to patient care in somewhat different ways appropriate to the times and to his own background: Dr. Falk as a surgeon and diagnostician; Bill Graham as a chemist and patent attorney; and Vern Loucks as a restless strategist with a uniquely personal management style. Confronted with turbulence in health care markets and financing in this country and around the world, he insisted on looking at the system in new and different ways, sometimes discomfiting for subordinate managers. Alternate Site care was, in the eighties, the most prominent symbol of Loucks' leadership. That is what makes subsequent events in regard to Alternate Site care so remarkable.

OTHER SERVICE BUSINESSES

Not all service businesses that were launched at the time were equally successful. In 1982 Baxter acquired Medcom, a medical education and services company. It was later divested. TMS (Travenol Management Services) was organized in 1983 to provide consulting services to hospitals based on Baxter's own experience with value improvement and quality leadership. TMS was later folded into corporate marketing.

The largest Baxter service business outside Alternate Site was Hospital Information Systems. Systems in medical, pharmacy, patient care, billing, and other administrative areas had become a significant percentage of hospital expenditures. Quarterbacked by Steve Lazarus and supported by a marketing agreement with IBM, the company began to develop a hospital information business, largely through acquisition. Dynamic Control Corporation was acquired in 1983, then Stony Brook Systems and J.S. Data in 1984. In April 1985, the largest such acquisition, Compucare, was completed at a cost of about $75 million. George F. "Rick" Adam, with prior IBM experience and a Baxter corporate officer since 1982, became president of the Systems Business. The Systems Business was one of the approaches tried at the time to adapt to fast-changing market and competitive conditions. The business grew, but never achieved profitability. More important, there weren't the technological and marketing interconnections between this business and other parts of Baxter that had been so important in the company's successful growth formula. Earlier chapters have shown how solutions technology, early blood containers, dialysis, Fenwal Blood-Pack units, Viaflex containers, and then CAPD meshed and contributed to each other. The company's operating and financial performance through 1983 had been due to cumulative effects of quasi-independent business units skillfully managed so that their individual advances and competitive advantages became common assets. From that viewpoint, Hospital Systems was too much of a stand-alone business. It was subsequently spun out to an IBM-Baxter joint venture, IBAX Healthcare Systems. Loucks recalls some of these ill-fated service acquisitions of the early eighties wryly, but with good humor. "Some of these service markets were still in their infancy and we ourselves were still learning how to incorporate services in our overall strategy. To say I was disappointed with the results of several of those acquisitions would certainly be an understatement."

The experience didn't dampen his willingness to make acquisition a strategic avenue. After this early eighties period of adaptation and experimentation, two major acquisitions in 1985 and 1987 set the tone and direction for Baxter in the late eighties and early nineties.

NEW PRODUCT ADVANCES CONTINUE AS WELL

Baxter's rededication to product innovation continued to produce results. The CS-3000 blood cell separator (introduced in the late seventies) was well accepted. In 1981, the TMO membrane oxygenator was brought to market. The Autoplex anti-inhibitor coagulant complex system for hemophilia treatment was completed and introduced.

Emphasis was being placed on flow control devices through licensing agreements with Sharp, Oximetrix and other companies. A new blood additive, CPDA-1 (citrate phosphate dextrose adenine), was developed, extending the shelf-life of whole blood from 21 to 35 days.[6] Travasorb fat emulsion products for parenteral nutrition were also marketed. And, as mentioned earlier, development work was proceeding on new thermoplastics, such as polyolefin, to meet specific requirements of different medical applications. Polyolefin was "kinder" than other packaging materials to red blood cells.

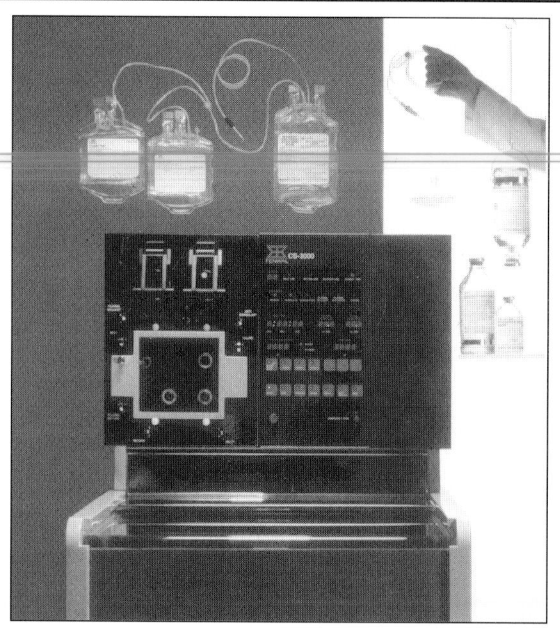

The CS-3000 uses centrifugation to separate whole blood into nearly pure pools of fractioned blood: white cells, red cells, plasma, and platelets. This technology provides multiple uses of blood products from one donor, extending the blood stock available to hospitals.

Probably the most significant product development of the early eighties for Baxter was premixed drug admixtures and frozen drugs, building on Viaflex and Mini-Bag container technology, which allowed premixed drugs to be "piggybacked" on the closed infusion system for nutrients and electrolytes. In the case of some patients and some medications, this method of drug administration was therapeutically more effective and offered hospital labor savings together with improved pharmacy control. Baxter was quickly successful in reaching cooperative agreements with Merck, G.D. Searle, Smith Kline, Rhone Poulenc, and Hoffmann-LaRoche to package and provide drugs in this new form, and also in working through stability and other technical issues that storing drugs in solution introduced. Marsh Abbey recalled how difficult it was to negotiate these contracts. "The concept of supplying drugs in bulk was foreign to these companies. It was like negotiating a birthright. One of those contracts took two full years from the beginning of the discussion to the inking of the document."

Frozen drugs were then developed as a solution to some of these issues. By 1985 the drug admixture and frozen drug business had grown to $74 million in volume and become another significant Baxter contribution to quality of patient care.

Loucks made another significant investment decision at this same time. The decision was in regard to the new field of biotechnology. The emerging field was beginning to attract significant attention from health market watchers and a big rush from investment analysts. Early developments held the promise of remaking many aspects of clinical care. Loucks decided to keep Baxter closely involved through several minority investments in biotech ventures. Baxter's joint efforts with Genetics Institute have now produced a recombinate Factor VIII (antihemophilic factor) which substantially eliminates the risk to hemophiliacs of AIDS and hepatitis B infections from live human blood concentrate.

The strategic decision, which so far has proven to be sound, was for the company to *not* "acquire" its way into the business. Individual biotech firms were specialized in narrow niches, their cash flows were negative, and acquisition prices sky high. Instead, Baxter chose to form alliances, distribution agreements, and joint ventures with biotech firms which provided a specific technology or therapy fit. This approach was aided by the number of Baxter management alumni who headed or held key positions in those companies. Bill Gantz, for one, had resigned in March 1992 to become CEO of Pathogenesis. Even more recently, his successor, Jim Tobin, left to become president of Biogen. The management development philosophy Graham had told Loucks about in their employment interview in 1965 was paying off in unexpected ways. Loucks' strategy in the early and mid-eighties of playing the biotech field rather than picking a niche was another example of heading away from the Wee Willie Keeler strategy. Or was it?

CHANGES IN PRODUCT MIX THROUGH ACQUISITION AND DIVESTITURE

Other than service businesses mentioned earlier, acquisitions and divestitures were a relatively minor strategic factor during this early eighties period. Auto Syringe was bought in 1982 and Hyland Diagnostics—part of Baxter's first strategic acquisition exactly thirty years before—was sold. A portent of things to come, the New Zealand, Mexico, and Philippines IV solutions businesses of American Hospital Supply Corporation were acquired in 1983 along with the name rights AHS had acquired from Don Baxter years before, solidifying Baxter Travenol's world-wide claim to the Baxter trade name. In 1982 the Cardio Pulmonary business was sold. In 1983 Omnis Surgical Corporation was formed as an independent company with a nucleus of cardio products and Discase injection, and Victor Chaltiel became its CEO. The intention at that time was to take Omnis public, but investment market conditions and later events upset those plans. Baxter acquired Extracorporeal Medical Specialties, a manufacturer of dialysis machines and devices in Tampa, Florida, from Johnson & Johnson in 1984.

BAXTER MANAGEMENT CAPABILITY AND DIVERSITY CONTINUES TO GROW

Indicative of continuing management developments were the number of people taking on broader responsibilities. Ray Oddi, who has figured in this history since 1954, became Baxter's chief financial officer in 1981. That same year, Dr. Grady Harris and Steve Lazarus were elected senior vice presidents, and Piccolo, Bob Rain, and Wayne Custead became corporate vice presidents. In 1982 Gantz was elected chief operating officer, Piccolo group vice president, Abbey senior vice president, and Donna C. E. Williamson and Rick Adam became corporate officers. The following year Madsen was named senior vice president and Robert J. Lambrix joined Baxter from Armco as vice president for finance. In 1984 Jim Tobin, who had led the successful premixed and frozen drug effort, was elected a corporate vice president. At the same time Lambrix was elevated to senior vice president for finance as another step in the well-planned program to succeed Oddi, who was planning his retirement. Overall, it was a balance of old guard and new talent.

CHANGES AT THE BOARD OF DIRECTORS LEVEL

At the time of the 1980 transition from Graham to Loucks, Baxter's 14-member board consisted of relative newcomers Gaylord Freeman (former chairman of First National Bank of Chicago); William Hewitt (chairman of Deere & Company); Charles S. Munson; Clinton E. Frank; William Wood-Prince; and W. Irving Osborne (former chairman of Pullman); balancing long-term board stalwarts Graham, Ralph Falk II, Marian C. Falk, Jack Knowlton, and Everett Travis.

Until recently the balance between Baxter management and outside board members, had tilted in management's direction. Also, a number of board members had, of course, long been associated with Graham. Loucks began to add to the board individuals who might support the aggressive, high-risk strategy then taking shape.

Charles F. Knight (chairman and CEO of Emerson Electric Company) replaced the retiring Travis in 1981. Fred Turner (then chairman and CEO of McDonald's) was added to the board in 1982. Then in 1984, the Honorable John L. Louis was elected a director, as was Gantz. The board now consisted of 13 members, of whom only three were inside directors: Graham, Loucks and Gantz. It was well prepared to face a difficult challenge in 1985, and then to undergo further change itself as a result of surmounting that challenge.

1983—BEGINNING OF A STRATEGY SHIFT?

Three events in 1983 signaled the beginning of a shift in strategy. The three separate events must be put in perspective in order to track strategic direction. The company had reached a size approaching $2 billion. The new CEO had to not only hit more solid singles, he needed to hit some home runs or triples. Alternate Site appeared to be heading over the fence. There needed to be more of those.

1983 was another strong profit year for Baxter, and one of its first events was another two-for-one common stock split (the seventh since 1959).

The second event was the phase-in, beginning in August 1983, of the DRG (Diagnostic Related Groups) prospective payment system for hospital reimbursement under Medicare Part A. What the new system did, in brief, was replace full cost recovery billing with cost or price caps for a mix of over 400 individual treatments or procedures. Picture a business today with open-ended contracts for services paid for as costs are incurred, facing a tomorrow when its services will be reimbursed through an artificial fixed-price system. That's a fair portrayal of the shocks DRGs sent through the hospital and hospital supply system. Granted, the change affected government reimbursements only. It was clear, however, that the new pricing standard would spread, and that when it did, all kinds of inventive cost shifting would occur among different classes of payers. Looking back at 1983, Loucks said, "That set of events meant the federal government *might* be able to control its own costs. In doing so, however, costs would be shifted to others. Look at the statistics. They're paying 88 cents on the dollar for Medicare and only 44 cents on the dollar for Medicaid. That is killing the states. It's certainly not helping business either."

Congress passed the Tax Equity and Fiscal Responsibility Act (familiarly known as TEFRA), Public Law 97-248, on August 19, 1982. President Reagan signed it into law on September 3. Title I provisions related to savings in health care and income security programs (specifically subtitle A on Medicare, Part A), imposed a stringent percentage cost increase limit for hospital reimbursement. It further directed the Secretary of Health and Human Services to:

> "Establish case mix indexes for all short term hospitals and . . . set limits for each hospital based upon the general mix of types of medical cases with respect to which such hospital provides services for which payment may be made under this Title."

The HHS Secretary was to develop final regulations no later than March 31, 1983, and the prospective payment system was to be phased in over a three-year period beginning a year after passage of TEFRA. Combining this new development with what had already been brewing in hospital group purchasing, Baxter growth rates and operating margins were certain to be adversely affected.

The third event was a Baxter first-of-its-kind. An investment analyst conference was held at the Hamilton Hotel in suburban Itasca, Illinois, from November 29 to December 1, 1983. More than 100 analysts from around the country attended as the market—in a late rally on Tuesday, the first day of the conference—hit a new Dow Jones high of 1287.20. The pros and cons of such a conference had been debated within Baxter before proceeding. Other major health care companies had not stepped forward to address how these profound changes would impact their business performance. So it took a certain amount of courage to take a public position on hospital system changes, the outcome of which was still very uncertain.

Baxter's message to the analysts was bluntly honest and well received. Loucks believed he had to get the message out about the market's deflated outlook. No one else in the industry had stepped up to the plate. When the conference was planned in the spring, hospital demand hadn't yet softened to the extent it did by the fall of 1983.

Reflecting on reactions to the conference, Loucks said, "We did the right thing to get the word out. That's not much consolation though, because when the hospital market fall came, it was like we'd been hit with an atomic bomb. We got the daylight kicked out of us in 1984." Baxter common stock bid price fell from 23 7/8 on November 29 to 21 3/8 on December 2 as daily trading volume swelled from 369,000 shares to 3,064,000 shares over that four-day period. That, however, wasn't the point. The conference wasn't held for the purpose of supporting the market price of Baxter stock. Loucks' purpose was broader and longer-term. He wanted to present a new strategic baseline for the company's position in the changing health care environment. That purpose was accomplished.

1984

As the new strategic baseline was drawn, Loucks recommended to the board of directors a series of actions to adjust to the new U. S. health care environment and its uncertainties. Baxter took a 1984 $116 million write-off (after tax adjustment) for plant shut-downs and other changes in income recognition. As shown at the end of this chapter, net income after the adjustment fell to $29 million, the lowest level since 1973.

The Philippines operation was closed and its manufacturing equipment transshipped to Baxter's Mexican plant. Facilities in Hays, Kansas, were also closed. The shut-down of Hays was the first closing of a domestic plant since the period of adjustment after World War II. The company continued to pay the cost of maintaining Hays facilities for two years after closing for the benefit of that small community.

There were reasons other than market environment for facility consolidations. Antagonistic labor unions in the Philippines escalated their violence to the point where the Baxter plant was totally sealed off and supplies had to be flown in by helicopter to keep operations going. The court system under the Marcos government failed to provide any relief for this problem.

Another more significant factor was that the world-wide manufacturing system, led for so many years by Ed Nawoj and then Madsen, had become sufficiently productive per unit of space and per labor hour that it could operate with a smaller number of facilities.

The announced Hays closing in 1984 was a particularly sad event. It was, however, planned and executed in a manner that was extremely sensitive to employee and community impact—so much so that it could have served as a model for the federal plant closing legislation that passed later.[7] A task force of Hays management, corporate manufacturing, human resources, employee benefit, and communication people worked for months on means of cushioning employee impact. Community support, sale and alternate uses of the facility, phased transfer of production, and similar issues were discussed. All of this had to be precisely timed in connection with required financial notifications and public announcements of the write-off. Loucks was on the telephone with Baxter staff until almost midnight the night before the employee meeting in Hays and the financial announcements. Some months later, Loucks and Graham both received letters signed by many Hays hourly employees thanking the company for the careful employee-oriented approach that had been taken.

Also in 1984, Loucks had a high-level corporate task force led by Gantz working on organization streamlining. As pointed out before, organization structure had never been a major element in Baxter corporate strategy. The guiding principles for organization remained flexibility, fluidity, and individual leadership. The 1984 task force did recommend some business unit consolidation and cost reductions. There were, however, no lasting changes in organization design. Tobin, who was very active in this effort, believes the introduction of technology organization units in 1984 was a basic change in Baxter's thinking and a constructive one.

As 1984 ended, Baxter was in a relatively strong position. Observers of U.S. hospital trends still disagreed about how far hospital admissions and lengths of stay would fall and about how many hospital closings would occur. The basic strategic question facing the company was whether and how its long-term growth rate of 20 to 25 percent annually (still 15 to 18 percent in these more difficult times) could be continued when its core domestic markets were now likely to grow at only 6 to 8 percent. No clear answer to that question had yet been found. The first half of 1985 would surface a specific opportunity and a company response that only a few years before would have been unimaginable.

END NOTES

CHAPTER XVIII

1. The corporate name, Baxter Travenol Laboratories, Inc., had been adopted and approved by the shareholders in 1976.

2. By 1989 U.S. physician income had grown to a total of $118 billion, a 59 percent gain from 1985. Per capita physician income had grown to $155,800. That was a 24 percent gain above inflation since 1985. *Forbes,* 27 May 1991, p. 125.

3. This is 1990 data, abstracted from *Fortune,* 29 July 1991, p. 50.

4. *Fortune,* 1 July 1991.

5. Baxter annual report, 1982.

6. Baxter annual report, 1983.

7. Worker Adjustment and Retraining Notification Act, 29 United States Code, Section 2101, effective February 4, 1989.

CHAPTER

XIX

THE 1985 BAXTER-AMERICAN HOSPITAL SUPPLY COMBINATION: A SUDDEN AND SUCCESSFUL STRATEGIC STROKE

November 25, 1993, was the eighth anniversary of Baxter's combination with its former rival, American Hospital Supply Corporation. It passed largely unnoticed, obscured by events swirling around Baxter for most of 1993, and having been immediately preceded by a company news release explaining future strategic direction, announcing further realignment and employment reductions, and providing details of the expected large write-off for the year.

The company's Deerfield headquarters appears the same now as in 1985, with a few exceptions. The Deerfield complex, including the executive building (Building One), is more lightly populated, reflecting the slimming down that followed 1985. Many of the old familiar faces are missing. No doubt much of that would have happened anyway due to normal attrition and retirement. And construction of the Parkway North Center, immediately north of the Baxter campus, has taken away the area's somewhat rural appearance.

Appearances notwithstanding, this is an organization completely different from the one of ten years ago. The American Hospital merger, which caused most of that change in character, remains one of the most controversial chapters in Baxter's history. A bold, brilliant strategic stroke, some say, who give great weight to what perhaps might have befallen Baxter without the 1985 merger. Maybe so, argue others, but deficient in follow-through and execution. Still another faction adamantly maintains the concept was ill-advised from the start. Often in the intervening years it was thought the time of proving which faction was closest to being right had arrived. The crucial test began developing in 1993-94.

The 1985 acquisition of, and merger with, American Hospital Supply was startling at the time—almost unthinkable—because of the tangled historical relationship between the two companies, their respective sizes, and the way Baxter had internally generated most of its growth. The decision and action on American Hospital Supply was lightning fast—initiated by Vern Loucks in mid-June of 1985 and culminating in an agreement between the two companies less than a month later. This milestone action, though, probably should be viewed as the result of a transition process that began when Loucks became CEO in 1980, or perhaps even earlier. Loucks had been weighing appropriate responses to health care market and competitive changes, and discussing them with his management team for some time before 1985. The period of 1980-85 should be considered a time of strategy review and development similar to the period of 1945-52, which followed the beginning of Bill Graham's tenure at Baxter.

Why was Baxter's merger with American Hospital Supply different in intent and result from other major mergers of the eighties? Even though that era is only a few years back, it might be useful to reset the stage. This is the era now being referred to by some as the "Decade of Greed." Michael Milken became its symbol. Corporate raiders became almost as widely known as *Raiders of the Lost Ark.* Corporations were accused of short-term shuffling of financial assets, of overleveraging, and underinvesting, all at the expense of their employees.

For the U.S. health care system, the eighties were the decade in which our national policies were declared to have failed. It was also the decade of biotechnology and of AIDS. Still, more broadly, the U.S. economy began the eighties in a recession, staggered under the weight of a crushing federal budget deficit, and ended the decade headed into another recession.

Why did Baxter's 1985 strategic maneuver appear likely to be successful? Because it clearly wasn't a financial grab of the kind critics attribute to the eighties. Because in the midst of all the adverse events summarized here, the company stuck to its knitting and was willing to bet on the long-term future of its core business. And Loucks had an unusually broad view of what he wanted to accomplish through the combination with American Hospital Supply. It went well beyond Baxter's own competitive position to include the whole structure of the hospital and health care business. He spoke repeatedly during this time about "improving and taking costs out of the entire system."

We've tried to illustrate how patterns and themes keep recurring throughout Baxter's more than 60-year history. Here's still another example. In the 1950s and early 1960s Bill Graham used to talk about "having to manage on two levels": one level being the cooperative distribution relationship with American Hospital Supply; and the second being the battle to prevent American Hospital Supply from gaining control of Baxter's manufacturing and technology base. Now we see Loucks attempting simultaneously at different levels to maintain the company's growth and earnings momentum, to fashion broader distribution systems and corporate programs like its American Hospital rival's, and to develop a new strategic vision. The generally unsuccessful, small acquisitions of the early eighties were part of that process, just as development of Piromen, Choloxin, and other such products had been in the early fifties when Bill Graham was thrusting out in various directions in order to overcome the constraints of the American Hospital distribution agreement. These were far different times. Baxter was no longer a small company struggling to establish its viability and capable of being readily shaped by a single strong leader. In part, the company was a product of its history and its past successes. Short-term investment expectations formed a new set of constraints. How Loucks went about transforming the company for a new health care age and the resistance and obstacles he had to overcome in the process are major themes of this and later chapters.

The book, *Strategy of a Megamerger,*[1] describes in detail the events and immediate aftermath of the 1985 Baxter merger with American Hospital Supply. However, because that earlier book was written during 1987-89, conclusive evaluation of the merger still wasn't possible. The original timetable for achieving the merger's financial targets was slowed by dilutive effects of the 1987 Caremark acquisition and by market and management factors.

The merger was risky and audacious because of the competition, even dislike, between the two companies. It wasn't going to be easy to make the combination work. The impression is sometimes given that mergers either work or don't work due to some combination of economic factors. Few really understand the enormous commitment and hard work that goes into making them successful. Also, the time necessary to make mergers work is frequently underestimated, as it certainly was here. Once it had been established that a Baxter offer for American Hospital was financially feasible, there was no doubt about Loucks' commitment to making it work. The opportunity to make a run at American came just after the 1983 and 1984 Homestead Group meetings[2] had helped to shape a sense of future strategic direction.

Loucks recalled, "We had tried to build our own corporate marketing program like American Hospital's.[3] And we made some progress.

But I can remember when I'd bring up Baxter's corporate marketing with key hospital people, they'd tune me out. So when American Hospital came on the scene, we already knew what a good strategic fit it would be. . . . Of course, that was based on looking from the outside in, on what we *thought* American was doing."

THE ACTION BEGINS DOWN EDENS EXPRESSWAY IN EVANSTON

Loucks was the first industry executive to say publicly—at the Baxter investors conference in late 1983— that the hospital business was going to get worse; American Hospital Supply was beginning to show the effects by 1984. Foster McGaw remarked in 1965 after American and Baxter broke up that "two of American's divisions were hospitalized." In 1984 some of American's businesses showed signs of illness for the first time in a long time. American Hospital's 1984 sales increased a meager 4 percent over the previous year. The hospital sector's operating earnings fell 9 percent. Since only 40 percent of its total sales came from self-manufactured products, many observers thought American particularly susceptible to a hospital industry downturn.

Big, hearty, compelling Karl Bays, American's chairman and CEO since 1971,[4] had a plan. He had been considering for several years how to break out of what he called "the hospital supply pocket," and go after a bigger share of hospital dollars, which represented almost 40 percent of national health care expenditures. This was called at the time the "supermed strategy." It contemplated a single organization which provided hospital services, incorporated manufacturing and distribution of necessary supplies, planned and developed facilities, and had substantial financing capabilities.

When Bays began to implement this vision, he didn't estimate the magnitude of the risk of putting American Hospital Supply "in play." The possibility that another health care company might try to move in on the opportunity he was seeking to create was judged remote. After all, while the health care waters were churning, the changes didn't include major mergers and acquisitions. Bays' advisors made the mistake of underestimating and misreading the competition, particularly American's smaller neighbor in Deerfield.

How did Bays' vision of health care's future differ from that of Loucks? Given the different nature of Baxter's business, Loucks had to consider global as well as domestic market trends. American Hospital's operations were primarily domestic. Loucks was also perhaps more focused on the role of technology and innovation in solving health care's problems. And he was convinced even then that the entire health care system in the United States had to be rethought and reformed.

From 1983 forward, Loucks' strategic view and objectives have remained remarkably consistent. He has continued to maintain that new pressure on U.S. hospitals created both need and opportunity for a totally new kind of hospital company to work with them, and, if Baxter could rise to the opportunity, there would be more than adequate growth and earnings as a reward. "Let's not focus on all the negatives," he said. "Despite cost and other pressures on the health care system, patients are going to be treated." Bays' strategic view, on the other hand, contemplated American's integrating forward into the hospital business and competing with hospitals.

Still, Loucks was grappling with the same immediate problems that troubled Bays—a market shift that was almost certain to constrain growth and profit margins. In an August 1984 strategy review, Tobin spoke persuasively about how Baxter's traditional niche leadership approach might now penalize the company in the new health care environment.

Loucks responded forcefully. "You find a way," he said, stabbing a finger in Tobin's direction, "to make corporate marketing and distribution systems work in our favor, rather than against us."

Then, in Baxter's March 1985 board meeting in Florida, Director Fred Turner raised the prophetic question of whether Baxter could continue to go it alone in the new health care environment, or whether the company should seek to combine with another health care supplier in some way.

LOCUS SHIFTS TO NASHVILLE

Bays and Dr. Thomas Frist, the CEO of Hospital Corporation of America (HCA) of Nashville, Tennessee, had been talking for some time about combining their companies to form a "supermed" organization. Both men were widely known leaders in their respective health care fields. HCA was then the leading for-profit hospital chain. Subsequently, it suffered setbacks as the market deteriorated. Figure 23 shows distribution of revenues and beds among the leading U.S. for-profit chains as of 1990. Bays said, "Tommy Frist and I knew the idea was ahead of its time. With a squeeze on the industry, though, and possible consolidations we believed we had to move then or take the risk of letting the idea get away."

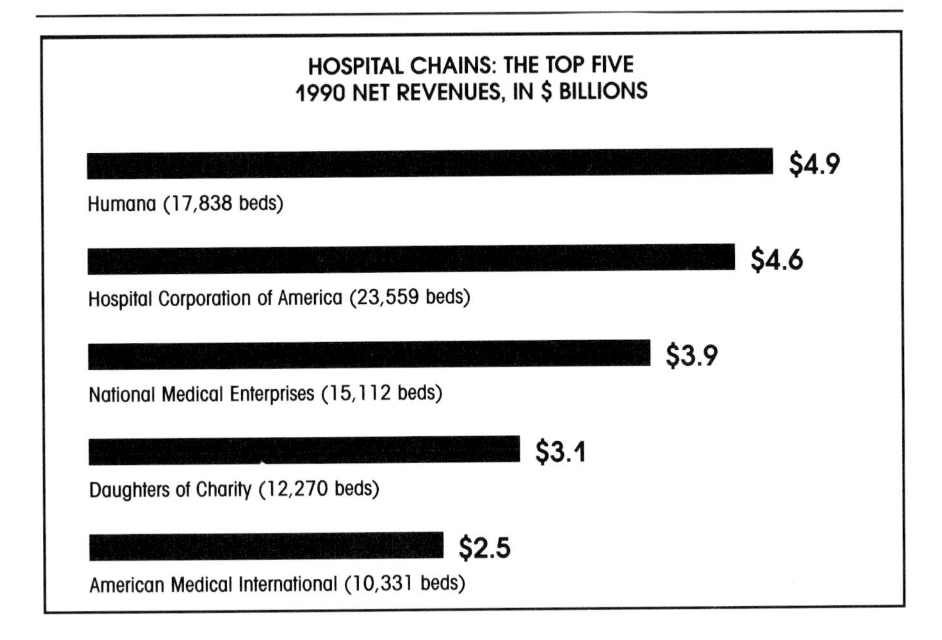

Figure 23[5]

By January 1985, American Hospital, with the assistance of Merrill Lynch Capital Markets and HCA, had developed a plan. They would form a joint holding company, Kuron, to operate out of Nashville. The American Hospital Supply subsidiary would continue to operate out of Evanston with a smaller staff. The mechanism to accomplish this was a straight stock swap with no premium for either party to the transaction.

This was very much Bays' personal vision of the future. Few other key executives were in the loop. Hal Bernthal, American vice chairman, was. Jerry Myers, the chief financial officer, and John Crotty, vice president for planning and services, both helped Bays put the plan together. Other key American executives, however, were very much on the periphery. When the plan began to roll out, this proved to be one of its vulnerabilities. Other American executives like Frank Ehmann, Tom Quinn, and Will Pierie seemed to have misgivings as they were brought aboard in February and March. At best, they supported the deal out of loyalty to Bays.

However, unspoken queasiness about the Kuron concept among some American executives was a minor problem compared with what lay ahead. American Hospital and HCA made their plans public in New York City on April 1, 1985. Without a transaction premium, the stock market reaction was negative. The price of both stocks fell in response. Some analysts who followed the stocks said cynically, there's no strategy in this deal. Frist simply wanted to get at American's cash flow and Bays was worried about the effect of market changes on his distribution margins. The two companies were exchanging weaknesses, not building new strengths.

Hospital customers were overwhelmingly negative about a principal supplier linking up with a major for-profit competitor. Bays had, of course, anticipated that. Planning estimates before the announcement were that American could lose up to $400 million in annual hospital volume before bouncing back. Still, American people who were closest to customers were unprepared for the depth and vehemence of the feelings expressed. It's one thing to look at an abstract number estimating customer defections, quite another as a sales representative to face angry hospitals daily, hearing McGaw's message of the primacy of the customer played back.[6] Terry Mulligan, an American corporate officer who had been one of the architects of the corporate program and became head of corporate marketing for Baxter, used to read the old Dale Carnegie classic, *How to Stop Worrying and Start Living,* before briefing other American officers on the worrisome hospital market situation. The well-worn volume is still on his Deerfield office bookshelf.

HCA left the "selling" of the plan to overcome these negative perceptions to American Hospital. That may have been where the biggest problem was encountered. The concept was visionary, but very little was done to identify and enumerate specific immediate benefits for hospitals and the health care system. Were there going to be cost savings? Service improvements? New answers for hospitals to the new problems they were encountering? In the absence of solutions to these issues, many concluded that the only tangible benefits were for two groups of "stakeholders": employees of the companies and maybe—only maybe—stockholders.

American and Merrill Lynch had carefully researched which other health care players might seek to overturn the American-HCA deal, even though it had a stiff "lock-up" provision. This risk was substantially discounted—in error, it turns out. Baxter was dismissed from consideration out-of-hand because of its smaller size and the large 1984 write-off it had recently announced.

UNEASY CALM PREVAILS—UNTIL JUNE[7]

Events continued along this track for a time. American "huffed-and-puffed" to overcome the bad start in selling the HCA combination. Baxter stuck to its position that if Kuron became a reality, there would be no serious effect on its business. This seemed borne out by HCA's announcement during the time that it would renew Baxter's supply contract. The common stock prices for HCA and American Hospital Supply fell about 25 percent. Dates for stockholder approval (July 3, 1985) and for closing were drawing near. The hospital industry was still buzzing, but outside Evanston and Nashville interest and controversy faded. Frist, Bays, Myers, Crotty, and others involved in crafting the deal no doubt heaved sighs of relief by the early days of June that the intended outcome was in their grasp. The planning meetings ("love-ins") of HCA's and American's management staffs hit no snags. Bays was to be CEO of Kuron. From American, Ralph Seaman, human resource vice president, and his key staff, Tony Rucci, Herb Walker, Frank LaFasto, and others, were working with HCA counterparts to design and staff the holding company organization and develop required policies.

BAXTER BIDS AND KURON CRASHES

Rapid-fire decisions in Deerfield brought the plan to an effective halt on June 20. On that date Baxter startled American Hospital Supply, Hospital Corporation of America, and the financial world by making its own bid for American Hospital Supply.[8] A different kind of uncertainty prevailed after that, but there was little question that the HCA-American Hospital Supply merger was dead. Frist recognized that almost at once and prepared his exit plan. It took longer—into July—for American executives to concede that the HCA plan was foreclosed. Had they written it off earlier, the final outcome might possibly have been different. It had been a tough, uphill climb since the public announcement on April 1. Now the scramble back downhill was even tougher. It took its toll on American managers and employees alike. The real battle was about to begin, and they had not recovered sufficiently to wage a strong fight.

WHY BAXTER MIGHT HAVE BEEN CONSIDERED AN UNLIKELY TAKEOVER BIDDER

Over its history, Baxter had not been notably acquisition-minded. Putting aside the Wallerstein financial deal of 1957, only the Fenwal acquisition in 1959, and the very first acquisition, Hyland Laboratories, had had a major and lasting impact on Baxter's business and technology. Other acquisitions had been essentially "niche-fillers."

Baxter's growth and market leadership had been achieved principally through internal resources. Furthermore, most recent small acquisitions (Auto Syringe, Medcom, Dynamic Control, and Compucare—just completed in the spring of 1985) were marginally successful at best.

Baxter wasn't in the acquisition game. It certainly was an unlikely entrant in the developing arena of hostile takeovers. As one observer of the events put it with some puzzlement, "Baxter doesn't do this kind of thing."

The period leading up to the release of the HCA and American prospectuses was hectic in Evanston and Nashville. The mailing of the prospectus regarding the formation of Kuron on May 20 was a key milestone in the preparation for their respective shareholder meetings in early July.

Meanwhile, the continuing publicity surrounding that transaction caused a key Baxter financial executive to do his own operational analysis. Up to that time, Baxter's interest in the deal had been focused on market and competitive effects. This particular individual asked himself whether the situation represented not a competitive threat, but an investment opportunity for Baxter.

It was Mel Kalas, vice president-financial control, who began to ponder the question. Using annual reports from prior years, he prepared pro forma financial analyses for a merger of Baxter and American. He ran the same analysis over and over again, with his confidence in the answer growing with each pass. His "scratchpad" numbers indicated that at $42 per American share, 50 percent stock and 50 percent cash (compared with the $35 stock swap price in the proposed HCA transaction), buying American Hospital Supply could make sense for Baxter Travenol. He finally concluded, "The numbers aren't airtight, but a percentage point or two isn't going to change the conclusion. People are going to think it's crazy, but even so I've got to run this by Lambrix."

Kalas wasn't entirely alone in considering a possibility that most others would have dismissed out of hand. In a nearby office, the young director of financial analysis, Harry Kraemer, was also running American Hospital numbers and constructing hypotheses of his own. Kraemer, who would become Baxter CFO in November 1993, had developed a keen interest in acquisitions and other financial transactions while employed at Northwest Industries and earlier as a graduate student of Al Rappaport's at Northwestern University. He and Kalas would make up a complementary and highly effective team as their first tentative ideas took more definitive shape and began to lead to action.

KALAS PUTS THE BALL IN PLAY

Kalas broached the idea with Robert J. Lambrix, then CFO, on May 27. Lambrix said no. Kalas insisted on a second turn at bat. On Friday, May 29, he took Lambrix through his draft presentation. With more time and more data, Lambrix began to buy into the merits of the proposal. "Okay," he agreed, "I'll take the idea to Loucks and Gantz on Monday. But I want you to work over the idea and the numbers with Harry Kraemer on the weekend. We'll meet in the cafeteria Monday morning at 7:30 to see if the analysis still looks positive."

Kalas was enthusiastic about that approach. Before Friday afternoon's meeting adjourned, Lambrix telephoned and scheduled an 11:30 a.m. Monday meeting with Loucks and Gantz for the stated purpose of reviewing second quarter earnings outlook. Kalas immediately shared his thoughts with Kraemer to see if he agreed with his logic and enthusiasm. Kraemer did.

SOME KEY QUESTIONS

For years under Dr. Ralph Falk and Graham, the company had struggled to free itself of American Hospital's distribution embrace. Now here it was seeking to embrace American Hospital Supply. With United States hospital growth flagging, and American Hospital Supply pursuing a strategy of breaking out of the hospital supply "pocket," was it prudent for Baxter to commit even more deeply to this sector? Conversely, how much longer could Baxter expect to be able to go it alone?

Unlike the HCA-American Hospital plan, Baxter's proposed acquisition of and merger with American turned on required synergies of about $400 million. Are synergies of this magnitude realistic? Would American's distribution franchise prove to be worth the price Baxter ultimately had to pay? And did this turning point represent a basic change in the strategy Baxter had consistently pursued since the 1950s? Whether or not it was a strategic change, how long would it take for this move to pay off? Would investors and managers have the patience to see it all the way through?

THE GAME HEATS UP: JUNE 3 THROUGH JUNE 20

On Monday morning, June 3, Loucks called to cancel the 11:30 a.m. meeting with Lambrix because of other pressing business. Lambrix found it necessary to tell him the real subject of the meeting. "Look, Vern," he said, "what I really want to cover with you is a proposal for

Baxter to make a run at American Hospital Supply. Mel Kalas and Harry Kraemer have been working on it. I think we've got something here, and there isn't much time."

Loucks laughed, "You must have been smoking something over the weekend, Bob." But he agreed to let the meeting stand as scheduled, and as he hung up the phone Loucks thought to himself "This could turn out to be the vehicle for the strategy we've been developing. Can we make it happen, though, and make it happen in the right way?"

The sale in the 11:30 meeting proved easier than getting the meeting to take place. Loucks looked at the numbers and immediately saw the potential. His directions to Lambrix were succinct, "Find a top investment banker who agrees with us that this is feasible and makes good business sense . . . and will work with us to get it done. We have to move fast . . . within the next several days."

Lambrix's first investment banking inquiry produced a negative response. Not until the June 3 meeting with Goldman, did the Baxter finance team learn of the lockup agreement that AHS and HCA had put in place to preclude any other party intervening in their proposed merger. Goldman Sachs, which turned up later representing American Hospital Supply, told Lambrix the deal wasn't doable. Kraemer pressed for a second investment banking opinion, and Lambrix got Loucks' agreement to talk with First Boston. By Friday, June 7, First Boston responded that "they had an angle." On Saturday the key First Boston people—Joe Perella, Dick Bott, Bill Lambert, and Mike Koenecke (missing Bruce Wasserstein, who wasn't available, but later became the investment banking "wizard" of the deal)—came to Deerfield for a strategy meeting.

That same week Loucks had initiated the legal review process in regard to antitrust and other issues through Marsh Abbey, then Baxter's general counsel. The pressured weekend and the following week of June 10 brought further actions, which Loucks orchestrated masterfully. He began to bring other executives into the decision loop: first Tobin, then Lance Piccolo and Steve Lazarus. Their support would be essential if and when the high-risk decision got to the board of directors. Loucks kept Graham informed from the start.

Preliminary planning began for a board meeting, which, when it took place, turned into a three-day marathon. Work raced ahead on acquisition financing involving an estimated $2.5 billion. By Saturday, June 15, those discussions with First Chicago were well along.

On June 13, less than a week before the planned Baxter board meeting, Loucks was rocked back on his heels when Graham said to him, "I've been giving a lot of thought to this situation, Vern. I don't believe I can support it because of the financial risks and earnings dilution."

Ray Oddi recalled that he was just as surprised as Loucks. Loucks paused for what seemed like a long time before replying, "Bill, this is the first time we've come down on opposite sides of an important business decision. That makes me uncomfortable, but I believe we ought to bring the matter before the board of directors and let them make the call." And that's what the two men decided to do.

The June 18-20 Baxter board meeting thoroughly aired and dissected the facts. Support progressively swung to CEO Loucks' recommendation that a $50 per share offer be made for the stock of American Hospital Supply. Before the board adjournment at 9:35 a.m. on Thursday, June 20, approval of such action was unanimously voted.

By that afternoon, Abbey had personally delivered to American's Evanston headquarters the first "Dear Karl" letter from Loucks.[9] It was a carefully drafted "non-offer" letter in First Boston code language inviting American Hospital to enter into discussions with Baxter and offering to withdraw if the American board wasn't interested.[10] In reality, there was no way now to withdraw. The game was going to be played to the end, whatever the end was.

"IF 35 IS FAIR, THEN 50 IS FAIRER"

Twenty-four days—June 21 to July 14—was the time in which the game got played and the outcome was decided. It went exactly as Loucks and Wasserstein strategized. Baxter's execution was close to faultless. Because it was quick and followed the game plan, though, doesn't mean it was easy or stress-free.

Baxter kept the pressure on American with the slogan "If 35 is fair, then 50 is fairer." How could it be fair to American stockholders to spurn an offer that was 43 percent higher than the HCA price? Meanwhile, Loucks sought "quiet negotiations" with Bays as a primary strategy, while readying a fallback plan of pursuing an adverse tender offer or proxy solicitation.

The strategic response of American Hospital Supply was not nearly as effective. Maybe nothing American could have done would have worked. The Baxter maneuver had neatly boxed off some of the options. Beginning with a curt rejection of the Baxter invitation by the American board on June 21, American pursued a number of sequential defensive tactics. First, Bays and his key colleagues put principal reliance on the preemptive provisions of the HCA agreement and the belief that a Baxter-American merger wouldn't be permitted even under antitrust policies which were becoming less stringent. This was only a form of denial. And Frist, CEO of HCA, was already backpedaling away from the April 1 agreement.

American mounted a vigorous financial PR campaign pointing out that the $50 offer wasn't sound, and wasn't really $50 at all.[11] A $3 billion "defense fund" was lined up with the banks, although how it might be used was never clear. "White Knight" alternatives were considered, but only perfunctorily. Bays tried to interest Loucks in a "commercial alternative" under which Baxter would have privileged access to the American distribution system *without* a merger of the two businesses. Many Baxter people thought it was a "red herring." Whether it was or not, it certainly would have been a throwback to the old days of American-Baxter relationships.

Then toward the end of the first week of July, with Bays inclined towards putting the improving Baxter offer before his board for an up or down vote, the strategy in Evanston shifted to getting the best price for American's shareholders and the most favorable consideration for American employees. This is where Bays and American did best.

On Friday, July 12, the American board authorized Bays to enter into formal negotiation with Baxter. Negotiations proceeded throughout the weekend on per share price, treatment of American executives and employees,[12] and a "hell-or-high-water" liquidated damages clause to protect American should the Baxter merger fail for any reason. By 4:00 p.m. Sunday afternoon, July 14, when both boards met to review the weekend's progress, the game was over.

It was a dramatic ending and new beginning on that Bastille Day for a business relationship that dated back sixty years to Baxter's very beginning. The relationship had had many stages. Originally, Baxter solutions represented for American Hospital the most attractive opportunity to integrate backward into manufacturing. Later, the two companies developed different philosophies about the hospital supply and medical products business. American's was based on service and distribution; Baxter's was based on technology and market niche leadership. By now, American had developed its own technology position in its $600 million medical sector with heart valves, heart catheters, beta blocking drugs, interocular lenses and lasers, and a variety of other products.

Would all that history get in the way now? Did the deal mean that Baxter's niche strategy was behind it? Time, and further environmental changes in health care in the United States and other developed countries, would tell.

JULY 15 BEGINS A NEW ERA

The two boards reconvened on Monday morning and unanimously approved the terms of the agreement. The final price was $51 per American common share.[13] Baxter took on an almost $2.5 billion burden in bank debt. It would be years before the new company could work through the dilution.

American Hospital stockholders could expect to do well if the merger closed as expected. Ground rules for treatment of American's employee benefits and employment and severance "rights" were exactly as Bays had specified during final negotiations. Yet the best that could be hoped for by Baxter on July 15 was that American people were not too antagonistic and that they could be won over. Hospital customers, while supportive of the outcome, were still in a wait-and-see mode. And, of course, there remained a substantial element of uncertainty since the merger could still fail on its way to closing for any one of a number of reasons. Other newsworthy mergers had collapsed in 1985. It was far from a sure thing for Baxter and American.

Loucks spoke to Baxter managers and employees during this time about the amount of work and change that still lay ahead. "We're not in the last inning yet. We have to work together to build a totally new organization. It's not just the widely respected American Hospital Supply organization that's changed forever by this planned merger, the old Baxter is gone too. None of us can completely control the way all these changes take place."

Yet many of those who listened to him were saying to themselves, "This episode is over or almost over. How soon can we get it behind us so we can get back to work and the way things were?"

STRATEGY ASSESSMENT AS OF JULY 15, 1985

Even now, many years after the dramatic events of the spring and early summer of 1985, the strategic soundness and import of Loucks' strategy are still being assessed. The major strategic issues then and now were as follows:

- Why commit so heavily to the hospital sector when its growth rate and profit margins were clearly becoming more constrained than other parts of health care?

- Was American Hospital Supply Corporation, particularly its distribution system, worth the price Baxter ultimately paid?
- How would the actions that now needed to be taken—combination of two very competitive organizations and a heavy hand to squeeze out the synergies—impact on Baxter's long-successful strategy? Did the merger with American in fact require an entirely new strategy?

On the first issue, the hospital business was and always had been Baxter's mainstay. Representing almost 40 percent of domestic health care expenditures (HCE), hospitals had been through economic cycles before. Had hospitals not been facing pressure and consolidation in the mid-eighties, the opportunity to acquire and merge with American probably would not have come along. Furthermore, hospital products and distribution had historically been somewhat oligopolistic in structure. Pressures on hospitals would likely accentuate that pattern, providing a competitive advantage for Baxter with its larger scale and superior ability to manage and control costs. It appears for all these reasons that Baxter was wise to concentrate its investment risks in the area where it enjoyed its greatest marketing and technological strengths.

What about price? This was one of the more controversial issues at the time of the merger. Lambrix, Kalas, and Kraemer all opposed a $50 or higher offer level. When Loucks decided on $50 based on Wasserstein's advice about "breaking the glass jaw of the HCA deal," Abbey believed that American Hospital had no leverage to force the price higher. Still, the numbers Kalas started out with—$42 or a 20 percent premium over the HCA exchange—were probably not compelling enough to make the deal happen. In retrospect, the actual price does not appear to have significantly increased Baxter's risk overall or watered down the attractiveness of the transaction. The swing between 46 (probably the bottom of the range at a 30 percent premium) and the actual of 51 (a premium of 45 percent) represented an investment difference of $375 million—a considerable amount. However, just the two largest divestitures[14] soon after the merger produced an almost $1 billion offset to the merger cost. At worst then, the higher premium gave Baxter a longer, steeper hill to climb to reattain its past earnings level.

Of course, the third and last issue of corporate strategic direction was the most difficult, and managers and employees of both companies continued to have problems grasping where all this change would take them. What had happened to Wee Willie Keeler and the

Baxter niche strategy? If distribution margins were being squeezed, what could Baxter do to strengthen the American Hospital distribution system, and would it be enough to keep major manufacturers like Johnson & Johnson, Becton Dickinson, and 3M working profitably through this channel?

Actually, the strategic shift wasn't as much of a departure as it might have appeared. Loucks had in mind four key elements of a new strategy. The first was increased emphasis on services. This was already well under way before 1985, but the combination with American Hospital Supply stepped up the pace.

The second was a new form of supplier-hospital partnership. In that respect, Loucks and Bays had the same idea, but different ways of carrying it out. To implement his vision, Loucks needed a broader product-line and a superior distribution system. American Hospital provided both.

The third strategic issue was the need to take cost out of the health care system. As a strategist, Loucks was thinking about how to contribute to this goal system-wide, not just about the $350 to $400 million in merger synergies. It was, in fact, Loucks' broad view of the whole hospital and clinical care system in the United States, and all the costs associated with it, that set this merger apart. The combination of American and Baxter redefined the hospital and medical products industry and wrote entirely new rules for successful competition in the field, just as Baxter's many innovations had earlier. Significant savings were passed along, and continue to be passed along, to hospital customers.

And if the resolution of these three issues (service orientation, new forms of hospital partnership, and health care system cost-savings) worked as planned, then the whole hospital supply business could be made a new kind of market with different characteristics. Baxter could now supply about 75 percent of a hospital's total needs. Dominating the new market called for a new set of competitive advantages: scale economics, broad- and top-level hospital relationships, and breadth of product-line. These were quite different from the competitive assets the company had employed in the past. The "hospital penetration strategy," as it is now called,[15] led first by Bob Simmons and now by Mulligan, has been successful. In larger U.S. hospitals, Baxter continued to increase its dollar receipts per patient bed and per day of patient stay.

While Loucks was still shaping and beginning to "sell" this long-term business strategy, he had to focus much of his attention and energy on an immediate strategy for executing the merger. The merger could still fall apart. Glitches in execution could create obstacles for the long-term business strategy. That had happened to others.

MERGER EXECUTION: JULY 15 TO NOVEMBER 25

With the ink barely dry on the merger agreement, Loucks quickly formulated rules for merger execution. Some of his subordinates thought a couple of them were designed only for internal PR. The subordinates had it wrong; he was deadly serious about all of them. American executives and employees, on the other hand, began more and more to take Loucks at his word, although that certainly didn't mean they were committed to the new organization and its business strategy. By the end of 1987, all but a handful of American Hospital Supply's "magic 43"[16] cadre of executives had chosen to depart. This was unfortunate, but perhaps inevitable regardless what actions might have been taken. Most key executives—Bays,[17] Ehmann, Pierie, and Quinn, for example—stayed long enough to contribute to the success of the merger. That was the minimum Loucks was counting on.

The key decision rules were as follows:

- The combination of organizations would be "fast and friendly." Loucks wanted the organizational design and essential staffing done before the merger closing. It was. He also insisted on an open, cooperative process to salve pre-merger antagonisms.
- Slating procedures for selection of personnel would be fair and subject to both top management and human resource oversight. The best people were to be selected regardless of organization affiliation.
- Employee communication would be honest, timely, and proactive. Here Loucks was capitalizing on one of his own greatest management strengths.
- Merger execution would be led by a small transition team. For most of the execution and immediate follow-up period, it consisted of four team members: Dick Egen, executive-in-charge, Don Johnson, Gary Bang, and Ed Kleid. A fifth member, Vince Mihalik, was added before the team was "sunseted."
- Integral business units were to be maintained for the transition period so that disruptions in customer service, sales, and market relationships would be minimized. (In retrospect, this decision rule may have contributed to later execution problems.)

- Synergies were to be vigorously pursued and tracked in detail. The $400 million target remained a linchpin of the merger and one of the most visible indicators of its progress and success.
- Management's focus would be on *business* aspects of the merger. If those proved to be right, then the "softer" elements of culture, organization values, management style and employee commitment would fall into place in due time. (This decision rule has been questioned by some, inside and outside the organization).

By September, an organization had been designed and approved; the top 20 corporate officers had been selected[18] and were working on their own organizations and staffing; the personnel slating and selection process was cranked up, as were severance and outplacement policies and supports;[19] the 10 major business units were well-positioned to be further reduced in number at appropriate times; and Department of Justice-required divestitures were proceeding—painfully. All of this was done while maintaining the "Chinese wall" between the two companies required by antitrust regulation until actual merger closing. Loucks, Bays, Gantz, and Ehmann had every reason to be pleased. Egen worried particularly about slippage in Department of Justice approval schedules right up to the actual closing, but his team overcame every manageable obstacle. Employees were "down" as the process ground on and as they grasped the reality that their organization destinies were not in their own hands, but instead driven by events they couldn't control. Baxter employees sometimes resented the consideration extended to American managers and employees by Loucks and others. They found little comfort in the assessment offered by Loucks on several occasions. "It's like a Marine Corps recruit depot. Everybody's got to get the same haircut before we build a new team."

Two basic decisions made by Loucks at the very beginning of the process seemed risky at the time, but have proved out well, based on subsequent results. They were (1) his decision to press ahead as fast as he did to define the organization, rather than let the dust settle, and (2) choosing to treat everybody in the new organization equally.

In the management climate of the 1980s, these approaches seemed innovative, particularly considering how other organization changes and combinations were then being handled.[20] Perhaps they were truly innovative, but in retrospect, it seems more that Loucks was simply following the old management precept of doing the right thing at the right time.

EVALUATION OF MERGER AND BUSINESS STRATEGY AS OF 1985-86

It wasn't possible to evaluate results conclusively at the time the detailed account of the merger was written.[21] It was still difficult to do so in 1994 because of continuing rapid changes in the health care environment.

By far the most difficult of the immediate merger execution tasks proved to be getting the necessary operating synergies. They were a moving target and measuring results presented unanticipated complexities. Baxter captured some of the more obvious synergies—in corporate staffs, warehouse closings, other real estate sales, and common services—fairly quickly in late 1985 and early 1986. Then there was a lag and Loucks had to step up the pressure in 1987. Finally, after successive consulting projects by Booz Allen & Hamilton in 1987 and A.T. Kearney in 1990, Baxter did deliver on its synergy objectives as the decade of the nineties began. As a result, Baxter's G&A ratio, operating margins, and net income showed significant improvements in 1990 and in 1991. Its common stock price rose, reflecting these improvements. As a matter of fact, the company's common stock price hit $40 per share at the end of 1991, almost exactly what the 1985 shareholder value model prepared at the time of the merger optimistically predicted. That per share price compared with $23.25 in 1983 (post-split), $13.25 in 1980 at the beginning of the decade, and with $13 in 1985 when the merger was being finalized.

Reflecting on the years from 1985 to 1990, Loucks later said, "Remember, the 30 percent IV price drop in what had become a bilateral competition with Abbott cost us $125 million in 1987 alone and well over $250 million between 1986 and 1990. The 1987 Caremark acquisition was dilutive. Then in 1990 we took a $566 million charge for further restructuring designed to produce an annual $275 million cost improvement."

Baxter saw an opportunity in the changing situation of hospitals. The situation called for a leading hospital supplier with new characteristics: more service- and quality-oriented; able to identify and share cost savings with hospitals; in a position to meet the broadest range of changing hospital needs. Following the 1985 merger, Baxter's share of the U.S. hospital market grew at the expense of other national competitors. At the same time, however, smaller regional competitors became stronger market factors. This latter trend continues to be a matter of concern for Baxter. Does it mean that the company's size makes it less flexible and nimble in adapting to regional and local differences?

Baxter had the opportunity to create a new hospital supply and service market environment where success and competitive advantage factors are quite different from what they were when commercial dialysis or blood transfusion and blood components were first introduced. The company after all had begun its existence by redefining the function of manufacturing intravenous solutions. Now it was attempting to redefine and reengineer marketing, customer service, and logistics functions. That undertaking has proven inherently more risky and difficult in part because of continuing changes in the marketplace. Over the several years following the 1985 merger, Baxter's sales to hospitals increased substantially.[22] The "hospital penetration strategy," as it has come to be called, has been a strategic success. Nor has it necessarily foreclosed Baxter from other markets and other technologies.

KEY EVENTS IN THE YEARS IMMEDIATELY AFTER THE MERGER

There were many milestones as the new company moved forward from the 1985 merger. The more notable were new acquisitions and divestitures, clarification of corporate identity, organization development, effects on Baxter's position in global markets, and resultant new priorities for technical innovation.

Up to this time, hard-nosed bargaining and wheeling-dealing had not been thought to be one of Loucks' strongest assets. He certainly changed that perception through actions begun in late 1985. For the two largest divestitures completed in 1986 he insisted on, and got, significantly higher prices than his internal or external advisors thought possible—almost 30 percent of the total price paid for all of American Hospital Supply. Not only did this significantly reduce the merger debt burden, it sharpened Baxter's strategic focus. Graham's opinion is that, excluding Loucks' management of organization and people after the merger, his approach to divestitures was perhaps the most successful element in the whole merger process. Targeted synergies for the consolidation process were $400 million, which have taken years of hard work to accomplish. From the point of view of debt reduction, the divestitures of Flint and American Critical Care alone, on the other hand, yielded $1 billion with considerably less time and effort.

DIVESTITURES AND ACQUISITIONS

Loucks began to form a strategy for divestitures long before the November merger closing. Bruce Wasserstein of First Boston, Ray Oddi, former Baxter CFO, Bob Lambrix, then CFO, and Tim Anderson, then corporate development vice president, were all involved in divestiture strategy development with Loucks. Loucks was confidently optimistic about the time it would take to complete the planned divestitures and the prices the major ones would command. When it came time to put that optimistic plan into action, Ray Oddi very ably took the lead, drawing upon his years of Baxter financial experience.

The Justice-mandated divestitures in the fall and winter of 1985 were "tune-ups." The Oxygenator business was the first such sale. Haemonetics, American Hospital's blood business, and McGaw Laboratories, the focus of so much of the connection and competition between Baxter and American, were larger and more difficult transactions. Then, parts of the company's medical and procedure glove business were also sold. Since these deals were negotiated prior to the merger, each company had to take primary responsibility for conducting the mandated divestitures from within its organization.

After the merger closing, the strategic divestiture plan went into effect and the pace picked up. The American Cystoscope business was sold. American Medical Optics was sold to Allergan in April 1986. Both had been important parts of American Hospital's successful "technology engine," the Surgical Critical Care Group. The group had been configured to balance American's hospital supply and distribution business. That strategic role was no longer necessary after the merger.

When a company is actively in the marketplace, it tends to buy as well as sell. Baxter made an important move to strengthen its French operations with the purchase of Dubenard Hospital Company from Sanofi in November 1985. It purchased a small generic pharmaceuticals producer, Ascot, in January 1986. In June and July Baxter made two important acquisitions in its global (specialty) business areas: Hemascience Laboratories and Pandex Laboratories. With the addition of Hemascience and Pandex, and for other reasons as well, Baxter's blood products business, considered a mature "cash cow," seems to have entered a new era of vitality and innovation.

Abbey Medical was divested in September 1986. Also in September, as already mentioned, the two largest divestitures, Flint and American Critical Care, were consummated, recovering about 27

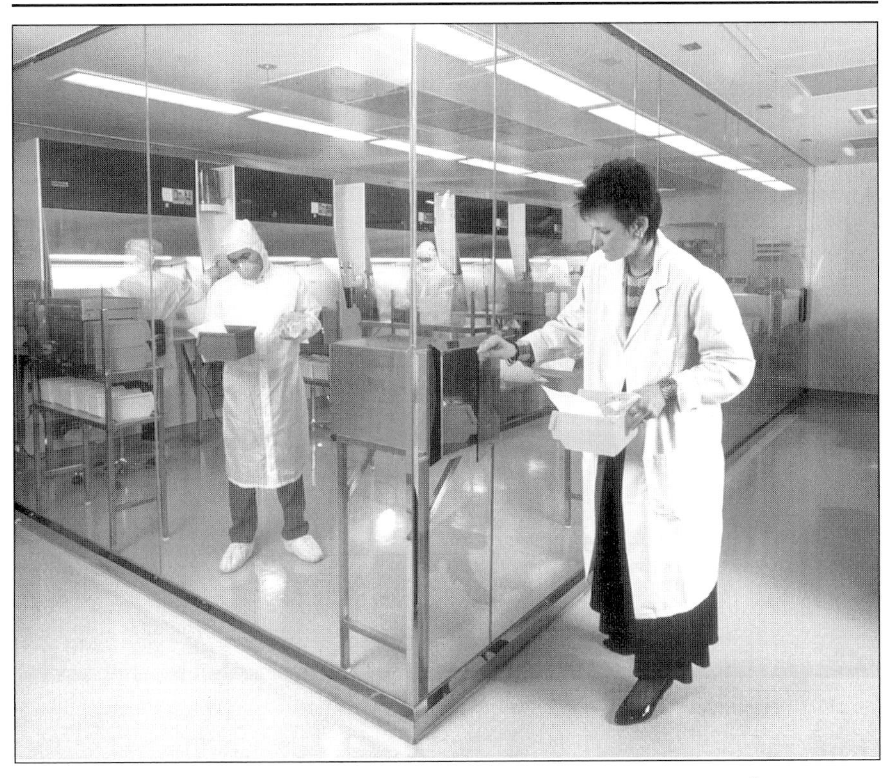

At Toronto General Hospital, the Baxter compounding center uses a clean room to mix pharmaceutical compounds according to specific patient dose instructions. This system assures a quality drug delivery program.

percent of the total American Hospital Supply investment. And before the divestiture strategy began to wind down, Discase lyophilized solution, an injection treatment for spinal disc disease developed by Baxter, was sold in August 1986 and American's surgical staple business was sold to 3M in March 1987.

Then in August 1987 Baxter's largest acquisition ever was completed. This was the $520 million deal for Caremark. Baxter and Caremark had been running very close in the number one and number two positions in Alternate Site and home care. In fact, so significant were their combined sales positions that Abbey thought it desirable to include with the U.S. Department of Justice submission, prior to the deal, an exhaustive list prepared from local yellow pages of the thousands of "mom-and-pop" home care services operating in the cities where Baxter and Caremark also operated. The full strategic significance of the Caremark acquisition may have been obscured because it came so hard on the heels of the 1985 merger. Loucks says now of the combination with Caremark, "Just as quickly as the merger with American Hospital transformed our position with hospitals, our acquisition of Caremark took us to the next level in Alternate Site. It really laced things up for us." By 1992, the fast-moving market situation had shifted again, and Baxter reluctantly altered its strategic position regarding the Alternate Site business, including Caremark.

The Caremark acquisition is another example of Loucks' bias for action. Jim Sweeney, founder of Caremark, had worked in product management for Baxter in the seventies and also worked at American Hospital Supply. Several times earlier, Baxter had put out feelers to Caremark about acquisition, without result. That changed on a winter day in 1987. Sweeney and Loucks passed each other on Fifth Avenue in Manhattan in early 1987. Sweeney called to Loucks, "Call me, Vern. There's something I want to discuss with you." From there, the deal was put together quickly.

Loucks is justifiably proud of this decision, made at the price of additional dilution in 1987. He pointed out, "The market multiple for an investment in high-tech home or Alternate Site care has increased since we bought Caremark in 1987. While the operating margins in this business are somewhat lower than the corporate average, the growth rate and return on invested capital are considerably higher."

Caremark was another step away from being a transaction-oriented company, and a step closer to becoming what Loucks calls a "process-oriented" organization. The entire system was in place for Baxter to serve patients wherever they were treated. It was Loucks' alternative to Bays' vision of "a broader playing field." Because of the dominance of Caremark in its markets, Loucks endures with good humor the barbs he sometimes gets for paying so much for the venture creation of a Baxter graduate.

At a 1989 alumni dinner-roast for Graham, the guest of honor made it a point to look at the audience and ask, "Where's Sweeney? [Sweeney left the company a short time after the acquisition.] He is still an alumnus, isn't he? I'm not sure how many re-employment bonuses of that size we can afford, Vern." As described later, this would all change again in 1992 when Caremark was spun off to become a separate, publicly owned New York Stock Exchange listed company. It was still another indication of how quickly, despite its greatly increased size, Baxter could respond to changing conditions.

NEW FOCUS ON PATIENT CARE

The reader has no doubt observed how certain key themes keep recurring in Baxter's history. In part that's because, as health care raced ahead over 60-plus years, the same issues continued to be encountered. Loucks, during the preparation of this history, observed how some of the conditions of the mid- to late eighties were reminiscent of the 1930s when Don Baxter Intravenous Products was struggling to get started.

Some hospitals now as then are financially pressed. There is concern again about access to needed health care, particularly for the unemployed and underemployed. And general economic conditions are again uncertain, following a decade described by some as filled with financial excesses.

Loucks' decision to emphasize health care *services* and to develop the world's largest alternate-site care network with the acquisition of Caremark had enabled Baxter to serve more patients directly across a wide range of therapies. Dr. Falk would probably have enthusiastically approved, even though he could not have possibly foreseen these new methods of treating patients outside hospital settings.

SOME EXPERIMENTAL AVENUES

During this same period, investments in biotech ventures in the early eighties began to produce some new product breakthroughs (for example, monoclonally purified Factor VIII for treatment of hemophiliacs). The long-developing joint venture with Nestlé in the field of clinical nutrition, Clintec, became a business reality. Clintec is now a business of several hundred million dollars, headed by Dick Egen as CEO. The Hospital Information Systems business, another initiative of the early eighties, was spun off as Spectrum Healthcare to a 50/50 joint venture with IBM (Spectrum was renamed IBAX in June 1991). So even when the post-merger waters were choppy, longer term development efforts continued.

CORPORATE IDENTITY

There were immediate pressures in 1986 to change the name and corporate identity of the new company. Much of this reflected the emotions of the post-merger era; for example, the idea to rename the company Baxter American to give both groups of employees a rallying point. Loucks turned a deaf ear to all these suggestions. In 1987-88, after an excellent study by the firm of Landor & Associates, the logo was changed to a starkly simple Baxter.[23]

Workers mount the new Baxter logotype at the Deerfield headquarters.

The blue color on a white field which had been used by both Baxter Travenol and American Hospital was retained. Since the Baxter name had been used for years by American in its solutions distribution activity, and since American had long ago purchased the original California Don Baxter Company, the name Baxter was probably the best unifying symbol of all. The only loss for the nostalgic was the familiar Baxter "flag" logo known variously as the "mortar-and-pestle," the "reclining B," or simply the "crushed box." Baxter employees didn't know quite what it signified, but it had been around a long time, and many employees missed it.

FURTHER ORGANIZATION DEVELOPMENTS

Organization improvements and adjustments to developing strategy proceeded smoothly, although employees and some managers complained loudly about the number of reorganizations between 1986 and 1989. The elegance of the original pre-merger, November 1985 organization design was that it allowed the process of compacting the organization to go on in a nondisruptive way. One of the more difficult tasks along the way—the execution of which was assisted by Bain Consultants—was the rationalization of the domestic sales forces, consisting of more than 2,000 personnel. Later, because of the changing role of distribution as the linchpin in the new Baxter system, the "first dollar" commission system for distribution sales representatives was eliminated. Sixty-eight sales representatives left soon after that change, but distribution sales increased that year by 10 percent. There had been some profound differences in sales and management philosophies between the two companies. In Piccolo's words, "American's system incentivized people to become top sales producers, while Baxter's incentivized people to move into management." Actually, the two systems and philosophies complemented each other very well, particularly as corporate marketing's role took hold and became even more effective than it had been in either prior organization.

By 1991 there were just three major business groups. They were global businesses, reporting directly to President Gantz; hospital businesses, reporting to Executive Vice President Tobin; and Alternate Site businesses, reporting to the other executive vice president, Piccolo.

The overall organization was a clear expression of Baxter's strategic thrust and an interesting combination of the two prior companies' organizational structure. For example, Baxter Travenol World Trade (BTWT) had been a fiercely independent part of Baxter. It was gone now, merged with high-tech or medical specialty businesses. The old Surgical Critical Care Group, successfully run for American Hospital by Will Pierie, was gone but its strategic core remained a key part of the global businesses. Now some of Baxter's leading medical specialties—renal and blood therapy—were better integrated within the organization reporting to Gantz. All three parts of the hospital business—IV systems, hospital products, and distribution—were integrated under Tobin. All Alternate Site businesses (with the exception of renal) were integrated under Piccolo.

Of course, below the top organization level, the diversity of product-market areas had increased markedly. It is important to understand the number, nature, and size of the divisions or strategic business units in order to grasp Baxter International's strategy for the future.

Without naming them all, the global businesses in 1992, before organization changes continued to shift the key executives, were organized and led as follows:

- Renal, headed by Don Joseph, which is both a market and a product-oriented business.
- Diagnostics, then headed by Tony White, a technology and market-oriented organization, and itself composed of many distinct businesses.

- Blood Products, led by Dale Smith, a product and technology-oriented business.
- Medical Specialties, led by Mike Estes, essentially technology-oriented and with heavy emphasis on Edwards and Bentley, which are market-driven.

Tobin's businesses included:
- IV Systems, led by Lester B. Knight,
- Corporate Marketing, headed by Mulligan,
- Hospital Products, headed by Bob Funari, and
- Hospital Sales and Distribution, led by Jim Connelly.

Piccolo's Alternate Site Businesses included:
- Caremark Home and Alternate Site Services, directed by Charlie Blanchard,
- Prescription Services, headed by Kris Gibney,
- Orthopedic Services, headed by Paul Zimmerman,
- Health Cost Management (Corporate Services), headed by Donna C. E. Williamson, and
- General and Industrial Products, led respectively by Diane Munson and Don Martin.

So the company's products and services were now being delivered to many points throughout the hospital as before, as well as to various alternate care sites, group practices and clinics, doctors' offices, laboratories, dialysis centers, blood banks, industrial plants, other corporations (Health Cost Management), directly to patients in their homes, and even to general consumers (mail-order pharmacy services). Just when it appeared in 1991 that this organization and strategic pattern was set for the future, a further basic change in strategic array and key Baxter executive players was already developing. Market tensions were building between the company's strong positions in its original hospital business and its fast-growing Alternate Site services.

IMPACT ON BAXTER'S GLOBAL BUSINESS

Post-merger changes provided a new surge for the company's global businesses. American Hospital had, before the 1985 merger, made a lesser commitment to businesses outside the United States. Baxter now ratcheted up sales goals per patient and per hospital bed for most of its traditional products in other developed countries.

Baxter also implemented a much more sophisticated organization to integrate marketing, manufacturing, and technology around the world, and to create the flexibility to manage different businesses in different ways depending on their requirements and individual stages of growth.

Gantz reflected on Baxter's increasingly successful international strategy, "We had a classic management success in international in the seventies. After an investment period leading up to the time Graham sent Loucks and me to Europe, we began through the seventies to reap significant returns. This was timely because inflation was sapping the U.S. economy. In the early eighties, exchange rates turned against us. Now the cycle favors us again. And we've got a much more diverse portfolio to work from. Of course, with EEC 92, we're going to have to build a broader manufacturing and distribution system, quite different from the country-specific systems that served us so well in the past."

EFFECT ON TECHNICAL DEVELOPMENT

What are the company's technical and R&D priorities after the sea-changes of the American Hospital merger? Some are the same, some are new and different. Blood therapy products and human-blood substitutes command a very high development priority.

Development work on the CS-3000 blood cell separator began in the mid-seventies, long before the merger period. The machine was introduced at the American Association of Blood Banking meeting in Las Vegas in November 1979. The CS-3000 wasn't fully perfected as a closed system until late 1984.

Baxter's Pete Bloom explained the issues, "At first, we weren't entirely clear where we were going or what we had with the CS-3000. Before this machine, there was no such thing as a completely closed equipment system. Consequently, the F.D.A. imposed 24-hour dating on blood platelets, making them impractical. The platelets we derived with the Fenwal Multiple Blood-Pack container system required six to eight donors to make one therapeutic dose. That increased the risk of infection and patient refractory response [rejection].

"The trick in making a closed system was to keep the tubing that fed the blood centrifuge from kinking. Baxter became aware of a technology for keeping the electrical wiring that fed a rotating radar tower from tangling. It was called 'Omega One, Omega Two.' We acquired the rights from a man named Adams. The Adams centrifuge

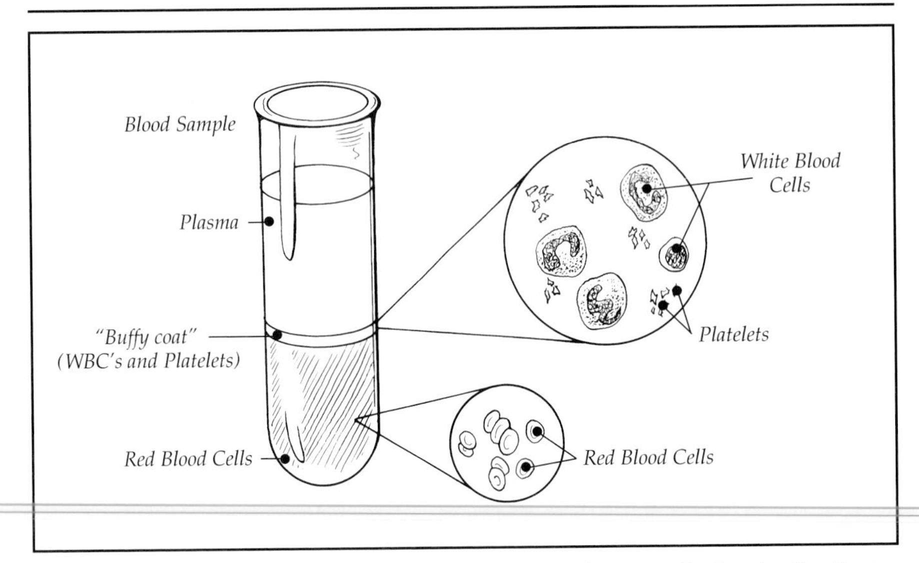

Whole blood is separated into various components by centrifusion in the Baxter Fenwal Division CS–3000. The apparatus facilitates collection of nearly pure pools of white cells, platelets, red cells, or plasma. Each of these components has an important therapeutic value.

principle wasn't fully perfected until 1984. It was a rocky road. When we got it perfected, it completely changed the market. One competitor, IBM, abandoned the market, selling its business to Cobe. The other competitor, Haemonetics, didn't catch up with the closed system until 1988 or 1989.

"Eliminating random donor platelet therapy revolutionized certain types of cancer therapy, making it possible for oncologists and hematologists to treat their patients without the risk of the patient bleeding to death. In 1989, we introduced the CS-3000 Plus, with expanded memory, more automation features, and on-screen coaching. We have a commanding market share, and more breakthroughs are on the way. . . . By the way, the CS-3000 apheresis kit is by far the most sophisticated disposable kit that Baxter manufactures."

Renal is also heading into a new era of innovation beyond hemodialysis and CAPD. With the addition of American's business, diagnostics became a strategic priority. (However, after continuing efforts to achieve market leadership, the company determined it should divest itself of the diagnostics business.) Major investments are being made in cardiovascular products of various types. Biotech investments of different kinds continue. And Baxter has broad investment interests in transplantation: bone marrow, kidney, LVAD (left ventricular assist devices), and others.

Bone marrow transplants involve giving the patient large doses of chemotherapy and/or radiation to destroy any cancer cells and diseased or damaged bone marrow, and then replacing it with healthy bone marrow. An autologous bone marrow transplant uses the patient's own bone marrow harvested earlier. Four thousand such transplants were performed in the U.S. in 1990, up from 800 in 1982.

Advances in health care services involve innovation too, although it is innovation of a different variety. The Baxter ValueLink system in hospital distribution, and the infrastructure system for CAPD, are also innovations, but requiring very different management attitudes and skills, and a significant amount of new investment.

The same internal pathways for one product or service breakthrough to connect and contribute to other Baxter businesses seem still to be operating well, although corporate size and product-line diversity make the process more difficult to manage. On the other hand, a much richer portfolio of technical strengths certainly has been created.

FINAL THOUGHT ON STRATEGIC SHIFT

In 1991, while reflecting on the changes of the 1980s, Loucks said, "We now manage a *process* for delivering health care products and services. Wherever we can, we much prefer to do it in partnership with hospitals. When that's not feasible, we may work in partnership with corporate payers or in other ways. What we did in the 1985-87 period is smash together all the niches so that Baxter could relate to the total health care delivery system. In that sense, the 1985 merger was simply a question of 'scale economics and preemptive strategy' (preemptive in that competitors will find it unattractive to duplicate Baxter's investment in the total process)."

Gantz also reflected on how Baxter strategy evolved between 1980 and 1985, "Between 1980 and 1983, after Vern succeeded Bill Graham as CEO and I became COO, we continued to execute Graham's long-successful strategy. There were some considerable pressures on us because we had allowed the new-product pipeline to run somewhat dry.

"Having relied on Graham's technical genius for so many years, responsibility for innovation was too tightly centralized for a $1.5 billion company. We had all sat at Graham's knee long enough learning strategy so that we were comfortable pushing more of the technical and innovation responsibility down into the organization.

"Vern and I put heavy emphasis on a process improvement program so that we could produce additional funds for R&D investment. Cost improvement became value improvement. With the leadership of Don Madsen and Ray Oddi, and the assistance of Bain Consultants, our operating margins and earnings were substantially improved. We reinvested some of that gain into innovation with excellent results. That was the period that produced drug delivery systems; Alternate Site infrastructure investment; monoclonally purified Factor VIII; and the foundations of Clintec. At the same time, we substantially reduced the risk of peritoneal infection with CAPD.

"Then in the fall of 1983, the bottom fell out! After DRG's came in, sales were 'pole-axed.' By November, we were forecasting weekly—and actuals were still falling short of forecast. Fortunately, we had a CEO who reacted instantly. He said, 'The market's changed and we're going back to the drawing board.'

"Fortunately too, we had a still-active former CEO who said, 'Whatever it takes to make the strategic adjustment, Vern, I'll support you.' So beginning in late 1983 and the first quarter of 1984, with our net $116 million write-off reflecting future manufacturing over-capacity, our basic strategy in regard to hospitals and Alternate Site began to change drastically.

"But guess what! Marketing 'niching' in the classic Bill Graham style is still very much with us. In global businesses we're still niching opportunities just exactly the way Graham would have. The principal differences are that the market niches are so much bigger, our distribution advantage transforms our basic approach, and the range of resources we can bring to bear is much broader."

So the answer to the question of whether Baxter's strategy remained constant is that it did and it didn't. It appeared to be a successful strategic adaptation. Some key strategic issues, however, still loomed in 1991. Among them were:

- Integrating distribution within Baxter's overall business
- Discordance between the hospital and Alternate Site businesses
- Improving hospital margins, particularly on prime vendor (non-manufactured) products
- Adjusting European strategy to EEC 92 initiatives
- Continuing to master the process of service innovation
- Investing in the developing potential of Pacific Rim health care markets

It is, of course, pure speculation to consider where Baxter might be today without the American Hospital Supply and Caremark combinations of the mid-eighties; and equally so to project American Hospital's position had events taken a different course.

The strategic thrust was, again, hitting the ball in an unexpected direction. Baxter demonstrated once more an organizational flexibility unique for a company of its size, which made it possible to continue adapting to basic changes in global health care.

At this point, this becomes a history of *two* companies: Baxter and American Hospital Supply. A prior history of American covers its remarkable record from its founding in 1922 until 1964.[24]

From 1985 to 1987 Baxter completely transformed itself. American Hospital Supply, as an equal part of the new enterprise, was transformed as well. Baxter ended 1992 more than four times the size it attained in 1985. Operating income (pretax) in 1991 approached $1.1 billion, 60 percent of what total Baxter sales were in 1985. The long-successful market niche strategy is still alive and well, embedded in a much larger framework.

Baxter's two largest and most powerful competitors in medical and hospital products (Johnson & Johnson and Abbott Laboratories) both combine this business with other businesses, such as consumer health care products or "proprietaries," infant nutrition, and pharmaceuticals. In that larger context, one could say that Baxter and American belonged together; that, given their history, they represented "two halves of one whole." That certainly appears to have been the consistent view of McGaw as he pursued a combination with Baxter through much of the 1940s and 1950s. McGaw exchanged gracious letters with Loucks shortly after the 1985 merger agreement.

All the history didn't make the combination, when it ultimately occurred, any easier or less risky. The reason was that the objectives of such a combination had totally changed. In McGaw's day, the objectives had been primarily internal: management control, vertical integration of manufacturing and sourcing, and customer identification of supplier name and brands. By the mid-eighties, the objectives had become primarily external: adapting to a new marketplace, building new scale economics, creating totally new processes to replace the old transactional way of doing business with hospitals, and capturing "customer share of mind" rather than simple brand identification. What made the merger difficult was that many of the key participants in both companies saw the combination in terms of the old imperatives, rather than the new ones. It took strong leadership on Loucks' part to attempt to change perceptions of employees as well as customers.

Loucks reflected on those difficult years, "1983 and 1984, as tough as they were, served the purpose of getting us very, very focused. Then along came the American Hospital Supply opportunity. You could say it fell right in our laps. But we never assumed we'd just do the deal and that would solve the problems we faced. Good thing we didn't because we ran into some tough problems.

"First, as happens in acquisitions and mergers, American was not doing some of the key things we were counting on as well as we had thought they were. As we moved to fix some of those things, I'd have managers say to me 'Let's give people time to adapt and adjust,' and I'd have to tell them, 'Look, we don't have time.'

"Also, we ran into heavy pressure on prices. From 1977 to 1988 we got no real price relief, and in 1989 the price relief was only 3 percent. We pushed our overall corporate margins to the 37 to 38 percent range. The hospital penetration strategy is a success. Customer service innovations like ValueLink are producing commanding share positions. The result is that it took us five years instead of four to accomplish the business objectives we publicly announced at the time of the 1985 merger."

Baxter in 1991 ranked about 60th in profits and market value, about 100th in sales, and 200th in asset value, among top U.S. industrial companies in the various business directory listings[25]. The company's major challenge continues to be increasing its rate of return on equity beyond the level that prevailed in the post-merger years.

While both Baxter and American were performance-oriented companies, it is quite apparent that the 1985 merger has created an even more performance-oriented culture in the new company. That result is essential because of the new realities in the U.S. and global health care markets. In the seventies, Baxter management thought its strategy might hit the wall first at $250 million and then at $1 billion in annual sales. That didn't happen. It's abundantly clear now that no current strategy, however soundly conceived, will be as long-running as the strategy that propelled Baxter through the sixties and seventies (and, for that matter, that guided American Hospital Supply for even longer). Global competitive pressures simply won't permit it. Baxter has to begin preparing now, and it is Loucks' principal preoccupation, for the next juncture at which it appears likely that company strategy might again hit the wall. The company faces the next turning point with a strong capital and market base and with a young, experienced management team.[26]

ORGANIZATION LEADERSHIP LESSONS

Leadership, as distinguished from management, and how leadership transforms large organizations have become major themes in American business literature.[27] There are important and perhaps unique lessons in Baxter's 1986-1990 period of transformation for Baxter people seeking better to understand their own history . . . and lessons for others as well.

The team working in 1985 and 1986 on the combination of the Baxter and American organizations perhaps didn't fully grasp at that time what they were about. In general, they assumed they were working on merger tasks of combining and rationalizing. Loucks, from the start, saw it differently. He knew that he was beginning a process of transformation. He knew also that, before it was done, it would test his leadership abilities.

The reader will perhaps remember that we've referred several times to "managing on multiple levels." That's what Graham had had to do in the periods described as the years of thrusting out in new directions (the late forties and early fifties) and the growth years (the mid-fifties to the early eighties). Now we see Loucks having to do it again in the era of health care system transformation. Managing on multiple levels means two things. First, it means overcoming inherent conflict and contradiction among varying primary objectives and constraints. In the situation of Baxter and Loucks in the mid-to late eighties those varying principal factors were:

- *cost*—the clear and present imperative to take significant costs out of the system;
- *people*—managing the process of change in such a way that it increases, rather than reduces, their stake and their commitment;
- *strategic thinking*; and
- *new system design*—that is, rigorously relating the interests of the company to the needs and interests of the total health care system.

For example, if Loucks had moved more quickly to achieve maximum Baxter cost-savings, as some critics said he should have, the human dimension would have been adversely affected. Then too, those pressing at the time for greater economies were thinking of relatively simple programs such as Baxter head count reductions.

Loucks, on the other hand, was characteristically thinking of taking costs out of the total system in a way that would yield Baxter a significant competitive advantage.

Like Graham before him, Loucks had a strong bent for humane leadership. That common approach was certainly one of the reasons why the transition in 1980 had gone smoothly. The stories are legion about how Loucks reached out to help individual employees with health, financial, or other problems. Early in his CEO tenure, he had people around him like Sam O'Kelly whose responsibilities included keeping Loucks in close touch with employee perceptions and needs. As the process of staff reductions surged during 1987 to 1990 (and still continues today), therefore, there were certainly personal pressures and concerns for Loucks. Perceptions of him among some employees shifted from "Is he too good a guy to make the tough decisions?" to "Is he so relentless in the drive to control costs that he no longer cares about employees?"

The second meaning of managing on multiple levels has to do with the phenomenon of the organization's different perceptions and expectations, which diverge at times of stress and change. Even superior communication will not eliminate that phenomenon, only reduce its intensity.

Achieving these two things—balance among conflicting goals and convergence of individual and organizational interests among different groups of people—are, most simply and realistically, the essential tasks of leadership in transforming or renewing any large organization. They're not new, though some management observers say they are. They are, in fact, old as the hills. They're just more difficult in today's complex and brutally competitive environment. Loucks carried out these tasks with great skill and patience.

Time will tell how well the transformed Baxter will consistently deliver market, technological, and profit leadership. Some Baxter employees chafe under frequent organization adjustments and realignments. However, that has always to some extent been Baxter's way and it is certainly an inherent part of the current CEO's view of organization agility necessary for leadership.

CONTINUING CHALLENGE OF PINNING DOWN MERGER RESULTS

At the end of 1991 the outcome of the 1985 merger appeared positive. The sense within Baxter was that the most difficult and hazardous part of the eighties journey of change had perhaps already been traversed. The hope that calmer waters lay ahead was, however, to prove illusory. More shocks and reversals still lay ahead, as will be described in the following, concluding chapters.

Whatever position one chooses to take on the original idea of merging the two companies, harvesting promised merger benefits has been slower and more difficult than anyone, including Loucks, expected. Many different reasons for that could be cited. For example, Loucks believes that the health care market has undergone such rapid transformation that Baxter has had to keep accelerating and adjusting its plans, particularly in regard to its internal cost structure. Some others observe that Baxter simply underestimated at the beginning of 1985 the complexity of what it then set out to do. As time stretched out, the investment community, with its well-known bias for short-term results, grew increasingly impatient and began to question the merger benefits it had originally accepted rather well.

Another factor cited as a possible primary cause was that Baxter was perhaps trying to do too much at one time, and that as a result its focus was blurred. Certainly, communicating the company's direction crisply and clearly to investors, customers, and even employees proved difficult in the late eighties and early nineties. Still, that has always to some extent been a challenge for Baxter because the company is nearly unique even among its major health care competitors.

Within the company one may hear the opinion voiced that the merger didn't produce faster and more conclusive results in large part because employees have grown somewhat weary and dispirited due to the many waves of change that have broken over them since 1985. They need, these employees say, some notable successes to encourage them to "keep hanging in there."

Whatever the reason or combination of reasons, final votes on the success of the 1985 merger are yet to be counted. Baxter top management continues resolutely along the path it has chosen, undeterred by expression of outside doubts, and holding in reserve other attractive strategic options it might elect to pursue at some time in the future. It could be said that one of the central goals of strategy is to multiply the number of available, attractive strategic options. The American Hospital Supply merger did that. It's up to Baxter management to continue to make the right choices going forward in a complex and uncertain health care environment.

END NOTES

CHAPTER XIX

1. For a detailed account and chronology of events from 1984 to 1987 refer to Thomas G. Cody, *Strategy of a Megamerger* (Westport, Connecticut: Praeger Publishers/Greenwood Publishing Group, 1990).

2. The Homestead Group, referred to in other parts of the text, was a group of about 20 Baxter officers who participated with Loucks in strategy formulation.

3. *Corporate marketing* was the term used by both American Hospital Supply and Baxter Travenol for a unified sales service and contracting effort for all products across hospital department and specialty lines.

4. Karl Bays died on November 7, 1989, just a month short of his fifty-sixth birthday.

5. "Business World," *The New York Times Sunday Magazine,* 9 June 1991.

6. Although Foster McGaw was still alive and Karl Bays said he discussed the HCA plan with him, McGaw no longer played any role in the company. He died in early 1986.

7. Since events from June to November 1985 are recounted in detail in Cody, *Strategy of a Megamerger,* they are more briefly summarized here.

8. June 20, 1985, was the date of the first Vern Loucks "Dear Karl" letter opening the Baxter-American acquisition/merger skirmish. Twenty-five days and several letters later with the Baxter offer substantially "sweetened," the American board approved Baxter's offer.

9. There were four "Dear Karl" letters—June 20, 22, 25, and 27—which progressively clarified terms and strengthened the offer.

10. Because of the HCA-American "lock-up" provision and SEC and NYSE rules, this invitation could not be "an offer."

11. Goldman Sachs valued the terms of the June 20 "Dear Karl" letter at $39.57 per American share.

12. Sunday, July 14, negotiation between Bays and Loucks at the North Shore Hilton on American's "15 point memorandum" produced favorable (some thought overly-generous) treatment for American Hospital employees.

13. Some analysts include the payment to HCA in calculating per share purchase price, thus raising the price to $53. Loucks points out these were one-time costs, transactional in nature, which should not be included in the valuation equation.

14. The two divestitures were Flint, sold to Boots Ltd., and American Critical Care, sold to DuPont.

15. Baxter's hospital penetration strategy set high "hurdle bars" for sale of all company products per hospital patient bed. Achievement of these targets has represented much of Baxter's volume growth in recent years.

16. The "magic 43" were the top American executives included in the company's highest level of benefits.

17. Karl Bays became chairman of the new company. He resigned in June 1987 to become CEO of Whitman Industries.

18. There was excellent "balance" in officer selections. Five of the ten senior line officers came from each of the prior organizations, mirroring the balance at the top with Bays, Loucks, Gantz, and Ehmann.

19. Both personnel selection and severance policies were professional, effective, and humane—due in large measure to the efforts of Tony Rucci, who became senior vice president of Baxter and left in 1993 to accept a position with Sears, Roebuck and Co.

20. See for examples the description of the General Motors reorganization in 1984 and Chrysler's acquisition of AMC in 1987; *Fortune.* 16 November, 1992, p. 74.

21. Cody, *Strategy of a Megamerger.*

22. Baxter's share of U.S. hospital purchases is well over 20 percent, substantially more than that of any other individual competitor.

23. The full new corporate name was Baxter International Incorporated, and the name of the principal domestic company was Baxter Healthcare Corporation.

24. Sturdivant, *The Story of American Hospital Supply Corporation: Growth Through Service.* (Evanston, Illinois: Northwestern University Press, 1970).

25. See, for example, Forbes 500 annual directory, from April 27, 1992.

26. As of 1994 Loucks was 59; James Tobin, president, was 49; Lester B. Knight, who assumed Tobin's hospital responsibilities, was 36; and Tony White, responsible for global businesses was 48.

27. See, for example, various books by John Kotter of Harvard Business School, and recently, Noel M. Tichy and Stratford Sherman, *Control Your Own Destiny or Someone Else Will* (New York, New York: Doubleday, 1993), which describes how Jack Welch is transforming General Electric.

CHAPTER

XX

BUILDING MOMENTUM: 1986-90

The 1985 turning point, like earlier points in the company's history, had elements of suddenness and at the same time of underlying continuity. The suddenness and the reasons for it have been made clear. There was a question in the late 1983-84 period as to whether the base the company had built over the years was adequately defensible. Wilbur Gantz described that critical time, "I still recall November 1983 as the DRGs took effect. At about the time of the investors conference, things turned worse much more quickly than any of us thought possible. We'd forecast weekly to be up 10 or 12 percent and then come in flat. Remember, this was a company accustomed to planning and building three to four years out, just to keep up with demand."

The 1985 combination with American Hospital allowed Baxter to build a new base almost instantaneously. And it was accurately a new base, rather than a new strategy. The underlying continuity may not be quite so apparent.

The continuity, which not all the participants in the events of 1986 to 1990 grasped at the time, consisted of three major elements: a commitment to the principles of total quality management (TQM), renewed and strengthened customer orientation, and a *long-term* approach to market and organization change—all of them obviously closely related. It was these three elements of continuity, together with strong leadership, which made this combination of Baxter and American successful, compared with other 1980s mergers of similar size and significance.

Actually, there was a fourth important factor, sometimes overlooked: the strength of American Hospital Supply's human resource function, which was preserved in the new Baxter and which served the company well in the difficult post-merger years. Related to that factor was the diversity that combining the Baxter and American staffs encouraged.

Ongoing quality management programs proved to be a strong unifying force. In the year or two following the merger, some of the traditional human resource programs for knitting together the cultures of the two predecessor companies proved only partially successful. However, the emphasis on total quality management, which was well underway prior to the merger, provided concepts around which people from Baxter and American Hospital could readily join. The Quality Leadership Process (QLP) became a major management focus directed to customer requirements, customer satisfaction, and the teamwork necessary to meet them. Vern Loucks' involvement in these kinds of management programs had been active since the early to mid-seventies. From time to time, differences in the management and strategic approaches of Graham and Loucks, the two men who have most influenced and shaped Baxter over the last almost half-century, have been described. In respect to follow-through and attention to operating detail the two are very much alike. Mary Wrenn, who was one of the first women on the New York Stock Exchange, and an early discoverer of Baxter stock, paused when asked what made Baxter uniquely attractive as an investment. After reflection, she said, "You know, beyond the vitality of the industry and Baxter's innovation, it really came down to something very basic. That's Bill Graham's follow-through on every opportunity and every problem." Loucks continued as a champion of quality programs from that time forward as they contributed to operation improvements.[1] Although total quality management and quality leadership weren't designed as cultural unifiers, they served that purpose nonetheless.

Michael Merson of Helix Healthcare Systems in Maryland said recently, "It is relatively easy to differentiate Baxter from others because Baxter has a much richer management philosophy. They don't think and act as a provider, but rather as a integral part of the health care system and health care community. When Helix was formed a little over six years ago as a small regional multi-hospital chain, Baxter offered us all kinds of assistance and services. They loaned us executives such as Frank LaFasto. They brought all our executives to Deerfield to discuss the most effective ways to work together. They found all kinds of ways to meet our needs. When the world of health care delivery is changing as dramatically as it is, you need to work with people who are a real part of your community."

Don C. Black, president of Child Health Corporation of America in Shawnee Mission, Kansas, strongly supported Baxter's later spin-off of Caremark International. He explained, "Baxter is the only company that's stepped up to the plate to be a hospital company. It's paid off for them and for us. We have one hospital in our system that does $30,000 a bed with Baxter. And as their process becomes even more efficient, other materials can also move through it: food, perishables, pharmaceuticals."

Black went on to point out the challenges still facing Baxter as a hospital company, "Baxter has to prove they won't give preference to their manufactured products. The mindset has to be like Santa in *Miracle on 34th Street*. We don't have it here at Macy's, but we can get it for you at Gimbels. They have to keep working at the task of matching with specific customer needs. Because Baxter has gotten so big, a good way to do that is to look at what makes some of the smaller regional hospital distributors effective.

"As hospitals go to a capitated approach (instead of fee-for-service), the salesman has to act even more like he's in the customer's employ. Being in charge of hospital X is a big job. Baxter probably should look at its career ladders to keep the same person at the same hospital for a long, long time. And Baxter also needs to build a better Alternate Site distribution system. They've given their competitors a big hill to climb, but there's still a lot to do."

Both American Hospital Supply and Baxter had long been strongly customer-oriented. Baxter's customer orientation evolved over time to what might best be characterized as a market-share approach; American Hospital's evolved as a service-based approach. Changes and pressures experienced by American hospitals in the mid-eighties were powerful motivation for the merged company to look at customer requirements even more intently and in a new way. Terry Mulligan described the process, "While the name 'Corporate Program' was started and utilized at American Hospital Supply Corporation, the concept has been drastically expanded and accelerated since the merger. What originally was intended for a few hospitals and hospital systems, and supported by a few people at American, is now working for over 2,000 of our hospital customers and supported by nearly everyone at Baxter. This is now a part of the fabric of the company. From 1986 to 1990 sales under the corporate program tripled. By 1991, 76 percent of Baxter incremental hospital sales in the United States came from corporate customers. This success has in turn led to teamwork initiatives throughout the company and annual teamwork awards focused on and actively involving specific hospitals."[2]

Managerial teamwork is one of the hallmarks of Loucks' style. Those who are still nostalgic for the Camelot period when he first became CEO talk most frequently about that characteristic and how the new team meshed then. So it should be no surprise that corporate

BAXTER SALES AND EARNINGS
1986 - 1991*

Year	$ Net Sales	$ Net Income	$ Net Earnings Per Common Share
1986	5,700,000,000	192,000,000	0.63
1987	6,223,000,000	323,000,000	1.10
1988	6,861,000,000	388,000,000	1.31
1989	7,399,000,000	446,000,000	1.50
1990**	8,100,000,000	487,000,000	1.65
1991	8,921,000,000	591,000,000	2.03
Compound annual growth rate	9.4%	23.3%	30.0%

* Calculations prior to the spin out of Caremark, Int'l.
** Excludes $566,000 pretax restructuring charge

Figure 24

marketing, which involves most parts of Baxter in intricate teamwork, and partnerships with hospital customers should emerge strongly again after the travail of the merger. No surprise either that the executives who were then around Loucks—people like Tobin, Knight, Piccolo, White, Mulligan, Lambrix, and Rucci—are all strong team players.

Heightened customer orientation and quality leadership both served to emphasize organizational teamwork. The scale and complexity of the new company required a new management approach and style. Teamwork was an important part of the answer.

The third element of continuity was a persistently long-term outlook. It was certainly necessary, because achieving the merger's financial and operating targets was not a task for summer soldiers. Loucks stuck to the long view, which had been a Baxter tradition since Graham first began to run the company. It took longer to hit the targets than had been estimated and promised. Contributing factors were market sluggishness, competitive pricing, and the dilution undertaken to acquire Caremark in 1987. By far the major time factor though was what Loucks likes to call "gaining-share-of-mind." This refers to gaining customer attention, comprehension, and commitment for a new message and a new way of doing business. The concept applies equally to employees. There is probably no way to short-cut that process. Baxter is still working on it today.

Baxter products are seen more frequently in hospitals than white lab coats.

DISTRIBUTION—THE LINCHPIN

Every strategic shift of the kind attempted here has a linchpin. The linchpin in this case was the American distribution system. Distribution was the foundation of the value-added processes Baxter envisioned, linking it even more closely to its hospital customers. Obstacles were encountered along the way. First, as is bound to happen in any merger of competitors, the American distribution system was *not* doing all the things that Baxter as an outside observer had thought it was. So new investments had to be made. Second, because of the typically lower margins in distribution, management approaches for leveraging that part of the business had to be developed and tested. That, in turn, led to questions about how distribution should relate to other key parts of the company's business not just internally, but in the eyes of the customer. Working through these complex issues took time and led to progressive evolution of new strategy.

STRATEGIC SHIFT

Baxter strategy evolved from 1986 to 1990 in several distinct phases. In the first of these the company solidified a new base which was stronger competitively. The base was large enough in scale to take advantage of hospital industry consolidation and allowed the company to adapt its established niche positions. In that first period of about 1986-87, the risks of being a niche supplier to an industry buffeted by DRGs and other cost pressures were substantially reduced. Remember, as recently as the early 1980s Baxter had derived 60 percent of its operating profits from IV solutions—a product line which was particularly susceptible to pricing pressures.

That, in turn, led in 1987, 1988, and beyond, to the very successful hospital penetration strategy, directed by Mulligan and the Baxter corporate program organization. The corporate program is simply a way of focusing intensively on an individual hospital's or hospital system's particular needs, and then (not so simply) harnessing all of the company's products, capabilities, and resources to meet those needs—as the corporate marketing people like to say "seamlessly." It's a classic way to gain share and make money in a mature market segment. Hospital customers are generally very positive about what the program does for them. Most other hospital suppliers have been forced to respond from a position of relative competitive disadvantage.

Dr. Monroe E. Trout, chairman of the board, president and CEO of American Health Care Systems in San Diego, as well as a doctor, lawyer, and retired senior vice president for R&D of Sterling Drug, had this to say about Baxter's hospital partnership role during a 1992 interview:

"Early on, after I joined American Health Care Systems I decided we had to do business with suppliers in a different way. We had 1,500 different contracts, most for one-year periods. The benefits of longer-term contracts with a few major suppliers seemed obvious. I went around and talked with supplier CEOs. Some of them threw me out. Some were polite, but not willing to commit. Then I met Vern Loucks. He not only shared my point of view, but went on the line with his board of directors to make a $6 million credit facility available so that we could make my vision a reality. We have one of the best business relationships in the industry because it's based on complete trust. Beyond the initial commitment he made, I find he's not afraid of rolling up his sleeves and digging in. Busy as he is, I can pick up the phone, get through to him, and he will personally solve the problems of one of our hospital administrators. As a result, our business with Baxter has grown eight times during this partnership [from 1987 to 1992]. I have great confidence that he and Baxter will solve the problems that Caremark activities are causing for Baxter's hospital customers.

"The relationship is strong because it has compelling mutual benefits. It's good for us and good for Baxter."

Later, on April 30, 1993, Dr. Trout spoke in support of Baxter during the annual stockholders meeting at which concerns were expressed about management actions leading up to the March 25 agreement with the federal government regarding violations of the anti-boycott provisions of the Export Administration Act.

After the 1987 acquisition of Caremark, Alternate Site business strategy proceeded along a parallel track. Baxter focused on developing and managing the overall process for delivery of care in new non-traditional settings (that process including distribution, billing and reimbursement, patient education, coordination with physicians, and a number of other functions). Caremark was to be involved in some dramatic decisions during 1992. Beyond the immediate dilutive effect of the merger, there were investments to be made in Alternate Site infrastructure at the same time that hospital markets required investment as well.

In the hospital business Baxter continued to take strategic actions which blurred the lines between traditional supplier and provider roles. For example, the company expanded the inventory and logistics services it would provide within the hospital's four walls. It moved toward capitated pricing of hospital products because growing managed care alternative approaches to health care delivery, of course, were built on capitated, instead of fee-for-service, pricing. Blurring the lines was one of the reasons the question began to be asked with increasing frequency whether Baxter could responsibly play the two roles of largest hospital/medical product producer and distributor and largest provider of Alternate Site services.

Alan Weinstein, president and chief executive officer of Premier Hospitals Alliance, offers some challenging projections for the health care system and Baxter's role in it. "With or without the Clinton Reform Plan, suppliers are going to have to get better at marketing to *networks*. Their products will have to cover the whole range from hospitals to home health agencies. As sales people become more consultative, their incentive systems have to change.

"Suppliers also have to go at risk with providers through capitation. We're already seeing some of that from Baxter and others . . .

and traditional group purchasing systems and alliances are going to change as well. They probably won't be as exclusive as they've been. As networks materialize, are suppliers going to alienate hospitals and go direct? It's like the Caremark issue. Are suppliers also providers because they're at risk through capitation? Can they, should they do business with more than one network in a city even if they're competitive? . . . Tough environment, but if you have the horsepower Baxter does, the right culture to get together with your purchasers, and if you're nimble enough, you ought to do real well."

Finally, during 1988 and 1989, the company took a hard look at both its country-based international organization and its established niche businesses (renal, blood, and others). The decision was to make the niche businesses *global*. Specialty business managers were given a mixed (matrix) responsibility for product markets and parts of the world determined by geographical patterns of product use and technological leadership. The separate Baxter Travenol World Trade Organization in effect ceased to exist. Its leader since the 1985 merger, Lawrence Kinet, left the company.

The niche strategy didn't go away. It simply became embedded in a larger framework. Loucks said of that shift, "Changes in the marketplace made it imperative we adjust our strategy. Managing the broader process gives us a formidable base from which to defend ex-

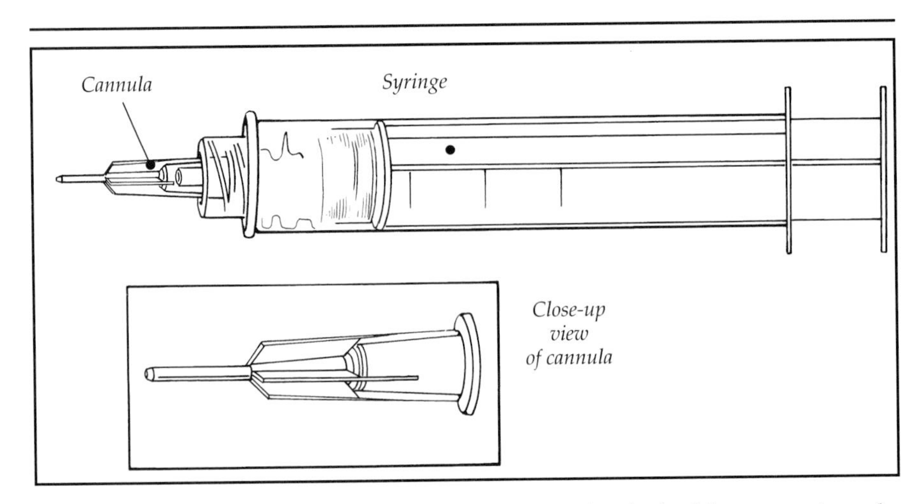

The innovative stick-free needle provides protection for the health care worker who can be free of the risk of accidental needle punctures. Exposure to blood-borne infections is minimized with this concept.

isting niches and the flexibility to target new ones. The challenge is to make all the necessary investments in product technology on the one hand and process technology on the other."

Perhaps the most accurate description of these strategic adjustments comes from Gantz. He said, "Remember, all of the current executive management team learned niche strategy from Bill Graham. Then the market upheaval of 1983 and 1984 convinced us we couldn't niche our way into the future. We had to embark on a broader course. However, we're still following the thread of what we learned. You could say that's now the hidden part of our strategy. Specialty businesses account for a substantial part of our business and they represent about $250 million of our $280 million R&D investment. In these areas we're niching in the classic Graham way, but with a much broader world-wide technology base on which to draw."

PAVING A PATH FOR THE FUTURE

Alternate Site created new benefits for the modern Baxter organization in that many more people at all organization levels became directly involved in patient service and care: customer service people and hotline operators, truck drivers, technicians, nurses, pharmacists, reimbursement specialists, education and family support people, and so on. This kind of multifaceted contact with the customer/patient creates a vitality and sense of mission that few other approaches can.

Baxter created an infrastructure through which an increasing range of long-term or short-term services could be provided cost effectively and in the most patient-friendly atmosphere. It involves patients and their families constructively in the management of their own care. And it can reach those for whom other care delivery options are neither appropriate nor practical. Beginning with therapies where it was the pioneer, dialysis and infusion, Baxter's Alternate Site system broadened to include other technologies and therapies, including some provided by other companies that could most advantageously be delivered through the Baxter system.

THE NEW IMPERATIVES

Well before health care reform began to assert itself as a primary force, the new imperatives of the health care system were already becoming clear, including:

- restraint of rising health care costs;
- improved access to the system;
- simplification of administrative paper work;
- and related to all of the above: broader, better-coordinated networks (managed care).

The company was heading down two somewhat separate tracks to meet those imperatives. The first was engineering a new manufacturing-distribution approach for meeting the needs of hospital systems and networks in a way that reduces overall costs. The second was creating a national alternate site care system within which a number of therapies could be delivered at lower cost. It was thought the two tracks, serving the same broad imperatives as they did, were complementary. However, this was still before the prospect of reform began to exert extreme pressures on both of those parts of the health care system. Was Baxter thinking ahead to how the escalating pressure might build conflict between the two tracks?

STRATEGY MIRRORS BAXTER LEADERSHIP

Loucks and Graham, Baxter's only two CEOs in the modern era, each reflected his own time and environment. Graham was the lawyer-scientist, probing questioner, sometimes stern controller who mastered the business by keen observation and analytical ability. His leadership produced a string of technological breakthroughs as well as consistently superior financial results. Loucks, an imaginative executive, built on his strong marketing skills, and used his insight into future directions of the marketplace to transform the company. As his imprint has progressively shaped Baxter, its business groups and units have become progressively more autonomous, due in part to larger scale.

Thirteen years into his tenure as CEO, Alternate Site direct services to patients were as much an expression of Loucks' management personality as was the first commercial artificial kidney a reflection of Graham's in the fifties and sixties. While each direct-patient therapy for hemophilia, immune deficiency, and other disease states remains a specialized niche, Loucks' strategic view integrated all these many disparate services into a single delivery system, just as the American Hospital Supply merger led to a distribution service network broader than Baxter's traditional hospital niches.

FINANCIAL RESULTS

The most difficult challenge of the late eighties for Baxter's executive management team was producing superior financial results. The strategy had been adjusted, but when would it pay off? Company management had clearly been focused and toughened by the merger process, but would that be enough to make the Baxter-American Hospital combination different from other 1980s mergers which had disappointed investors in too many cases? Loucks and his key advisors had to walk a tightrope, driving merger synergies, on one hand, and attempting to heal the post-merger organization trauma on the other. The two efforts were not easy to reconcile.

1986 and 1987 were reasonably satisfactory years, consistent with merger financial projections. Return on equity hovered in the 11 to 12 percent range, below rates to which Baxter had been accustomed and rates for leaders in the company's industry group. Of course, if the substantial goodwill added to the balance sheet due to the type of merger undertaken (compared with a pooling of interests) was removed from the calculation, then Baxter's effective return on equity (ROE) would have been higher. Not everyone agrees that return on equity is a suitable measure of Baxter's long-term financial performance. Bill Graham and Ray Oddi don't. Graham points out: "Relative ROE is established by the industry you're in. Even during our 29 record-setting years we never used it as a principal measure. Long-term earnings growth gives a more accurate picture and probably correlates better with stock price gains too. Still, the analysts have made it a big deal and therefore Vern has little choice but to emphasize it."

A warning flag went up for Vern Loucks in the spring of 1989. It looked like operating results were flattening. Former CFO Bob Lambrix recalled, "By midyear 1989 we were looking at earnings for 1990 that were as much as 25 percent under street estimates. Loucks went into action. He pushed for more restructuring, principally at the plant level. We brought James Wolfensohn's investment banking firm in for counsel. It looked like our long uphill climb since the 1985 merger was at risk of stalling."

Loucks was looking for $55 million more in earnings from manufacturing and distribution. Jim Tobin stepped up to the plate and identified ways to deliver those results. Lambrix put forward a plan, endorsed by Tobin, to reduce corporate staff by an additional 600 positions, cutting corporate burden significantly. Shortly afterwards,

Loucks announced dramatic actions to be taken in 1990 which would lead to increasing ROE to 15 percent. These actions changed Baxter's organization approach and management alignment significantly.

COMMON STOCK PRICE

Figure 25 shows Baxter common stock price ranges at the beginning and end of the years from 1986 through 1990. The stock performed well, ahead of the Standard & Poor's 500, but still short of Loucks' and the company's expectations. It wasn't until 1991 that the stock began to trade consistently in the $36 range. It closed on December 30, 1991, at a high of $40.38, consistent with original merger shareholder value projections.

BAXTER'S COMMON STOCK PRICE, 1986 - 1990

Year	$ High	$ Low	$ Close*
1986	21.250	15.125	19.250
1987	29.250	16.000	22.750
1988	26.125	16.250	17.625
1989	25.875	17.625	25.000
1990	29.500	20.500	27.875

*Figures taken from month of December.

Figure 25[3]

CONCLUSION

1986 to 1990 were difficult years. They required a long-term view, as did the years in the late forties and early fifties when Graham's strategy for the still fragile company was being developed. There were many strategic actions being planned and executed. A number of them were extraordinarily complex and difficult: for example, fashioning the former specialty businesses and Baxter Travenol World Trade into a combined global approach, and positioning distribution as an integral part of the overall enterprise. Baxter's accomplishments during this period can best be captured by looking back at its post-DRG market value on June 20,

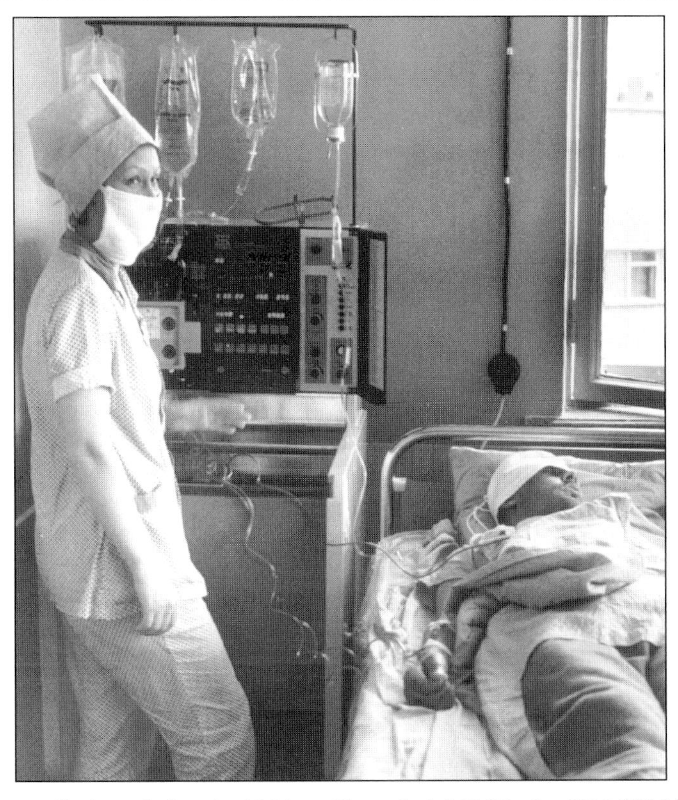

In treating radiation victims in 1986 at Chernobyl, USSR, the CS-3000 blood separator was employed for plasma exchange and bone marrow transplants. The technology helped save patients exposed to the nuclear plant's fallout.

1985, the date when the offer for American Hospital Supply was first made. Baxter's common stock closed on that day at $16.63. By late 1992, Baxter stock was trading at $35 to $37, an increase of about 117 percent.

MILESTONES

1980-1990

1980	CEO mantle passes from Graham to Loucks.
1981	Baxter-Travenol marks 50th anniversary.
1981	Ronald Reagan inaugurated as 40th president.
1981-82	U.S. economy slides into recession.
1981-85	Small to mid-size acquisitions: AutoSyringe (1982) Medcom (1982) Dynamic Control (1983) Extracorporeal (1984) J.S. Data (1984) Stony Brook Systems (1984) Compucare (1985)
1983	Diagnosis Related Groups (DRGs) introduced for prospective reimbursement.
1983	Approval of combined reimbursement rate for hemodialysis and CAPD.
1983	Baxter holds November-December investors conference to discuss U.S. hospital industry storm clouds.
1984	Passage of Tax Equity and Fiscal Reform Act (TEFRA).
1984	Baxter closes Hays (Kansas) plant and Philippines operations. Takes $116 million after-tax write off.
1985	Acquisition of and merger with American Hospital Supply Corporation. Graham becomes senior chairman.

1986	Death of Foster McGaw.
1987	Acquisition of Caremark for over $500 million.
1987	Chairman Karl Bays leaves to become chairman of IC Industries (later Whitman). Loucks becomes Baxter chairman.
1987	Booz Allen & Hamilton assists with merger synergies and continuing cost reduction.
1987	Gantz elected Baxter president.
1988	George Bush elected 41st president of the United States.
1988-89	C. A. "Lance" Piccolo and Tobin elected executive vice presidents and Baxter board members.
1989	Death of Bays.
1989-90	A. T. Kearney provides consulting assistance on synergies and cost reduction.
1990	Death of founder Dr. Ralph Falk's widow, Marian Citron Falk.
1990	Baxter restructuring charge.

END NOTES

CHAPTER XX

1. From 6 April 1992 letter from Dr. Robert H. "Patt" Patterson, M.D., who led the quality effort for most of these years.

2. Terry Mulligan, 16 April 1992 letter.

3. Source: Baxter annual reports for those years.

CHAPTER

XXI

1991 MARKS BAXTER'S SIXTIETH ANNIVERSARY

1931 to 1991—a lifetime apart measured by life expectancy of the 1930s. Two totally different eras because of the proportion of GNP now devoted to health care and even greater advances in the capabilities of clinical medicine. Yet bridging this immense gap between 1931 and 1991 were some basic similarities. Reflecting on the company's sixtieth anniversary, which passed without fanfare, Vern Loucks observed, "In the early thirties there were problems of access to health care. Now we have them again for different reasons. Thirty-four million Americans don't have health insurance coverage.[1] The role of hospitals was changing then. And now it's changing again. We face some immense public health concerns like AIDS and drug abuse, which are like the public health challenges of the thirties, except, of course, that they dwarf the earlier problems in both cost and social consequences. The health care system and hospitals in particular were financially pressed then and now. A policy debate was going on then about health care accountability. The answer in the 1930s was community responsibility and 'volunteerism.' Now we're beginning to see new initiatives by states and major employer groups to address overwhelming health care problems."

What kind of environment did Baxter face as 1991 rolled around? First, of course, 1990-91 brought revolutionary changes in the world order. These began with the crumbling of the Berlin Wall and realignment of Eastern Europe, and proceeded to the dissolution of the Soviet Union, where doctors were paid less than factory workers and the health care system lagged far behind most countries of the world.

In 1991 the U.S. economy was struggling to rebound from a recession that was long and difficult and finally determined the results of the 1992 presidential election. Labor market softness persisted, partly because this was the first modern recession where service employment declined markedly (except in health care services). As shown in Figure 26, health care employment in 1990 grew by 7.7 percent—a

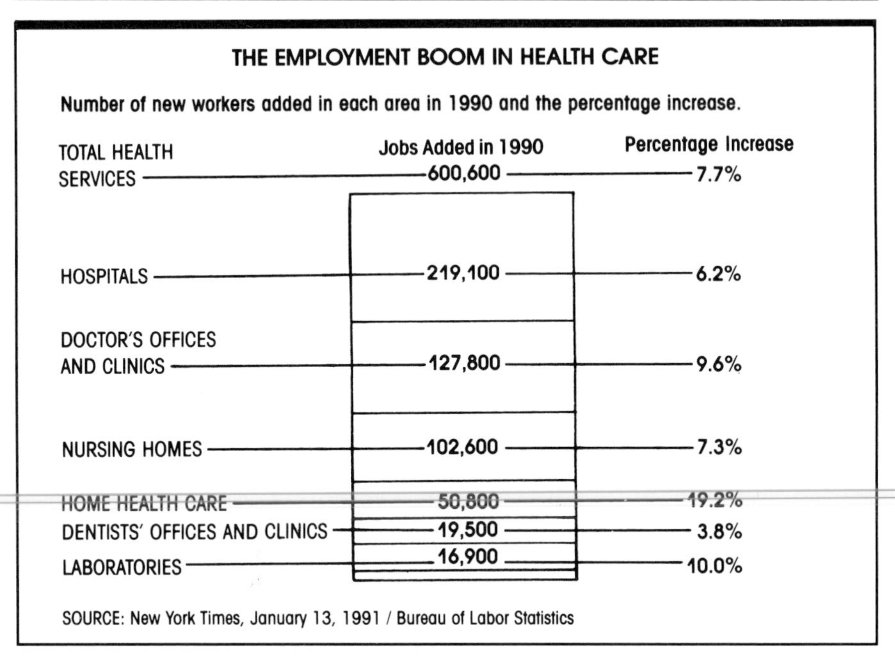

Figure 26: *Health care employment continues to grow robustly in every category except dental medicine.*

gain of 600,600 jobs to a total of 8.4 million. In the decade of the eighties the number of health care workers in the U.S. swelled by over 50 percent. The Bureau of Labor Statistics predicts that seven of the ten fastest growing occupations in the nineties will be in health care.[2]

MORE CHANGE IN THE HEALTH CARE ENVIRONMENT

Public policy debate about how to fix the nation's health care system intensified in 1991. What was different this time around was that much of the informed public appeared convinced that the system was "broke," and some large employers were running for cover because of their health insurance cost experience. The Financial Accounting Standards Board (FASB) required corporations to reflect retiree health care cost obligations fully in their financial statements. The federal government's efforts to cut nicks in the federal health care budget, first with hospitals, more recently with doctors and prescription drugs, and in 1991 by acting to prevent cost-shifting by the states under Medicaid share formulas, had proven only moderately successful. All the usual suspects were trotted out: the third-party payment system; America's tort system, encouraging defensive medicine; doctors who overtest and overprescribe; expensive new technology; the aging of America; and the system's paperwork burden, which has been estimated to consume as much as 20 percent of total health care expenditures (HCE).

Fueling much of the debate is U.S. per capita health care spending, approaching $2,500 per year in the early 1990s. That's $700 more than the second highest spender, Canada; $1,000 more than the number three spender; and $1,300 more than Japan. Higher per capita spending in the U.S. has not produced uniformly better health care statistics. U.S. infant mortality, for example, is often cited as a significant area where the U.S.lags behind some other countries. Statistics show that U.S. regions and cities with the highest health care costs are not those with the best health care outcomes. So the issue has become effectiveness as well as affordability. President Bush's budget director, Richard Darman, estimated during preparation of the fiscal 1991 federal budget that health care expenditures would soar to 25 percent of GNP in the early part of the next century unless basic changes took place, raising the question: would individual health care be treated as a right regardless of affordability?

Would the 1990s mark the decline and end of America's mixed health care system, which had combined government, nonprofit, community, professional, and business interests for so long in an uneasy alliance?[3] The mixed system is the hallmark of the American approach to health care. If it changes radically, then the health care business will change and Baxter's successful strategy must also change.

What this history of more than 60 years of advances in hospital care and clinical medicine and Baxter's role in those advances clearly shows is that a period of explosion in health care knowledge and practice (for example, the 20 years between 1945 and 1965) then leads to a period of system rationalization and resource development and allocation (in this case, the almost 20 years between 1965 and 1983).

If this view is correct, then it is technology that drives and determines the U.S. health care system as much as method of payment and other factors. The current wave of innovation in biotechnology, immunology, genetics, diagnostics, noninvasive and microsurgery, new materials to substitute for human blood, bone, and skin, and a host of other discoveries may change the practice of clinical medicine and patient care more swiftly and more radically in the next 10 years than the breakthroughs which Baxter witnessed and contributed to over the last 60-plus years. If it is true, then it argues against rationalizing and restructuring the U.S. health care system now without knowing or estimating the likely impacts of these future developments.

Baxter is well positioned to adapt to and take advantage of advancing new technology across a broad front, thanks in part to the American Hospital Supply merger. Current advances may, moreover, make it possible for developing countries to raise their levels of health care to approach what is now taken for granted in advanced countries. Poorer countries with rudimentary health care systems represent about 80 percent of the world's total population. Their health care needs are enormous. Imagine the increase in market potential for Baxter and others[4] if health care services could be substantially improved for this large majority of world population through appropriate technology without all of the professional infrastructure of mature systems in western countries. Developing nations have already demonstrated that it is possible to short-circuit historical processes of economic and industrial growth. This same kind of speed-up could conceivably occur in health care development.[5] This future potential is a challenging new frontier for Baxter consistent with its long-standing dedication to finding new ways to serve human needs for quality health care.

1990—ANOTHER MOMENTOUS YEAR FOR BAXTER

As described earlier, warning flags began to go up for Loucks in late 1988 and early 1989. During the first part of 1989 he kept reviewing hospital business numbers. Discussions of net income results with operating executives grew more frequent and more insistent. Then on January 5, 1990, Bob Lambrix presented a corporate staff reduction plan to Loucks. It called for corporate staff cuts of 600 positions, reducing corporate functions to a minimum level necessary to support the office of the CEO, consistent with earlier recommendations of consultants Booz Allen & Hamilton and A.T. Kearney. By this time, business units were operating much more autonomously. Lambrix calculated the plan would produce after-tax savings of $35 million annually, equivalent to 12 to 14 cents per common share. Loucks immediately bought the plan. Tobin says that of those staff positions, over half were shifted to the businesses where they could be better directed and controlled. The total corporate staff reduction target for all functions and businesses was 6,400 positions. Loucks also put heavy pressure on operating executives to produce another $25 million in immediate operating profit improvements. Jim Tobin had been hitting his global numbers in a tough competitive environment.

He was concerned that a similar profit push wasn't manifest throughout other parts of the company. So when Loucks surfaced his concern and Bob Lambrix expressed his point of view, Tobin pushed hard for action. Tobin probably would have been named president anyway when Bill Gantz announced his resignation to head up a new biotech company early in 1992. He was the natural and expected successor, but his yeoman service during this period certainly built his already solid reputation for action and results.

These actions led to a $566 million restructuring charge for 1990, reducing 1990 net income to $40 million.

The stock market reacted positively. Baxter's price earnings ratio increased and the common stock price peaked during this period at $40.38. As noted before, Baxter's ROE in the following year approached 15 percent.

This single decision then for 1990 made the outlook immediately more positive, even though the issues looming on the horizon were difficult ones. The first of those was the question of how the health care system would change as the next century approaches. Continuing cost escalation meant something had to give.

Decisions in the early 1990s paved the way for solid earnings gains in 1991 and 1992. It certainly wasn't easy, however. Some

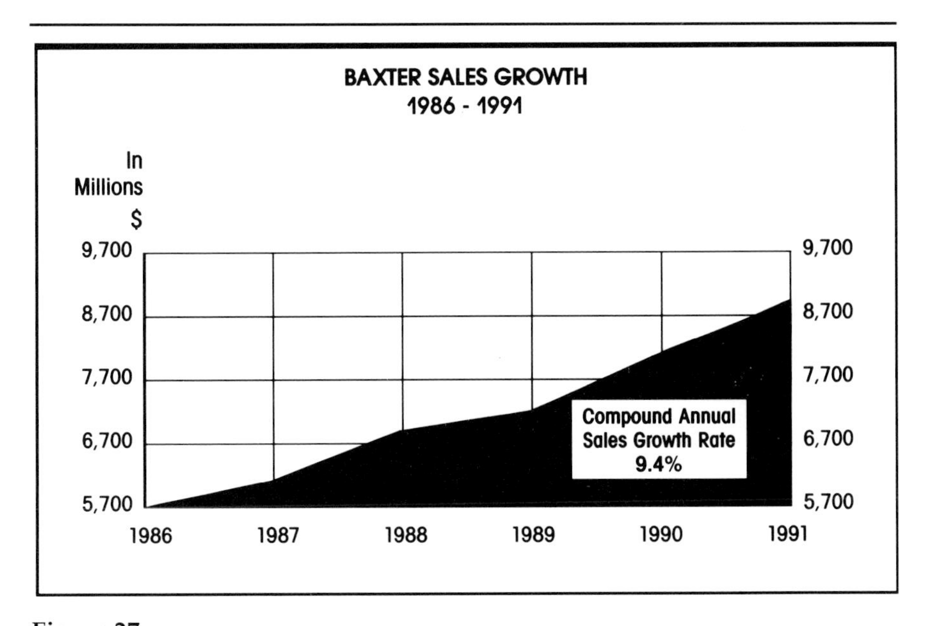

Figure 27

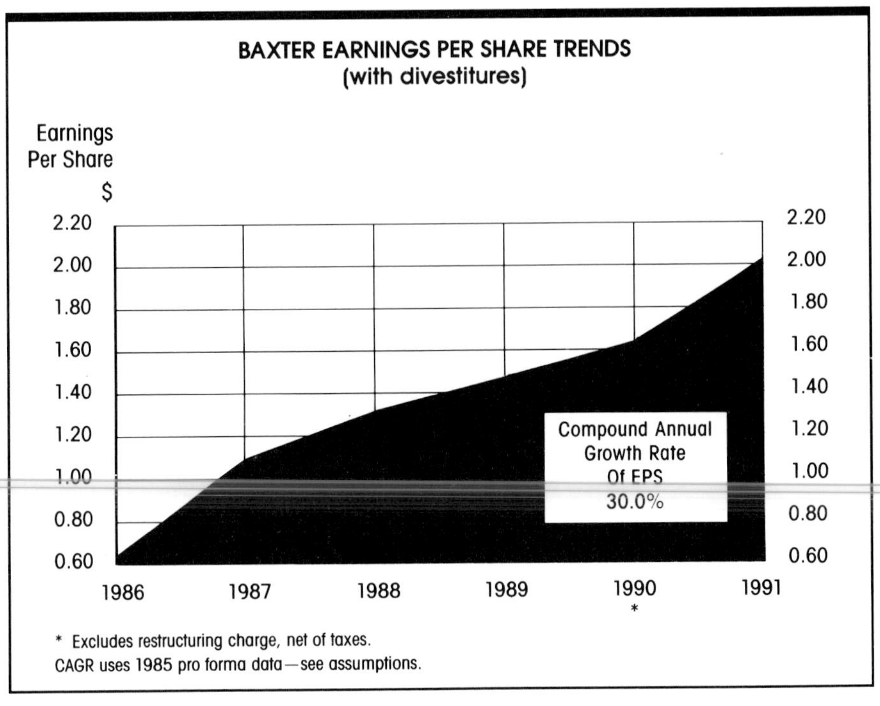

Figure 28

employees dusted off the old merger trauma words from 1985 and 1986. The reduction of corporate staff from about 2,000 to 500 positions, necessary as it was, created profound changes in style as well as substance. Wherever possible, administrative support and some professional functions were outsourced to independent contractors. Marsh Abbey's pain was evident as he oversaw the decentralization to the businesses of the "corporate law firm" he had painstakingly built. And parts of the Deerfield headquarters' six-building complex became cavernously empty. Implementation of these decisions through 1990 and into 1991 conclusively ushered out Baxter's long-established, distinctively practiced approach to corporate functional management. It had been on its way out for some time, but this proved to be the swan song. Not an appropriate management concept for a $9 billion company, some observed, while others clung to the view that it was an unwitting victim of hard-nosed cost management.

1990 continued a process of ongoing change that had begun in August of 1984 with the strategy review, described earlier, in which Graham, Loucks, Tobin, and several others had confronted the issue of how Baxter should adapt to its new environment. As CEO, Loucks engineered and executed one element after another of a new strategic design, many of them initially resisted or misunderstood by one part of the internal organization or another. Earlier we quoted Dr. Ralph Falk saying in the 1950s that he deserved every nickel of his gains on Baxter stock ownership for the single act of selecting and recruiting Graham in 1945. Similarly, Graham deserves much credit for selecting Loucks to lead Baxter through this difficult period.

We've also observed that the degree and frequency of change Baxter has repeatedly undertaken would perhaps not have been possible without the CEO continuity and stability the company has enjoyed (in effect, only two CEOs over almost 50 years of its post-World War II growth).

So it isn't surprising that in the midst of all the bewildering change of the late 1980s and early 1990s some basic Baxter values and characteristics have remained very much the same. First, the company appears to have done an effective job of recognizing the needs of, and balancing its responsibilities to, shareholders, customers, employees, and yes, the many different countries and communities in which it operates. In its Chicago homeland, for example, Baxter has provided leadership for other major corporations in operating an innovative inner-city school—Corporate/Community Schools of America—an undertaking to which Loucks has a deep emotional commitment. On one recent occasion he flew back from an important European tour because of a funding problem at the school.

"We don't make anything you eat, drink, or wear, so why should the public know Baxter?" Graham used to like to say in the sixties. And that introduces the second characteristic which is a distinctive approach to communications. Both Loucks and Graham have always preferred low-key, down-to-earth communication with customers, employees, and others. Both men, different as they are, intensely dislike "hype" and prefer to let results speak for themselves. By and large, their preference has served Baxter well.

And closely related to that is a third value, which is that Baxter has always taken a humanistic approach to all the people with whom it comes in contact—patients, doctors, hospital administrators, employees, suppliers, and others. Even during staff reductions in 1985-86 and 1990-91, that quality was apparent. Nothing contrived about that either; it springs naturally from the twin sources of deep commitment to patient well-being and the company's interactive, interpersonal, team-oriented management systems.

Fourth and finally, Baxter has always, since Graham's early years, been strategically driven, a tradition now enriched by Loucks. As pointed out several times, the company isn't bounded by any mate-

Baxter has served the medical needs of the U.S. Armed Forces for several generations. The company was in Kuwait for the war in the Persian Gulf in 1991. They served with relief supplies to Kuwaiti citizens, Iraqi refugees, and Allied troops, and remained in Kuwait after the war to help reestablish the medical infrastructure of the ravaged country.

rial resource or single technology or brand franchise. It has insisted its managers and people take a long and total view so that the only boundaries imposed are the limits of managerial imagination. An admirable set of characteristics, it appears—particularly the last one—to meet the requirements for corporate leadership and success in the new century.

On the other hand, Baxter's product/market array remained a vexing strategic question. Would this array be understood and appropriately valued by investors? Clearly, hospital customers did understand it, as will be shown by the events described in the final chapter. Which businesses would provide the profit leverage to propel Baxter to financial rates of return which its successful history leads it to expect? Caremark was producing excellent growth, but some thought its financial leverage was limited. Despite the enormous success of the hospital penetration strategy, the dominant U.S. hospital market was growing at less than 10 percent annually. The global specialty businesses are showing new vitality, but even a breakthrough like CAPD in 1978 would no longer by itself be enough to substantially affect total corporate numbers.

The answer, as for any large organization, lies in an intricate combination of actions, which Baxter already has underway. Principal initiatives are: R&D, which has the potential to yield big returns in artificial organs, transplantation, immunology, immuno diagnostics, and cardiovascular medicine; also market initiatives throughout the Pacific Basin; and development activities in less-developed parts of the world (including a surgical instrument manufacturing facility in Moscow). Countries whose medical infrastructures lag far behind ours and those of Western Europe represent enormous untapped potential for Baxter.

Clearly this question would not be answered for a time because as this history was drawing to a close, the company announced at its May 1992 annual stockholder meeting that it was studying the desirability of spinning out the Caremark-Alternate Site business as a separate publicly-owned corporation. The announcement was favorably received and produced a *New York Times* article to the effect that this was clearly an important way in the future for American corporations to create additional shareholder value.[6] Did these events mark the end of Baxter's long transition which began in 1983 or perhaps even earlier in 1980? Had management correctly anticipated health care's future and positioned the company well? Had the many changes since the landmark American Hospital Supply merger in 1985 been fully assimilated so that Baxter was operating from a solid base? The signs appeared encouraging. Subsequent events, particularly in 1993, were to demonstrate that the difficult transition was far from over. 1993 would be perhaps the most difficult year in Baxter's entire history spanning more than six decades. The events of 1993 attracted an unaccustomed kind of public attention to the company's decisions and actions.

END NOTES

CHAPTER XXI

1. In 1931, health insurance was still being invented as described earlier in this history.

2. *The New York Times,* 13 January 1991.

3. Eli Ginzburg, *The Medical Triangle: Physicians, Politicians, and the Public.* (Cambridge, Massachusetts: Harvard University Press, 1990). These essays debate the question of whether the mixed system will break down.

4. Estimated world expenditures for health care are two trillion dollars, of which well over one-third are within the U.S. and most of the balance of which are in other developed nations.

5. Peter Drucker, *The New Realities* (New York, New York: Harper & Row, 1989). While not a discussion of health care as such, this broad Drucker treatise is a lucid analysis of how new systems will emerge and be integrated.

6. *The New York Times,* 3 May 1992, Business section.

PART FIVE

ANTICIPATING HEALTH CARE REFORM

At 1993 year-end the dominant feature of the fast-changing U.S. health care scene was reform. Enactment of a plan was then still a number of months in the future. It would take, furthermore, years of progressive implementation for the full effects of a social and economic intervention of this immense magnitude to be experienced and understood. Nonetheless, choppy bow waves of Health Care Reform were already being felt throughout 1993 in the stock market and among hospitals, other providers, and by Baxter.

Among the top seven health care stocks in *Business Week*'s list of the top 1000 companies in market value[1], five fell by an average of four percent in 1993. Baxter's stock fell by a much greater amount. Investors were clearly rattled about most aspects of pending Health Care Reform. Baxter experienced a disproportionately larger effect in part because of the perception—not necessarily accurate—that its future was too closely tied to that of hospitals.

During the 1980s, growth of the U.S hospital segment (by far the largest part of total health expenditures at about 38 percent), lagged behind that of the overall health care index and was substantially outstripped by growth in spending for other components, such as physicians and drugs. Much of the slowing of hospital growth could be attributed to the prospective payment system (DRGs—Diagnosis Related Groups). Wasn't it likely, investment analysts asked, that an already somewhat deflated segment, with which Baxter had closely aligned itself, was going to have its growth rate and pricing depressed even more by the far-reaching provisions of President Clinton's health security plan?

At the same time, hospitals stepped up their pace of consolidation and network-alliance formation. Enrollment in managed care plans of various kinds spurted. Beginning in the second quarter of 1993, the rate of Baxter's sales growth in the U.S. began to slow markedly, ending the year up five percent for the total company. It was like 1984 all over again, perhaps even more ominous now.

At the beginning of 1994, Baxter faced still another critical strategic turning point, more difficult perhaps than the others met and surmounted over the more than sixty-year history described in these pages. National tension between short-term political rhetoric and longer-term reality of Health Care Reform was mirrored within Baxter as the company continued to adjust its strategies to uncertain, emerging market requirements.

1. *Business Week Magazine*, March 28, 1994.

The concluding chapter describes 1993 events as the company was affected by the immediate prospect of reform and as it prepared strategically for the health care environment of the 21st century, not just in the U.S., but simultaneously in other developed and fast-developing countries around the globe. This history has shown how Baxter has persistently stuck to its original goal of improving quality of patient care and consistently chosen the long-term strategic view. Presumably, those traits will continue to serve the company well at this time of change. Nonetheless, just as the outcome of the strategies undertaken by Bill Graham in the mid-forties wasn't completely apparent until the early sixties, so too the outcome of the eighties and early nineties strategies won't be determined until well after the final period covered by this work.

It seems appropriate to conclude this history at this juncture on the note of the future challenge. Baxter began, it has been shown, as an uncertain enterprise, with less than full control of its destiny, with the country mired in the depths of the great depression. Clinical medicine was in its infancy. Soon after, the still fragile company had to shift its pursuit of life-saving innovations to the distant battlefields of World War II. Out of this crucible and after Bill Graham's arrival in 1945, a successful strategy began to emerge. Over the intervening years and through several distinctly different health care eras, that strategy has been tested and challenged many times. The $8.9 billion health care leader with a global presence in more than 100 countries, where its products and services are vital to the well-being of countless patients in many vital therapies, is being tested and challenged again in ways that could not have been anticipated ten or perhaps even five years ago. Always in the past such challenges have sparked new bursts of flexibility, creativity, and innovation on Baxter's part. Will that occur again?

CHAPTER

XXII

INVENTING THE NEW BAXTER

By the second and third quarters of 1993, as already stated, Baxter growth and profit margins were being impacted by the prospect of Health Care Reform. The same sudden effect had been experienced before in 1984 after introduction of DRGs. The reason was the same: states, hospital systems, HMOs, and private payers scrambling to position themselves for the new competitive environment. Critics of Baxter's domestic hospital focus began a chorus of "we-told-you-so's." It didn't get any better as the year wore on.

OTHER ISSUES CROWD IN ON BAXTER

As if pressures on business strategy weren't enough, other serious problems began coming to a head in the second quarter of 1993. On March 26, Baxter pled guilty to one count of violating the Export Administration Act because of providing information to Syria about company operations in Israel. Other charges reported in the media, some of them clearly frivolous, were dropped. Baxter steadfastly maintained its one violation was inadvertent. Nonetheless, general counsel Marsh Abbey resigned and reverberations continued because of the false assumption that its guilty plea meant Baxter had abandoned its long-standing commitment to the Israeli health care system.

Less than five months later, in August 1993, the U.S. Veterans Administration went noisily public with charges that Baxter had made sales to V.A. hospitals of non-contract items while telling hospitals the items were on contract. Linked to earlier charges of improper Mideast dealings, and reportedly aided in a way not fully disclosed by a discharged, embittered former Baxter employee, the V.A. might have barred the company and its chairman and president from doing business with the federal government for one year. At year-end, the charges were quietly resolved. More damage had been done, however.

PRODUCT LIABILITY LOSSES CAST ANOTHER DARK SHADOW

Baxter's abiding goal of improving quality of patient care has involved the company in therapies where clinical benefits are greatest and where liability risks may be great as well: areas such as dialysis, cardiology, and blood therapies, including clotting factor concentrate for hemophiliacs. The company affirms its continuing commitment to such areas, but the potential risks have sharply increased due to government regulatory interpretation, broad construction of liability, and skyrocketing awards to plaintiffs.

On March 23, 1994, the largest settlement ever negotiated in a class-action lawsuit, in final process since the spring of 1993, was announced.[1] It required payment of $4.3 billion over seven years to women claiming they were injured by silicone breast implants. A number of companies, but principally Dow Corning, Bristol-Myers Squibb, 3M, and Baxter, were parties to the settlement. Baxter's share of the cost was an estimated $556 million, of which $424 million was expected to be recovered through insurance.

To put these events in perspective, Baxter itself never manufactured silicone breast implants. A small subsidiary of American Hospital Supply, Heyer-Schulte (acquired by American in 1974 for $7 million and sold for $14 million in 1984, which shows the modest size of the business), had manufactured them, giving rise to Baxter's liability. One of the lead Baxter attorneys on the complex case said, "Connie Chung began network coverage of the breast implant issue in January of 1991. In two years the number of cases rose from 20 to 4,000. Despite the fact that we were winning individual cases, this kind of litigation is a business for certain people, and we chose not to be in the business. We began global settlement efforts in September of 1992. . .you know the sad thing about all this is that claims are not supported by credible medical evidence. Doctors were put in an awkward position. Some women feel they were denied a treatment option, and the FDA threw up its hands and contributed to the panic. . ."

HEMOPHILIACS AND HIV

An even more tragic and ironic example of liability's two-edge sword is the scourge visited on hemophiliacs in the early to mid-eighties.

Hemophilia is a serious, painful, and potentially fatal disease from which an estimated 20,000 males in the U.S. (200,000 worldwide) suffer. The hemophiliac's lifeline is clotting factor concentrate (Factor VIII and Factor IX) made from the pooled plasma of many donors, and thus particularly vulnerable to infection. The infection of their lifeline, between the time the HIV virus began to endanger blood supplies (1981) and the time when a screening test was approved and preventive measures were implemented (1985), was devastating to them and their families.

A large claim on behalf of hemophiliacs in this and other countries is now pending against the National Hemophilia Foundation and clotting concentrate suppliers. During and after this critical period, Baxter took a number of preventive actions. The company was evaluating heat treatment to inactivate viruses from 1978 to 1980. It revised its own blood donor screening procedures in January 1983. In 1984, it entered the competition to develop an AIDs screening test and in October of that year it demonstrated that heat treatment in fractionation of some concentrates blocked transmission of the AIDs virus. In April 1985, Baxter began, immediately upon approval of a test, to screen all plasma donations for HIV, and then halted the sale of non-heat treated Factor VIII in the U.S.

Even more dramatic achievements came after that. The FDA approved Autoplex, an anti-inhibitor coagulant complex, in 1987. In 1988, Baxter introduced monoclonal-antibody purified Hemofil AWF. In 1990 and 1991, the company announced a program to supply free Hemofil and in 1992 received FDA approval to supply genetically-engineered recombinate. In 1993, a gene therapy approach for treating and ultimately curing hemophilia was announced.

The tragedy is that a generation of hemophiliacs suffered a cruel blow. Baxter and Loucks feel that tragedy keenly. The irony is that a company which has invested and contributed so much for more than thirty years to the treatment and potential cure of hemophilia finds itself caught in a storm of publicity and potential liability. In one of his many 1993 employee meetings in Deerfield to discuss issues confronting Baxter, Loucks spoke with intense feeling about this particular situation. "Some other companies confronted by similar problems have chosen to withdraw from high-risk therapies. Baxter has not done that, and I hope we're not forced to. Leaders in this industry should take responsible risks on behalf of patients. Even in the clear light of hindsight it's very difficult to say what different choice we could have made as the HIV virus was still in process of being identified and the ramifications of the disease it causes were being grasped."

SPOTLIGHT ON BAXTER

These widely publicized setbacks together with flagging 1993 results and concern about longer-term company effects of Health Care

BAXTER SALES AND EARNINGS 1992 to 1993	1993	1992
NET SALES	$8,879,000,000	$8,471,000,000
NET INCOME (LOSS)	(198,000,000)	441,000,000
INCOME (LOSS) FROM CONTINUING OPERATIONS	(268,000,000)	561,000,000
EARNINGS (LOSS) PER COMMON SHARE		
CONTINUING OPERATIONS	($0.97)	$1.99
EXCLUDING RESTRUCTURING AND LITIGATION CHARGES (ESTIMATED)	$1.95	$1.99

Figure 29

Reform focused a harsh spotlight on Baxter management and financial performance. Would this unwelcome attention distract Baxter management from what needed to be done or create a new sense of urgency?

1993 RESULTS

The end of 1993 approached with Baxter announcing, on November 16, a $925 million write-off for restructuring to deal with approaching Health Care Reform issues and to increase product liability reserves. $700 million of the total amount was for restructuring, $225 million for product liability. Figure 29 summarizes 1993 financial results.

About the sales and distribution consolidation planned in the restructuring, Terry Mulligan said, "Vern Loucks went out on a long limb in 1985 to bring together the complementary strengths of American Hospital and Baxter. Then we began to take sequential steps in order to consolidate the essential elements of Hospital Distribution, Scientific Products, and IV Systems. Now we've taken further steps—perhaps the ultimate ones—and the results are going to speak for us."

Harry Kraemer, named CFO after Bob Lambrix' early retirement in November 1993, amplifies that comment: "We've already taken

GS&A (general, selling, and administrative) expense down five percent. For a nearly $9 billion company that's a $450 million saving. These further steps will help to reduce GS&A expenses another three to four points."

THE "BEHIND-THE-SCENES" DRAMA OF 1993

Chronological reporting doesn't capture the real drama of what happened within Baxter during this difficult year.

About midyear, Loucks and the Senior Management Committee (SMC) initiated a no-holds-barred review of Baxter's strategy and business portfolio. Investment bankers Wolfensohn and Lazard Freres were intensively involved. Many tough alternatives were vigorously advanced. The Board of Directors was regularly briefed as the review proceeded.

In late October the committee concluded from the analysis that the company would retain all of its principal businesses rather than divest significant parts, at least for now. The last modifying phrase is key. Harry Kraemer, new Baxter CFO, said, "We're not locked into anything for the long term . . . stay tuned."

Spinning off the hospital distribution business—strongly advocated by some—appeared to be neither as beneficial or practical as originally thought. Perhaps a better job of integrating American Hospital and Baxter had been done than critics were willing to acknowledge. The earlier decision to divest the diagnostics business was affirmed, and it now appears that the decision is moving rapidly to a successful outcome. In general, though, Baxter restated its commitment to aggregation and integration of its major lines of business despite the preference of some short-term investors for disaggregation. Loucks points out, "The investments in technology to which we're committed require a large cash flow and the domestic hospital business produces $300 million in cash flow. Those who felt we should spin off that business didn't have an answer as to how we would replace $300 million." Continuing consolidation in U.S. health care markets driven by reform efforts may prove the deciding factor in showing Baxter's choice to be the right one.

COMMITMENT TO BAXTER'S STATED DIRECTION

Unlike the 1985-1986 period immediately following the American Hospital Supply merger, when the overriding objective was to retain key people regardless of their strategic commitment, late 1993 was a time for managers to sign on or sign off. The year brought tension and pressure in Deerfield and other locations due to negative publicity that challenged employee pride in their accomplishments and contributions, slowing markets, and debate over critical decisions determining the company's future. During these tense and pressured times an ad appeared in the *Wall Street Journal* over the signatures of a large number of Baxter employees with the simple message, "We're proud of our company."

Objectivity may be adversely affected in direction-setting decisions of this kind because people's organization and career futures are at stake. No doubt, there was some of that in this case. There were hints of some disagreement at the board level. However, at the end of the day, the board unanimously supported and approved the basic direction recommended by Loucks and the Baxter management team.

It was, behind the scenes, intense drama. When it was over, management ranks at the top of Baxter had been thinned. Loucks said, "There would have been some thinning of the ranks anyway since we're assigning so much more responsibility to our ten group business heads, where we have a rich combination of youth together with depth and variety of Baxter experience." Most notable in the realignment punctuating this drama was the departure of Jim Tobin, a Baxter stalwart since 1972 and president since 1992. He resigned at 1993 year-end, and shortly thereafter was named president of Biogen. Tobin's resignation was a loss, but, as is apparent, there isn't anything really new about Baxter providing high-talent executives to the biotech industry, nor its ability to surface outstanding new talent.

HAS BAXTER'S STRATEGIC FOCUS BEEN CHANGED BY 1993 EVENTS?

Yes, Baxter's strategic focus has changed, but probably not in the ways that some had expected. One of the principal themes of this history has been the evolution and adaptation of company strategy, starting with the initial design to overcome the company's inherent competitive disadvantages. From time to time at critical junctures the question has risen as to whether Baxter's existing strategy had run out of gas. The question loomed at the time of the 1962 breakup with American Hospital Supply, and again when the company reached $1 billion in sales. Baxter can't continue to grow, some said then, by remaining a niche player in medical specialty markets. And the question has become a chorus since the 1985 merger with American

Hospital. Too much of a commitment, critics keep saying, to the low-tech, low-margin supply part of the business.

THREE-PART BAXTER STRATEGY

The company's strategy is described in detail in the February 1994 chairman's letter to shareholders.[2] It is a three-part strategy, each part overlaid with the next and mutually supporting. So the company has never, in fact, abandoned one strategy and undertaken another. Instead, it has kept the best of what's already working and overlaid a new strategic dimension. Perhaps that's what always happens in the real world of strategy. However, one of the real-world complications is that some customers and many employees may not yet completely comprehend all aspects of Baxter's complex strategy. They tend to lock in on one aspect or another, depending on their experience and bias, rather than grasping all the overlays. Clearly, Baxter management has to work harder at communicating the strategy and it is working harder at this demanding task, seeking to ignite the organization's commitment to shared values and stressing teamwork and individual empowerment. It will probably require reinforcement from some visible successes for the management message to take hold. 1994 first quarter results suggest such successes may be near at hand.

Earlier chapters showed that Baxter's original success was due in part to its proficiency in strategic technology niches. That element is still there. Next, the company experienced great success in its international strategy, which was itself a niche approach, individual country by country. That element is still there as well. Both elements have changed and been strengthened by the overlay process.

The three key elements to Baxter strategy are to:

- Continue and expand global leadership in Baxter high tech specialties: dialysis, cardiovascular therapy, blood therapeutics, and the newer areas of immunology and biotechnology.
- Increase market penetration for Baxter's entire product line in the many countries where the company already has a presence; and capture the immense potential represented by still-developing countries now approaching a point where they can afford modern health care.
- Build the lowest cost, most efficient platform for delivering the wide range of products and services needed by U.S. hospital systems and other clinical care networks and sites.

So it's a strategy of differentiation in the first element; low cost strategy in the third; and a mix of the two in the second. Complex, to be sure but calculated to provide many competitive advantages.

Loucks believes the closest and most illuminating parallel to Baxter's integrated approach to emerging health care markets is the revolution simultaneously occurring in global telecommunications, popularly described as the information superhighway. The telephone companies, cable operators, software and media producers are all crossing traditional boundaries in their race to integrate, just as Baxter is attempting to do in health care. Of course there are substantial risks involved, but the risks of not making the attempt are greater still.

STRATEGIC PIVOT POINT

The part of the strategy most critical to the company's success, most difficult, and most closely watched, involves the U.S. hospital business. How, it is asked, can Baxter achieve its stated goals of sales and profit growth in high single digits and of driving its common stock price from the low 20s, where it's been stuck, up to the mid 30s and beyond, when so much of its volume (over $5 billion) is concentrated in the pressured U.S. hospital sector? Baxter itself acknowledges the difficulty of winning minimal price increases in this competitive market. Company management addresses concerns about growth prospects for this part of its business with three observations. First, domestic hospital business is clearly a misnomer; its scope is considerably broader than that. Baxter's distribution system reaches clinics, labs, alternate sites, even industrial customers, in addition to hospital systems. Further, the system has the capacity to serve existing and new customers with products that today go to market through other channels. Second, as Harry Kraemer puts it, "Baxter is targeting not just the $1.00 of direct hospital product cost, but also the additional $1.50 in product-associated costs incurred within the hospital. We've got to persuade customers to pay for the value of our reducing those costs." Third, and most important, the clear trend to capitation[3] of materials and services favors Baxter's economic muscle. Few, if any, other hospital suppliers will be able to play the capitation game head-to-head with Baxter. By taking on more of the risk through capitation, it stands to reason the company should earn a higher economic return.

WHAT'S NEW AND DIFFERENT?

The strategy doesn't sound much different, does it? What is different is consistently expressed by the three occupants of the office of

CASH FLOW PROVIDED BY CONTINUING OPERATIONS (IN MILLIONS)				
1989	1990	1991	1992	1993
$545	$716	$697	$742	$765

Figure 30[4]

chief executive, Vern Loucks, Tony White, and Lester Knight, and by CFO Harry Kraemer. All talk about new rigor and discipline in the management process, about tight management of the company's growing cash flow, and tough resource allocation decisions. Figure 30 shows favorable trends in Baxter cash flow.

They talk with the same urgency about driving this more rigorous approach into each of Baxter's ten businesses, at the same time allowing more latitude for the diverse strengths of each business to assert itself. So it all comes down to execution. Senior management seems to have responded well to the challenge. Now it's up to them to rally Baxter's 60,000 employees.

BRIGHT PROMISE FOR NEW BAXTER MEDICAL TECHNOLOGY

Innovation has been a basic strength of the company over the years. The durability of its leadership positions created by pioneering innovations—leadership in such areas as blood therapy, dialysis, cardiology, and IV therapy—has been unequaled, lasting for thirty, forty, and more years. Once such leadership is established, Baxter gives it up rarely and grudgingly.

The three-part strategy certainly doesn't reduce emphasis on this basic strength, assuming resource allocation is appropriate. Nor does Health Care Reform reduce potential for Baxter to leverage growth and earnings through innovation. In fact, the emerging health care environment may indeed favor the kind of innovation for which Baxter has become recognized, since it has often reduced the cost of health care.

The company's innovation pipeline appears full, with recent contributions such as "engineered" clotting factor (which FDA commissioner Kessler called a "a true milestone in hemophilia treatment") and significant new products like blood substitutes, now in

BUSINESS	GROUP VICE PRESIDENT
1. Renal	Donald W. Joseph
2. Biotechnology	Timothy B. Anderson
3. Cardiovascular	Olav B. Bergheim
4. Diagnostics	Scott T. Garrett
5. International Hospital/Intercontinental	Manuel A. Baez
6. IV Systems	Jack L. McGinley
7. Surgical	Michael A. Mussallem
8. U.S. Distribution	Darnell Martin
9. Field Sales Account Management	Joseph F. Damico
10. Health Systems, Corporate Marketing and Sales, Government Sales	Terrence J. Mulligan

Figure 31: *"Leadership Strategy, Leadership Strength."*

human trials, the Novacor Wearable Left Ventricular Assist System (LVAS), and ANTI-CD45.

Furthermore, Baxter has mastered new ways of harvesting and earning returns on new technology. Executive vice president Tony White observes, "In the old days we invested in technology, got regulatory approval, developed and educated the market, and then after a period of years we began to earn a financial return. Now we have a variety of options we can elect earlier in the cycle. We can license, form alliances, sell some ownership. Properly managing these and other options moves the financial return to an earlier point in the development cycle."[5]

RESOLUTION OF HEALTH CARE REFORM UNCERTAINTIES

Over the longer term, Health Care Reform may improve Baxter's prospects. Executive vice president Lester Knight, responsible for the U.S. hospital and medical products business, says: "When Vern Loucks took the gamble of acquiring American Hospital in 1985, he was ahead of market trends. The market resisted what we were trying to do. Now the market has caught up. That's an encouraging sign for us."

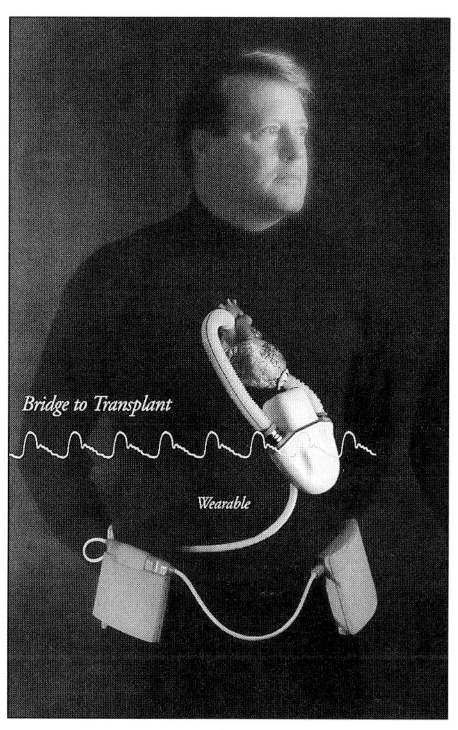

The Novacor Heart Assist System is a wearable electrical heart assist device.

The observation isn't meant to imply that adapting to Health Care Reform will be an easy passage for Baxter. Far from it. Reform almost certainly means short-term pressures for many health care providers and suppliers, including Baxter. This is already reflected in the company's downward revision of its growth and earnings projections. For the longer term, however, as shown in Figure 32, Health Care Reform initiatives are moving in parallel directions to Baxter's strategy.

It remains to be seen whether the company has made the best strategic decisions in this time of uncertainty, and even if so, whether it will continue to make the right calls as events proceed. As Loucks, Kraemer, and other senior executives have been saying, "Watch our results . . . and stay tuned." As 1993 ended, Baxter, recovering from the year's several blows, still faced challenging business conditions. Recent events, however, should be placed within the context of sixty-plus years of outstanding contributions, summarized in the table "Landmark Patient Care Contributions" at the end of this final chapter.

Large challenges have in the past stirred the company to put forth its very best efforts. The urgency with which Baxter management is

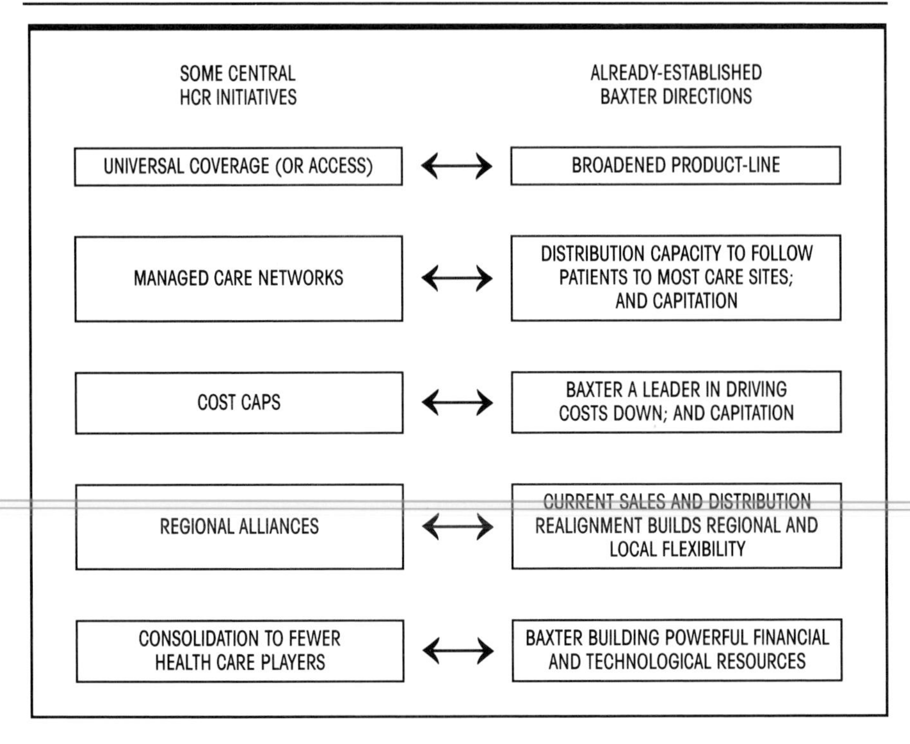

Figure 32

approaching the challenges of 1994 and beyond and the basic soundness of the company's business and competitive position suggest that history may repeat itself.

1994 first quarter results support that optimism. Sales increased seven percent from the year earlier period. Earnings were up nine percent to 47 cents per share. SG&A expenses were reduced 1.2 percentage points. Net debt remained flat, the first time in a first quarter that had occurred since the 1985 merger with American Hospital Supply. Operational cash flow was also strong. All in all, Baxter appeared to be solidly on track.

EPILOGUE

The last words belong to Bill Graham, who will mark his fiftieth—yes fiftieth—anniversary with Baxter in 1995, and to Vern Loucks, who will mark his thirtieth in 1996. Eighty years of service to others, forty years of CEO service for the two men. Most of them excellent years. And the tough years, Loucks points out, like 1993 and like 1962 when Baxter and American Hospital Supply separated, can be viewed as transitions in the dynamic and continuing evolution of health care. It is, indeed, a remarkable record.

You'll hear echoes here. Echoes of the 1980 transition from Graham to Loucks. Echoes of Graham creating an innovative strategy in the forties and early fifties; of Loucks doing the same in the more complex health care environment of the eighties. Echoes of the different market view of Baxter and American Hospital Supply, which Loucks sought to combine into one through the 1985 merger. By this time, Graham at 83 is in a reflective frame of mind. Loucks, approaching 59, is still in the heat of battle and his comments reflect it.

Looking forward after 1993's many challenges, Vern Loucks expresses cautious confidence:

> "No one can now foresee exactly what the health care system will look like after this upheaval. Nonetheless, Baxter is well positioned for the post-reform world. We have the right products, a competitive cost structure, strong management and teamwork particularly among the leaders of our ten business groups, solid values, and, perhaps most of all, a tradition of innovation that is as strong as ever. We will meet the challenge of Health Care Reform. Our performance in 1994 and subsequent years will speak for itself. . .I'm more concerned in some respects about what the health care debate will do to public attitudes about the system than I am about reform itself. All of us must continue to work hard at educating the public about how to make the health care system work better."

On February 21, 1994, Bill Graham was inducted into the Modern Healthcare Hall of Fame along with Clara Barton and several other notables. In his brief remarks he said:

> "It's clear to me that even if I could wind back the clock, I wouldn't go into any other career. I had the ideal career. I had the opportunity to run a successful business and, at the same time, to make a contribution to humanity. How can you do better than that?"

Then he quoted John Wesley as inspiration for him and for everyone who has the opportunity to work in health care:

> "Do all the good you can,
> In all the ways you can,
> (For) all the people you can,
> As long as. . .you can"[6]

MILESTONES

1991–1993

1991	Marian C. Falk dies.
1992	Wilbur H. Gantz resigns.
1992	James R. Tobin appointed president and chief operating officer.
1992	Scott Garrett and Jack McGinley elected corporate officers.
1992	Darnell Martin promoted to group vice president.
1992	Joseph F. Damico, Timothy B. Anderson, and Olav Bergheim become corporate officers.
1992	Initiation of surgical instrument joint venture in Russia.
1992	Spin-off of Alternate-Site businesses (Caremark International, Inc.) to shareholders.
1992	FDA approval to market Recombinate Antihemophilic Factor (a genetically engineered form of the human blood clotting factor VIII).
1993	Hemoglobin-based blood substitute DCLHb™ approved for testing in hospital settings.
1993	U.S. concludes investigation of Baxter's Mideast business dealings.
1993	European Community recommends approval of Baxter's Recombinate rAHF.
1993	Baxter establishes kidney dialysis products joint venture in China.
1993	Restructuring plans and litigation charges announced.

END NOTES

CHAPTER XXII

1. The New York Times, 24 March 1994.

2. 1993 Baxter Annual Report.

3. Capitation, a term made familiar by HMO pricing, refers in this instance to pricing product on a per patient or per procedure bases, rather than per supply unit.

4. Source: Baxter Finance Department.

5. Soon after, bearing out the bright promise for continuing Baxter innovation, the company and its Novacor division announced successful implantation of the LVAS in a 62-year-old Englishman in the first study of a wearable assist system as a definitive long-term therapy. This event at Papsworth Hospital NHS Trust of Cambridge University came also exactly ten years after the first bridge to transplant with the LVAS at Stanford University Medical Center in 1984. At the same time, Baxter announced the HomeChoice™ automated peritoneal dialysis system, simultaneously launched in three continents, as still another major advance in treatment of kidney failure (those Baxter advances stretching back to 1956). And, related to that, DNX Corporation & Baxter announced a new organ transplantation partnership, emphasizing several key technologies including xenotransplantation.

6. Original Wesley language has been modernized here.

LANDMARK PATIENT CARE CONTRIBUTIONS

1931-1939	Commercial development of IV solutions.
1939-1941	Introduction of Transfuso Vac and Plasma Vac, making modern blood transfusion and blood fractionation and therapy feasible.
1941-1945	Hundreds of thousands of American lives and medical knowledge advanced by use of Baxter IV and blood units in World War II.
1946-1950	Pioneering use of medical grade thermoplastics in administration sets.
1956	The first commercial artificial kidney.
1960-1961	Biocompatible, closed blood administration and separation system.
1961	First commercial heart-lung machine.
1968	First Factor VIII (AHF) concentrate for hemophiliacs.
1970	Viaflex revolutionizes IV administration.
1974	Minibag drug administration system.
1978	CAPD revolutionizes peritoneal dialysis.
1978-1980	Baxter introduces heat treatment to block viruses in Factor VIII and Factor IX.
1988	CS 3000 blood cell separator (closed system).
1990	Stick-free needle system to prevent virus transmission through accidental sticks.
1992	Monoclonal Factor VIII.
1993	Genetically engineered Factor VIII.
1993	Novacor wearable Left Ventricular Assist System (LVAS) enters investigational stage.

TABLE OF APPENDICES

PROSPECTUS

125,000 Shares

Baxter Laboratories, Inc.

Common Stock, $1 Par Value

THESE SECURITIES HAVE NOT BEEN APPROVED OR DISAPPROVED BY THE SECURITIES AND EXCHANGE COMMISSION NOR HAS THE COMMISSION PASSED UPON THE ACCURACY OR ADEQUACY OF THIS PROSPECTUS. ANY REPRESENTATION TO THE CONTRARY IS A CRIMINAL OFFENSE.

		Price to Public	Underwriting Discounts and Commissions (1)	Proceeds to Selling Stockholders (2)
100,000 Shares Offered by Underwriters	Per Share	$17.00	$1.15	$15.85
	Total	$1,700,000	$115,000	$1,585,000
		Price to Employees	Underwriting Discounts and Commissions	Proceeds to Company (3)
25,000 Shares Offered by Company to Employees	Per Share	$17.00	None	$17.00
	Total	$425,000	None	$425,000

(1) The Selling Stockholders have agreed to furnish an insurance policy indemnifying the Company, the Underwriters, and others against certain civil liabilities, including certain liabilities under the Securities Act of 1933.

(2) The Company is not selling any of the 100,000 shares offered by the Underwriters and will not receive any of the proceeds thereof. Such shares constitute Common Stock at present owned by the Selling Stockholders whose names and holdings are stated herein under "Selling Stockholders." The proceeds are shown before deduction of expenses of the Selling Stockholders estimated at $28,485.

(3) The proceeds are shown before deduction of expenses of the Company estimated at $6,445 and are based on the assumption that all of the 25,000 shares offered by the Company will be subscribed and paid for by employees. However, no representation is made that all or any portion of such shares will be subscribed and paid for. Reference is made to "Offering by Company to Employees" herein.

The 100,000 shares of Common Stock to be purchased by the Underwriters are offered subject to prior sale, to allotment and to withdrawal or modification of the offer without notice, to the approval of legal matters by Messrs. Mayer, Meyer, Austrian & Platt, counsel for the Underwriters, and by Messrs. Bell, Boyd, Marshall & Lloyd, counsel for the Company, and when, as and if delivered and accepted by the Underwriters. It is expected that delivery of such shares will be made on or about December 14, 1951, at the office of Lehman Brothers, 231 South LaSalle Street, Chicago 4, Illinois, against payment therefor in Chicago funds.

The Managing Underwriter is:

Lehman Brothers

The date of this Prospectus is December 10, 1951.

Selling Stockholders, 1951

The following table sets forth the names of all stockholders of the Company, the number of shares of Common Stock owned by each of them, and the number of such shares to be sold by them to the Underwriters:

Name	Number of Shares Owned	Number of Shares To Be Sold
Directors, officers and their respective wives and children		
Ralph Falk	41,250	8,250
Ralph Falk, trustee for Carol Falk	15,000	—
Marian C. Falk	114,375	22,875
Carol Falk	3,750	3,750
Harry N. Falk	45,000	9,000
Elizabeth M. Falk	11,250	2,250
Antonie Falk Kelley	11,250	2,250
William B. Graham	16,250	3,250
Naurice M. Nesset	19,562.5	4,437.5
Thelma Nesset	2,625	—
Ralph Falk II (son of Ralph Falk)	20,312.5	4,062.5
Carol Fullinwider	18,750	3,750
William A. Heveran	3,125	625
Rosalie Heveran	3,125	625
Other stockholders		
Lois K. Andersen	4,125	825
Bifin and Company	3,750	750
Daniel R. Borgen	3,125	625
Wayne D. Brandon	3,437.5	687.5
LeRoy Briggs	3,750	750
A. Lincoln Brown	3,750	750
Estate of Harold Brunn, deceased	3,750	750
Frances J. Burdick	1,875	375
Ethel C. Chapman	14,062.5	2,812.5
Joan G. Chapman	4,687.5	937.5
Horace Dawson	1,875	375
Harold Dedman	1,875	375
Ann D. Ensign	1,875	375
Isabella Ensign	1,875	375
Eben W. Erikson	7,500	1,500
Lloyd B. Erikson	1,250	250
Marie B. Erikson	1,250	250
Marilyn M. Erikson	1,250	250

David R. Falk	1,125	—
Henry L. Falk	12,375	3,600
John P. Falk	2,250	—
Estate of Lena S. Falk, deceased	12,000	2,400
Robert H. Falk	2,250	—
Theodore Falk	7,500	1,500
Corallyn Gewecke	625	125
Theodore H. Gewecke	5,625	1,125
A. Curtis Jones, Jr.	4,125	825
Winfield G. Jones	4,500	900
Emma Kleiner	3,750	—
Eugene M. Kleiner	3,750	—
J. M. Kleiner	6,375	3,525
Walter H. Kleiner	3,750	—
Foster G. McGaw	16,500	—
Edward J. Nawoj	3,125	625
Margaret M. Rau	2,812.5	562.5
Joseph E. Rau	3,750	750
Northwestern University	4,125	4,125
Josephine Rothchild	3,750	750
Barbara E. Smith	4,125	825
Kathryn Stanley	1,125	225
	500,000	100,000

The names and addresses of the several Underwriters and the number of shares to be purchased by each of them from the Selling Stockholders are as follows:

Name	Address	Number of Shares
Lehman Brothers	One William Street New York 4, N. Y.	24,000
Glore Forgan & Co.	40 Wall Street New York 5, N. Y.	10,000
Bear, Stearns & Co.	One Wall Street New York 5, N. Y.	5,000
Goldman, Sachs & Co.	30 Pine Street New York 5, N. Y.	5,000
Wertheim & Co.	120 Broadway New York 5, N. Y.	5,000
White, Weld & Co.	40 Wall Street New York 5, N. Y.	5,000

Listing of All Members of the Board of Directors: 1951–1992

Per Baxter Annual Report of	Board Member
1951	Ralph Falk M.D.
1951	H. N. Falk
1951	Ralph Falk II
1951	Wm. B. Graham
1951	N. M. Nesset Ph.D
1952	G. Preston Snow
1955	John M. Knowlton
1955	Fred Marquart
1957	Everett H. Travis
1960	Marian C. Falk
1964	Roy C. Ingersoll
1965	Charles S. Munson, Sr.
1966	Daggett Harvey
1969	W. Irving Osborne, Jr.
1970	John T. Kimbell
1974	William A. Jennett
1975	B. A. Bridgewater, Jr.
1975	Vernon R. Loucks, Jr.
1976	Gaylord Freeman
1976	William Wood-Prince
1977	William A. Hewitt
1978	Clinton E. Frank
1979	Wilbur H. Gantz
1979	Charles S. Munson, Jr.
1982	Charles F. Knight
1982	Fred L. Turner
1984	The Hon. John J. Louis, Jr.
1985	Karl D. Bays
1985	Silas S. Cathcart
1985	Harrington Drake
1985	Frank A. Ehmann
1985	Graham J. Morgan
1985	Henry G. Van der Eb
1985	Blaine J. Yarrington

1986	Mary Johnston Evans
1986	A. Bartlett Giamatti
1987	Martha R. Ingram
1988	C.A. (Lance) Piccolo
1988	Robert J. Simmons
1989	John W. Colloton
1989	James D. Ebert
1989	James R. Tobin
1990	David W. Grainger
1992	David C. K. Chin, M.D.
1992	Susan Crown
1992	Frank R. Frame
1992	Georges C. St. Laurent, Jr.
1992	David Satcher, M.D.

(Excerpts from an address by William B. Graham before the Investment Analysts Society of Chicago, on January 28, 1960.)

Magnificent Performers for the Public

I am pleased to be here, and welcome this opportunity to talk with you about Baxter Laboratories, where these days are active and absorbing ones.

For our pharmaceutical manufacturing industry as a whole, these are also active days. As your Chairman has requested, I shall comment today on industry activities as well as those of Baxter.

The accomplishments of the American ethical drug industry in recent years have been remarkable. At least some of us in this room are alive today—or have families intact—because of the drug industry's never-ending research efforts.

The ethical drug industry is, as you well know, a young one. For its inventors, it has been a good performer. For the public it has been a magnificent performer. Yet, it has reached a point in its growth which is apparently unavoidable for every young industry. It has become the target for a Congressional hearing, now underway in Washington.

Policy for Growth

At Baxter, the accent is on youth. We have brought together a group of young men, each an expert in his own field, to form what we consider to be one of the finest management teams in any industry. The average age of the key executives who report to me is 43 with an average length of service of ten years.

Our policy for growth at Baxter is a combination of internal research and development, and outside acquisitions. In this connection, I might say that during 1960 our search will continue for companies that can be integrated into one of our divisions to broaden not only their over-all product base but also their specialization as marketing units.

Last year, in an address before the New York Security Analysts, I predicted that we would make at least one acquisition before the end of 1959—actually, we acquired two companies, Flint, Eaton and Fenwal Laboratories.

We recognize the potential growth opportunities in many foreign countries, and are moving aggressively in this direction. One important step, started early last year, is the eventual consolidation of the international activities into one International division responsible for all products.

Our programs in various countries are in many different stages of development—in some cases they involve setting up a distributor; in other cases, building a manufacturing plant (for example, Colombia, South America). A company of our size can't build more than a few plants at any one time. Accordingly, locations are carefully selected, and the decision to build must be properly timed.

Financial Policy

Our financial policy has been to obtain most of our capital from internal sources. We have followed a conservative dividend policy. In the last three years, for example, we retained about 70% of earnings.

Our heaviest capital requirement in the last ten years was in connection with the acquisition of Wallerstein early in 1957. We accomplished this by a combination of straight debt and $1.8 million of convertible debentures. These debentures have now been completely retired or converted.

Effective December 11 of last year, our Common Stock was split 2 for 1. On the new basis, we now have approximately 1,275,000 shares outstanding, which is about 27% more than 10 years ago, after adjusting for the split. We consider this a relatively small dilution, considering that during this period the company has tripled in sales, in net worth, and in assets.

In 1959, we stepped up capital spending to a level of $1.5 million dollars, which is nearly double the 1958 expenditures.

A new issue of $2.5 million dollars of Preferred Stock, authorized by our shareholders at the 1959 Annual Meeting, has been purchased by Massachusetts Mutual Life Insurance Company. The funds realized have been used to retire all but $500,000 of our short-term debt. This issue consists of 25,000 shares of $100 Par 6% Preferred with no warrants or convertible features. It carries a 4% mandatory Sinking Fund requirement beginning November 30, 1964.

The diversification program that started in 1951 and 1952 began to show tangible results in 1955. The upward trend continued in 1956, with 1957 and 1958 both showing a sharp increase over the preceding year.

Excerpts from Gaylord Freeman's remarks on May 12, 1983, and February 10, 1989. (Complete copies of the Introduction were provided by Mr. Freeman on January 16, 1990, for partial quotation here.)

Introduction of Bill Graham to the Harvard Business Club of Chicago, 1983

If tonight you are meeting William Graham for the first time, you will observe that his face is open and, even at 71, he has a boyishness about him.

Charm, graciousness, modesty and humor are the qualities that you would first recognize and like. He is so pleasant that you may think that to be his main characteristic. His smile comes so quickly and with such warmth he hardly seems to be a serious individual. His modesty makes him so deferential that you may have the impression that he is not quite your equal but would like to be.

A simple, happy, deferential, open-faced man. He'd probably make a good salesman or perhaps a politician—"just a great guy." That is, until there's a problem and BAM! This jovial Santa Claus, without losing his smile, flashes a mind like a bear trap—as fast, as firm, and as sharp. The solution is presented, his associates informed and convinced, and Bill, still with that boyish smile, gives someone else the credit for the decision.

My present assignment of introducing Bill reminds me of how greatly I underestimated him only fourteen years ago. I had known Bill only slightly but admired him greatly when he came on the board of the First National Bank of Chicago in the spring of 1969. I had been impressed first, by his genial personality and second, by his ability. Since I had known him only superficially and had not seen him in the few civic groups with which I was acquainted, I thought, with some arrogance, that I should introduce him to the community—which I proceeded to do.

I was quickly humiliated when I found he knew everyone and everyone knew and liked him.

I am not the only one who has learned about Bill. He is a director of: Bell and Howell, Borg Warner, Deere, Field Enterprises, First Chicago and the First National Bank of Chicago, and Northwest Industries.

John Stafford, in inviting me to be here, pointed out that your Business Statesman award is restricted to one who has:

- Achieved outstanding personal success in business
- Made a distinguished contribution to his industry, and
- Made a distinguished contribution to the welfare of the Chicago community

Before you make too hasty a decision and grant any such award, let's examine the candidate's credentials on the basis of these three criteria.

First, has he in fact

> "Achieved outstanding personal success in business?"

You all know that despite the unemployment of the current recession, he *is* employed.

Before I put to a vote the question of whether he meets the first test—as to achieving outstanding personal success in business—I must acknowledge some uncertainty as to the meaning of that phrase. If it means that he achieved it all *personally,* he would disqualify himself. He would assert that he has had brilliant support from *Vern Loucks, Bill Gantz, Ray Oddi, Marshall Abbey,* and many others. But Bill hired each of them and personally trained them. So maybe he does qualify.

The second test is

> "Has he made a distinguished contribution to his industry?"

Baxter Travenol is considered a pharmaceutical company, but it's no pill puncher.

What do his competitors actually think of him?

I asked Karl Bays, Chairman of American Hospital Supply, who immediately responded:

> "To me, Bill is a builder, an innovator and a model of leadership. He built a small, regional producer of intravenous solutions into an international healthcare firm. Stressing innovation in products and medical technology, he achieved a truly impressive record in sales and earnings."

Then there was another response, unsigned, it reads

> "Why that son-of-a-gun. If he doesn't stop cutting prices and producing better quality products, we'll all go busted. Let me tell you . . ."

If I were to condense to a five-line jingle what I have said so far, it might read

> "It's true, Bill Graham is extremely charming but it's also true that he's quite disarming. Competitors think that Bill is nice but when they can't meet his specs or his price they find that statesman quite alarming."

Lastly in sequence, though not in importance, is the third test

> "Has he made a distinguished contribution to the welfare of the Chicago community?"

He has served on the boards of directors or trustees of

The Lyric Opera,
The Chicago Horticultural Society,
The Community Fund of Chicago,
The Crusade of Mercy,
The University of Chicago,
The Orchestral Association,
The National Park Foundation, and
The Evanston Hospital

Beyond that, he was not just a member, he provided distinguished service in each of these roles which can be seen from some of his awards. The Lewis Foundation gave him their VIP award. The St. Andrew's society of Chicago gave him the distinguished Citizen's Award. He was given the Weizmann Institute Professorial Chair in 1978 and The Chicago Boys Club named him Chicagoan of the Year.

Earlier this month Bill was awarded an honorary doctorate by Lake Forest College. He's scheduled to receive an honorary doctorate from St. Xavier later this month and on the 11th of next month he will receive another doctorate degree from the National College of Education.

Bill has demonstrated those other characteristics of a true business statesman. He is a man not only of business ability but of wisdom and of philosophy. He is one who recognizes that his business and, indeed all business, is but one part of the larger society. Business is crucially important for it brings capital and labor together to permit the production of all of the goods and services on which our society depends. But the consumer is also crucially important, as is the government which in part regulates the relationship between business and the citizenry.

Gaylord Freeman
May 12, 1983

Introduction of Bill Graham
Baxter "Alumni" Dinner, 1989

The last time I spoke about Bill I introduced him to the Harvard Business School Association of Chicago. I was absolutely delighted to talk about a man whom I so admired that I spoke and spoke. My enthusiasm was so great that I spoke and spoke some more. I was quite pleased with myself and continued to tell about many great things Bill has done and what a wonderful man he is. I began to realize it was somewhat long for an introduction but I continued until I said almost everything that I could. I may even have made up a few things.

When I finished the irritated toastmaster said "Thank you, Mr. Freeman; unfortunately, you have talked so long that we don't have any time for Mr. Graham to speak. We will present him with this token of our admiration; then if you will give Mr. Graham a hand, the meeting is adjourned."

Anyway, most of you are as well acquainted with Bill (though perhaps not for as long) as I, but you may have forgotten that when he became president of Baxter just 36 years ago, the company's annual sales in his first full year at the helm were less than $15 million. For the last full year of his leadership (1979) they were $1 billion, 200 million, an increase of almost one hundred times. When he took over, the corporation's profits were $535,000 for the year. The last year of his leadership they were $111,908,000, over 200 times what they were when he took over.

During the years when he was the boss, per share earnings increased at the compound annual rate of 21% per year and produced an average annualized rate of return on stockholder's equity of 15.4%.

I don't believe that any other corporate officer in the U.S. today has a record that can match. Bill is the outstanding corporate executive of the past half century.

It is often difficult, and a test of true wisdom, to take a longer view. Bill has long recognized that—and had not only the wisdom, but also the courage to take that long view. On this point let me quote (less than one page) from that earlier introduction because it not only is applicable to Bill, but to each one of you who has personally participated with him in carrying out his longer view of the role of corporate leadership. I quote:

> *Expenses for research come out of current earnings. Product development costs come out of current earnings. Management development costs come out of current earnings. Matching gifts to encourage employee involvement in, and support of, community affairs, come out of current earnings. But Bill, supported by each of you has had the wisdom and courage to build for the future view. He could have reported even higher earnings for a short term, but he has always played the long game. There are more than seventeen thousand patients worldwide (that must now be well over 25,000) who have been enabled to leave the hospital and live at home through programs in dialysis, nutrition, continuous chemotherapy, intravenous antibiotic therapy, respiratory therapy, hemophilia therapy and continuous diabetes insulin therapy—because he and you—each of you—has had the vision and the courage to forego even higher short-term profits in order to better serve the public as well as your stockholders. There are hundreds of thousands, perhaps millions, around the world who, after severe disease or surgery, are recovered and leading productive lives because of the sterility and low cost of your principal products—particularly the efficient delivery of intravenous fluids. Together Bill and you have faced and absorbed the development costs of such needed products—the work of a true statesman.*

Throughout these few remarks I have emphasized Bill's greatest characteristic—wisdom.

Wisdom is not a single characteristic but rather a collection of many traits, great sensitivity now, in his case, enhanced by age and experience.

Emotional sensitivity—colored by, kindness, and unselfish dedication. Some more intellectual or reflective wisdom, the result of his observation, analysis and evaluation of each day's experience and the identification of its meaning as applicable to other situations.

Wisdom is also bereft of vanity for it requires an honest philosophy without the prejudice of self. In practice it relies on suggestion rather than order, questioning rather than didactic and gentle deference.

But Bill is no pussycat—if he senses any action unworthy of a gentleman his reaction is (as we have heard tonight about how he pared the invitation list) immediate and all the more awesome because it is so rare. But it is this observation and evaluation combined with tact and sensitivity without ego that create the elements of true wisdom which characterize you, Bill, and for which so many of us love you as much as we admire you.

Gaylord Freeman
February 10, 1989

Selected correspondence from William B. Graham to Dr. Ralph Falk, 1948-51.

cc Mr. H. N. Falk

August 24, 1948
AIR MAIL

Dr. Ralph Falk
135 Warm Springs Avenue
Boise, Idaho

Dear Ralph:

The labor negotiations are still continuing with the next meeting set for August 30. At the last meeting we offered a wage increase of 10¢ per hour plus a cost of living adjustment up or down based on ½¢ per hour for each change of one point in the Bureau of Labor statistics index of cost of living. The committee indicated that although they had rejected our offer of 7½¢ an hour with the cost of living adjustment, they would be willing to recommend this last offer. Harry will undoubtedly give you more details as to the negotiations.

Sales for the month seem to be going along fairly well. Dollar volume should be in the neighborhood of a half million dollars which we feel is very good. However, a considerable portion of this will consist of Army business which is at a very low margin and sets which are also at a relatively low margin. Accordingly, although we think this should be a better month than July, it does not look like an outstanding month.

We are continuing to work on the plant expansion and are considering a number of alternatives, some of which look better than the original plans. We will wait until you arrive to discuss this situation with you.

Don Baxter has filed a trade-mark application on the name "BAXTER" for the entire country. We are preparing an opposition to this application based on our exclusive use of the name in our territory. We feel rather pleased that the issue has arisen in this way since it leaves us in the position to litigate this question on a more favorable basis than if we had filed the application, and since at the same time we are in a position to feel outraged that Don Baxter should do such a thing.

We have heard nothing from you regarding the photostat of the Protein Hydrolysate ad which Petersen sent to you and assume this met with your approval.

Production is going along well. Discard reports indicate that our discards are at an all time low.

Sincerely,

William B. Graham

WBG:H
cc Mr. H. N. Falk

December 9, 1950

Ralph Falk, M.D.
Beverly Wilshire Hotel
Beverly Hills, California

Dear Ralph:

Enclosed is the letter to American Hospital responding to their letter regarding "Travenol." Since you asked us to make certain changes in the letter after you had left, we thought maybe we should send it to you for mailing. This will permit you to check and see whether the changes are all as they should be. It also means that if any question ever arises as to whether this letter was mailed in the form in which you signed it, you can state that it was.

Sincerely,

William B. Graham

WBG:H
Enc.

December 6, 1950

American Hospital Supply Corporation
2020 Ridge Avenue
Evanston, Illinois

Attention: Mr. Foster G. McGaw

Gentlemen:

We acknowledge with some little surprise receipt of your letter of November 3, 1950 protesting the use of the trademark "Travenol" upon certain of our products heretofore furnished you for distribution as our selling agent.

As you well know, the distributorship contract between us makes no provision for your approval of any trademark we may care to use. The portion of the contract quoted by you as authority for interference of this character is quite obviously not concerned with trademarks.

It might be well to point out that the mark in question has been in use for over a year with no previous indication of your disapproval. During that time we have shipped you well over 5,000,000 bottles bearing this mark. You might also recall that you have attended several conferences at which the development of the mark "Travenol" was discussed. It is quite apparent that your concern over the mark "Travenol" is of recent inception and probably results from your recent acquisition of Don Baxter, Inc.

With regard to your fourth paragraph, we wish to point out that "it would appear logical and fair and good business practice to consult with" your manufacturing associate before purchasing control of a firm with which we have cross license arrangements. You may recall that the first notice anyone connected with this company had of your purchase of Don Baxter, Inc. was when you told us of it as a fait accompli. We hereby protest your purchase of Don Baxter, Inc.

May we point out to you that which you have apparently overlooked—that we are most interested in the trademark "Baxter"—that we have used it widely for many years and are still doing so.

"Travenol," as was recently discussed in a conference with you concerning the 1950 advertising, is one of a series of trademarks which we are developing for individual groups in our line of Baxter Solutions. Your assumption of ignorance of this fact leads to the inescapable conclusion that some ulterior motive is the basis for your letter.

In conclusion we say that we deeply resent the insolence implicit in the charge that our acts in protecting the future of our business and yours are "morally distasteful" to you, or are dictated by some ulterior purpose.

Very truly yours,

BAXTER LABORATORIES, INC.

Ralph Falk, M.D.
President

RF:H

July 20, 1951

Ralph Falk, M.D.
135 Warm Springs Avenue
Boise, Idaho

Dear Ralph:

Manheim called to say that one of the men from the Fry Company, a management consulting firm, had talked to him about our deal with American. It seems that Fry is doing work for American. This man told Manheim that as his own idea and not at the suggestion of Mr. McGaw, he thought he should get together with Manheim and see if they could work something out along the lines of some settlement of difficulties between American and Baxter Laboratories. I told Manheim, by all means, to meet with him and see what he had to say.

The stock deal set up by Manheim looks extremely interesting. It seems to me that there are a lot of problems involved about doing anything in the next few months, but it is certainly worth looking into. This is one we will put on the agenda for your next trip here.

In the meantime, with the possibility of a public offering of common stock, I would like to hold the preferred stock issue. As a matter of fact, if there is to be a public offering even within the next couple of years, I think we would be wise to cancel our plans for the preferred stock dividend.

I am going to be in New York for a couple of days next week on the invert sugar situation and will see Manheim at that time for his latest comments. I will ask him what his explanation is for the present price of the American stock. He was very much surprised to find this quoted at 37 bid and 39 asked.

The June statement is completed and is in auditing. It is not too good but is pretty much as expected. If there are no corrections, it will come out at about $40,000 profit after taxes and profit sharing. Joe will send this on to you as soon as the auditing is completed, which will probably be Monday.

One thing that we should bear in mind in our overall operations is that we are getting our expenses geared to a relatively high level which will undoubtedly minimize or even eliminate excess profits tax but, of course, that means that we should watch these items to see that they are ones which will do enough good in the long run to justify the present expense. The biggest item is probably the sales department which is one which should pay dividends in future years.

Two new papers on the use of Pyromen for allergies are coming out in the July-August issue in the Annals of Allergy. These are the Zindler and Wittek papers. Maurice is working on the Time Magazine publicity and is trying to schedule it for September or October.

Our present thinking on concentrations is to have a 10 cc. vial of 10 gamma/cc. and a 10 cc. vial of 4 gamma/cc. In addition for sample purposes, we propose to have a 5 cc. vial of 4 gamma/cc. These should all be ready within the next two or three weeks. The entire program from now to the end of the year should cost approximately $100,000 for direct mail and journal advertising. This is the amount we talked about in our original discussions of this back at the beginning of the year and still looks sound to us. We would like to have your approval on this amount subject, of course, to the fact that some portion of this—perhaps between $25,000 and $50,000—could be cut off if we should decide to do so in the latter part of the year.

Sincerely

William B. Graham
WBG:H

INDEX

Bold face numbers indicate illustration.
n indicates endnotes.

B

D

E

F

G

H

I

J

M

N

O

T

Y

Z